MATHEMATICAL TECHNIQUES
IN CHEMISTRY

MATHEMATICAL TECHNIQUES IN CHEMISTRY

JOSEPH B. DENCE

Washington University
St. Louis, Missouri

A WILEY-INTERSCIENCE PUBLICATION

JOHN WILEY & SONS · New York · London · Sydney · Toronto

Library of Congress Cataloging in Publication Data:

Dence, Joseph B
    Mathematical techniques in chemistry.

    "A Wiley-Interscience publication."
    Bibliography: p.
    Includes index.
    1. Chemistry–Mathematics.   I.   Title.

QD39.3.M3D46   540'.1'5   75-16337
ISBN 0–471–20319–X

Printed in the United States of America

10 9 8 7 6 5 4 3 2 1

*To Joseph E. Weber, friend and former teacher,
who first introduced me to the rites of chemistry*

Preface

This book was motivated by the fact that students, both upper-division undergraduates and beginning graduate students with whom I have had contact, showed a surprising lack of manipulative ability or knowledge (or both?) of the basic mathematics deemed essential for an understanding of many problems in chemistry. Such problems span virtually the entire range of chemistry and are therefore not restricted to those encountered by physical chemists. Ideas in elementary molecular orbital theory, enzyme kinetics, complex solution equilibria, thermodynamics, wave mechanics, ligand field theory, and the kinetic theory of gases all require mathematics of one sort or another for their full expression. None of these areas can be said to be the domain of physical or theoretical chemists alone; for example, molecular orbital theory is fast becoming a standard part of curricula and general usage, and developments in recent years of valence-shell electron calculations by such workers as J. A. Pople[1] leave no doubt that the intended readers of their literature are practicing organic and inorganic chemists. These readers and others less theoretically inclined, both in academia and in industry, will have to aquaint themselves with basic mathematical notions such as basis sets, orthonormal functions, and coordinate transformations if they are going to cope successfully with these important papers.[2] The day when an organic chemist can arrive at the laboratory, run his reactions, take his melting points and infrared spectra, and go home at 5:00 pm is drawing to a close.

[1] See, for example, J. A. Pople et al., *J. Am. Chem. Soc.*, **92**, 2191 (1970); **93**, 289 (1971); and other papers in the series.
[2] As an example of the sort of applied use to which molecular orbital theory is being put, read J. M. George, L. B. Kier, and J. R. Hoyland, "Theoretical Considerations of Alpha and Beta Adrenergic Activity," *Mol. Pharm.*, **7**, 328 (1971), as well as the monograph L. B. Kier, *Molecular Orbital Theory in Drug Research*, Academic Press, New York, 1971.

It is not entirely the student's fault for his weakness in handling many of these mathematical ideas because little of the mathematics presented in classrooms is directed toward applications. To be fair, it could hardly be otherwise. Mathematics instructors have enough on their hands just presenting the basic concepts of their subject without having to worry about whether they should provide numerous applications to physics, chemistry, engineering, or indeed to all three. Physics instructors recognized the truth of this situation long ago, so that for quite a while a course in mathematical methods in physics has been a permanent feature of undergraduate and graduate physics curricula.[3] Very few departments of chemistry have a similar offering; it is hoped that in the future the number offering such a course will increase.

If recent trends in the educational literature are any sign at all, the time for this and the time when mathematics and physical science departments start paying more attention to each other are fast drawing near. G. Matthews and M. Seed, in an article entitled "The Co-existence in Schools of Mathematics and Science," point out that the most important step is for mathematics and science instructors (at the secondary and the college levels) to actually meet and discuss common problems.[4] The late Professor C. A. Coulson, who has probably done more than anyone to render lucid the complex mathematical ideas in quantum chemistry, has pointed out that practicing chemists must recognize that the relation between mathematics and chemistry has changed drastically over the past few decades.[5] Several other articles in the recent educational literature have outlined newly instituted programs in applied mathematics that should be of value to undergraduate students majoring in the sciences. One article has even made a plea that a course in applied mathematics would be of great value to pure mathematicians![6] All humor aside, the point here is that mathematics is a form of communication just as language is, and that it should be regarded as such in the science classroom, at least as far as the practical variety of mathematics is concerned. Professor K. J. Laidler, upon accepting the Chemical Education Award of the Chemical Institute of Canada, has made this and other points very strongly, and I agree with him one hundred percent.[7]

This book should really be of use to a great variety of people in chemistry since the level of presentation nowhere approaches that of the famous

---

[3]Texts have scarcely changed in 50 years: compare any present-day text on the subject with the old classic E. Madelung, *Die Mathematischen Hilfsmittel des Physikers*, Julius Springer, Berlin, 1922.
[4]G. Matthews and M. Seed, *Int. J. Math. Educ. Sci. Tech.*, **1**, 21 (1970).
[5]C. A. Coulson, *Chem. Brit.*, **10**, 16 (1974).
[6]M. J. Davies, *Int. J. Math. Educ. Sci. Tech.*, **3**, 71 (1972).
[7]K. J. Laidler, *J. Chem. Educ.*, **51**, 696 (1974).

monographs on mathematical methods, and since the book emphasizes applications in chemistry. To that vast sea of workers in chemical industry (clinical and pharmaceutical chemistry, polymer chemistry, paper, wood and waste chemistry, materials science and other branches of chemical engineering, etc.), who have been away from university training for some time and who feel the need for a review of basic mathematical concepts, this book should be of some help. On the academic scene, the book is intended principally for undergraduate students who are pursuing a major's degree in chemistry and who have already completed at least one-half year or preferably an entire year of a standard course in the calculus. Beginning graduate students who have had a particularly brief mathematical education should also find the book useful. Although there are in existence many excellent books on mathematical methods (see the Annotated Bibliography at the end of this volume), most of these are directed toward physicists or to "scientists" in general. In this volume the applications are drawn entirely from various branches of chemistry. Without entering into any futile polemics, this amounts to an operational definition of chemistry and not to any preconceived notions as to what constitutes physics and what constitutes chemistry. Until such time in the future when the structure of Western physical science will have reached the point where departmental outlines disappear and students are taught "science" instead of physics or chemistry, it will still be possible to justify the existence of separate mathematical techniques courses.

For the benefit of instructors, the author has found that in his lectures the material contained in Chapters 1–4 and part of Chapter 5 can just barely be covered in one quarter. At institutions where classes are conducted on a semester schedule an additional chapter could probably be covered. The instructor can select such material from Chapter 6 ("Matrices, Vectors, and Tensors") and Chapter 7 ("Special Functions") as he feels is appropriate for his course. In these chapters, as in the preceding ones, material that can be skipped without seriously impairing the continuity of the text is marked with an asterisk. Such sections could be covered in fast classes or could be recommended to the more motivated members of class.

At the end of every chapter there is an extensive set of exercises; the beginning chapters, in particular, that presumably every user of this book will read, contain especially large doses of problems. The problems are graded into three levels: drill problems and problems that can be attempted by all readers, somewhat harder problems, which are marked by an asterisk, and challenging problems, which are intended only for very good students and very good classes and which are marked with a double asterisk. Some of the problems are of a purely mathematical type, but many are applications to various situations in chemistry. The author has a personal bias against including answers to exercises in a textbook; real learning should not be a test of willpower.

A matter for concern here is whether a user of this book needs an extensive knowledge of chemistry before he is able to work through the material and attempt many of the problems. It is assumed that all readers have more or less mastered the equivalent of a one-year standard course of freshman chemistry for science majors—a course in which the qualitative concepts of free energy, rate of a reaction, discrete energy states of atoms and molecules, and equations of state for gases have been introduced—and that with careful study a reader can apply the chemistry he already knows and the mathematics he is then acquiring to the solution of ostensibly new problems. In the classroom it is the responsibility of every instructor, of course, to exercise judicious judgment in the selection of homework problems for the class. With an exceptional class this is not apt to be a serious problem, and an instructor may wish to assign some problems from outside the text. A solutions manual is available to instructors from the publisher.

A final comment should be made regarding the selection of subjects that are covered in the book. Two large areas have been omitted: statistics and probability, and group theory. The first was passed over because it was felt that mastery of this topic was of less priority than of many others for undergraduate students. For many workers in industry who continually handle large amounts of data, statistics and probability are of very great importance, but some selection was necessary to keep the book a manageable size. The second was omitted because I felt incapable of approaching the excellence of treatment given by Professor F. Albert Cotton in his book *Chemical Applications of Group Theory* (2nd ed., Wiley-Interscience, New York, 1971). Of the subjects that have been included in the present volume, those contained in the first three chapters are drawn from traditional areas up through the calculus; these are topics that are required almost immediately in one's study of chemistry. The subjects of the last four chapters are more in the line of special, albeit important, topics.

In writing this book, the author has benefited directly or indirectly from numerous people. Professor James V. and Dr. Lidia M. Quagliano provided constant companionship and encouragement, particularly during the early stages of preparation. My longtime friend and colleague Professor Dennis J. Diestler consented to read Chapter 6 and was his usual zealous and critical self. Several of the more subtle and sophisticated mathematical points that are only hinted at in the book were discussed with Dr. Thomas P. Dence. Many thanks finally go to Mrs. Georgia M. Chuhay and to the rest of the editorial and technical staff at John Wiley & Sons, Inc., for expert assistance in the preparation of the manuscript.

Feedback and constructive comments are welcomed from instructors and students and particularly from readers in industry and elsewhere who have used the text, regarding any aspect of the book as a whole. It is expected that this work contains the customary faults of any first-edition work, and the author assumes full responsibility for them. "Now go, write it before them in a table, and note it in a book, that it may be for the time to come for ever and ever [Isaiah 30:8]."...or until I write the second edition!

JOSEPH B. DENCE

School of Medicine
4911 Barnes Hospital Plaza
St. Louis, Missouri   63110
September 1975

Contents

MATHEMATICAL TECHNIQUES
IN CHEMISTRY

ONE

Algebra and Elementary Notions of Functions

Dol Common: "Yes, sir. I studie here the mathematiques,
And distillation."

BEN JONSON

1 VARIOUS FUNCTIONS; COORDINATE SYSTEMS; GRAPHING

Algebra, indeed most of mathematics, is built upon the concept of the
function. The concept of function was unknown to Classical and Arabian
mathematicians. It is a product of Western culture and could only take form
after François Viète (1540–1603), a French lawyer with important connections at the courts of Henry III and Henry IV, had first introduced in a
systematic way general letters instead of numbers into algebra.[1] Briefly, a
function is a prescription for taking elements from X, called the *domain* of the
function, into *unique* elements of Y, called the *range* of the function (see
Figure 1.1). Each element x in X is an *argument* of the function, and each
element y in Y corresponding to an x is the *value* of the function. Some
mathematicians prefer to use the term *mapping* on occasion in place of
function.

Although X and Y are usually sets of real numbers, in some cases they
may not be. Mathematicians have constructed several different algebraic
systems that usually have most or all of the following properties in common.

---

[1]D. J. Struik (ed.), *A Source Book in Mathematics*, 1200–1800, Harvard University Press,
Cambridge, Mass. 1969, p. 74. There is much historically interesting material in this book.

1

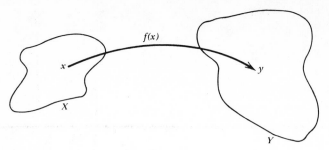

Fig. 1.1   A function or mapping.

1. Two operations analogous to addition and multiplication defined.
2. Existence of a zero and a unity.
3. Associativity: $a + (b + c) = (a + b) + c$, and $a \times (b \times c) = (a \times b) \times c$.
4. Commutativity: $a + b = b + a$, and $a \times b = b \times a$.
5. Distributivity: $a \times (b + c) = (a \times b) + (a \times c)$.
6. Closure: if a, $b \in X$, then $(a + b)$, $(a \times b) \in X$ (the symbol $\in$ means "is a member of").

Some of the above properties may be relaxed; multiplication in the algebra of matrices or of quaternions,[2] for example, is noncommutative. More on this is presented in Chapter 6.

Functions may take many forms; we distinguish two main types following Chrystal (see pp. 281–282, Volume I of his two-volume work listed in the Annotated Bibliography).

1. Algebraic: all arguments are involved in only addition, subtraction, multiplication, division, and being raised to a power.

2. Transcendental: one or more arguments appear as exponents, or as arguments of infinite series.

This definition of a transcendental function may seem unclear now; in Chapter 4 you will see how the logarithmic and the trigonometric functions are best understood in terms of infinite series. With this in mind, the following common examples of algebraic and transcendental functions should be familiar to you. By convention the dependent variable is regarded

[2]Hypercomplex numbers invented by the Irish physicist William Rowan Hamilton (1805–1865) around 1840. Vectors are an offshoot of quaternions, but with the rules for multiplication formulated slightly differently, a fact which caused scientists and mathematicians to square off against each other during the latter half of the nineteenth century. Hamilton was a child genius; in 1827, while still a college student, he was appointed Professor of Astronomy at Trinity College in Dublin.

as the variable placed to the left of the equals sign; the independent variable under consideration is on the right and has been underlined.

Algebraic	Transcendental
$P = \dfrac{nRT}{\underline{V}}$	$\Delta G^0 = -RT \ln \underline{K}$
$[H^+] = \underline{1 \times 10^{-2}M}$	$\lambda = \dfrac{2d}{n} \sin \underline{\theta}$
$\Delta S_{sys} = q\left(\dfrac{1}{T_1} - \dfrac{1}{\underline{T_2}}\right)$	$\psi_{1s} = \dfrac{1}{\sqrt{\pi a_0{}^3}} \exp(-\underline{r}/a_0)$

In this book we use the accepted notation ln to stand for logarithms to the base e (natural or Napierian logarithms).

Great convenience results when some of the properties of a mapping are represented pictorially as a *graph*. You should become intimately familiar with the graphs of several common functions (see Figure 1.2) and with a few of the not-so-common functions.

In the graphs in Figure 1.2 the coordinate system used is the familiar rectangular Cartesian coordinate system. However, many other types of coordinate systems are possible: oblique Cartesian coordinates, semi-logarithmic coordinates, polar coordinates, spherical polar coordinates, confocal elliptical coordinates, etc. You will meet some of these in later sections of the book. One value of a graph, of course, is that it allows you to estimate slopes, intercepts, and approximate points where two or more curves intersect.

An important point to realize is that it is possible to transpose a function originally graphed in one coordinate system into an equivalent function graphed in another coordinate system, provided one applies certain definite algebraic transformations to the original function. Thus consider the equation

$$\sqrt{x^2 + y^2} = \frac{y}{\sqrt{x^2 + y^2}}$$

which may be rearranged to give the equation

$$\left(y - \tfrac{1}{2}\right)^2 + x^2 = \left(\tfrac{1}{2}\right)^2.$$

If we now permit multivalued functions, then the graph is a circle of radius $\tfrac{1}{2}$ and origin at $(0, \tfrac{1}{2})$ as shown in Figure 1.3a.

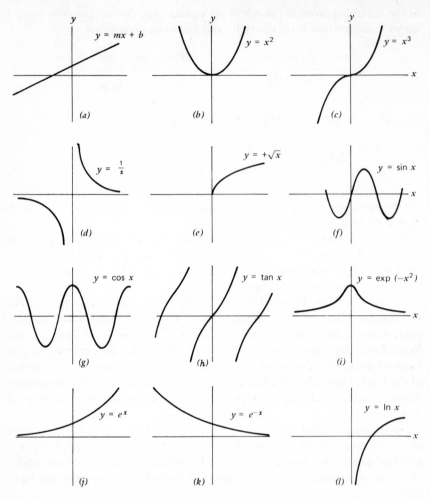

Fig. 1.2 Graphs of some common functions.

On the other hand, polar coordinates r, θ may be defined with reference to a right triangle (Figure 1.4) to yield the set of transformation equations

$$\boxed{\begin{aligned} x &= r\cos\theta \\ y &= r\sin\theta \end{aligned}}\,,$$

and if these relations are substituted into the equation above, the result becomes $r = \sin\theta$. At this point we can do one of two things: either erect a

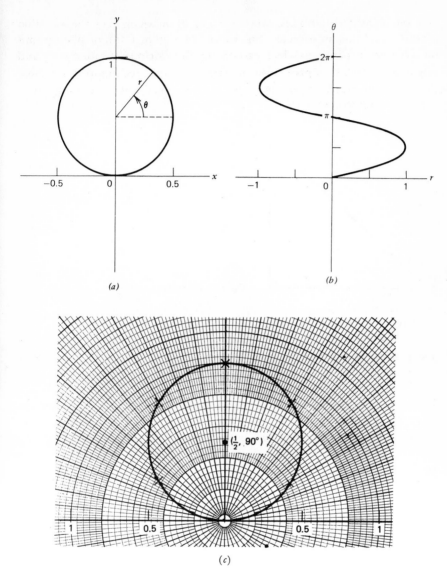

Fig. 1.3 Graph of a function and its equivalent in (*a*) rectangular Cartesian coordinates; in (*b*) polar coordinates, plotted on rectangular axes; and in (*c*) polar coordinates, plotted on polar coordinate axes.

new set of rectangular axes, labeled r and θ, in which case the equation $r = \sin\theta$ graphs as an ordinary sine curve (see Figure 1.3b), or plot $r = \sin\theta$ on polar graph paper, in which case the result is a circle of radius $r = \frac{1}{2}$ and origin at $(\frac{1}{2}, \frac{1}{2}\pi)$, thus preserving the original graph (see Figure 1.3c). Note that on polar graph paper the graph of $r = \theta$ would not be a straight line (what would it look like?).

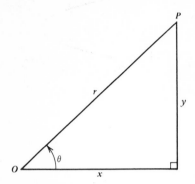

Fig. 1.4   Polar coordinates.

2   EQUATIONS OF THE FIRST DEGREE; DETERMINANTS

The general equation of the first degree is

$$Ax + By + C = 0$$

and its graph (Figure 1.5) is a line of slope $(-A/B)$ and of y intercept $(-C/B)$. Unlike other curves, the slope is constant for all intervals along the line. Often the equation is put in the form

$$y = mx + b,$$

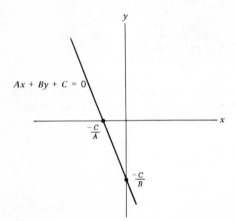

Fig. 1.5   Graph of $Ax + By + C = 0$.

from which the slope is m and the y intercept is b. In polar coordinates the first equation above becomes

$$r(A\cos\theta + B\sin\theta) + C = 0.$$

Note that it is not linear in θ. A line through the origin has the form $y = mx$; in polar coordinates this is simply $\theta = \tan^{-1}m$. Two other special cases are the following:

1. A line perpendicular to the polar axis: $r = (-b/m)\sec\theta$.
2. A line parallel to the polar axis: $r = b\csc\theta$.

Many ostensibly complex equations can be redefined so as to take on the form of a linear equation. For example, consider the famous *Eyring rate equation.*[3]

$$k = \frac{k'T}{h}\exp\left(\frac{-\Delta G^*}{RT}\right).$$

This equation is a relation between the rate constant, k, of a reaction and the free energy of activation, ΔG^*, of the reaction (Figure 1.6). The symbols k', h, and R stand for Boltzmann's, Planck's, and the gas constants, respectively, and T is the absolute temperature. The equation expresses a complicated variation of k with T. Now if we take natural logarithms of both sides and rearrange slightly, we get the equation

$$\ln\left(\frac{k}{T}\right) = \left(\frac{-\Delta G^*}{R}\right)\frac{1}{T} + \ln\left(\frac{k'}{h}\right)$$

which is of the form $y = mx + b$ with the slope m being the quantity $(-\Delta G^*/R)$, y being the variable $\ln(k/T)$, and the y intercept being the quantity $\ln(k'/h)$.

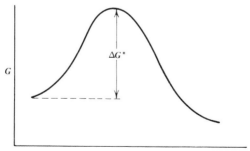

Reaction coordinate

Fig. 1.6   Free energy of activation.

[3]After the American chemist Henry Eyring (1901–   ).

Example 1. Kuempel and co-workers[4] obtained the following pseudo first-order rate data for the hydrolysis reaction:

$$Ru(NH_3)_5Br^+ + H_2O \xrightarrow{k} Ru(NH_3)_5H_2O^{2+} + Br^-.$$

$k(sec^{-1})$	$T(°C)$
1.2	15
3.8	20
5.4	25
8.3	30
12.2	35

Calculate the free energy of activation for the reaction.

Answer. A plot of $\ln(k/T)$ versus $1/T$ is prepared as shown in Figure 1.7 and a best-fitting straight line is drawn. The slope of the line is -11.9×10^3 deg, and this is to be equated to $-\Delta G^*/R$ according to the equation above. Hence $\Delta G^* = 11.9 \times 10^3$ deg $\times 1.98 \times 10^{-3}$ kcal mole^{-1}deg^{-1}, or about 24 kcal mole^{-1}.

Problems in which two equations of the first degree (in x and y) are to be solved simultaneously are common. They can arise, for example, in the balancing of complicated redox equations by purely algebraic means. These problems are usually solved by substitution; thus consider the redox reaction between zinc and dilute nitric acid. If we assign literal coefficients to the

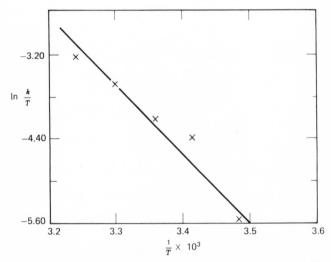

Fig. 1.7 Eyring plot for hydrolysis of the coordination complex $Ru(NH_3)_5Br^+$.

[4]J. R. Kuempel et al., *Inorg. Chem.*, **12**, 1036 (1973).

various species, we have the equation

$$a\text{Zn} + b\text{H}^+ + c\text{NO}_3^- \rightarrow a\text{Zn}^{2+} + c\text{NH}_4^+ + 3c\text{H}_2\text{O}.$$

As written, the elements zinc, nitrogen, and oxygen are already balanced. For hydrogen and for charge we may write the following conservation equations:

$$\text{H: } b = 4c + 6c \text{ or } b = 10c$$

$$\text{charge: } b - c = 2a + c \text{ or } b = 2c + 2a.$$

Three unknowns are contained in these two equations, but there is an infinite number of sets of coefficients that will balance the chemical equation (these sets are all multiples of one another). Let us therefore arbitrarily assign a the value of unity. Then substitution of the first equation into the second gives

$$10c = 2c + 2$$

and $c = \frac{1}{4}$, from which we get $b = 2\frac{1}{2}$. Finally, to clear of fractions so that the chemical equation is interpretable at the molecular level if necessary, we multiply a, b, c by 4. The final result is

$$4\text{Zn} + 10\text{H}^+ + \text{NO}_3^- \rightarrow 4\text{Zn}^{2+} + \text{NH}_4^+ + 3\text{H}_2\text{O}.$$

For very complex redox equations this method reduces the amount of labor to less than that required for the oxidation number and the half-cell methods. It rests on the one solid principle of conservation of mass. In contrast, the oxidation number method involves the use of numbers that at times seem questionable to students (particularly in the case of organic redox reactions), and the half-cell method requires splitting a perfectly acceptable reaction into two hypothetical ones.

The simultaneous solution of two or more linear equations in several unknowns can be given a simple geometric interpretation. Thus consider the following problem:

$$\left.\begin{array}{l} x + y = 7 \\ 2x - 3y = 4 \end{array}\right\} \; x = 7 - y, \text{ so } 2(7 - y) - 3y = 4$$

$$\boxed{y = 2, x = 5}$$

This solution represents the *point* where two lines intersect, these two lines being $x + y = 7$ and $2x - 3y = 4$.

When the number of variables is three or greater, it is often more convenient to use *determinants* and to apply *Cramer's rule*.[5] For example, if we wish to solve

$$x - 2y + 3z = 6$$

$$3x - y - z = -2$$

$$2x - 3y + 2z = 2$$

[5]After the Swiss mathematician Gabriel Cramer (1704–1752), who introduced the rule in 1750 although he did not use the concept or the notation of determinants.

we first write the system determinant:

$$D = \begin{vmatrix} 1 & -2 & 3 \\ 3 & -1 & -1 \\ 2 & -3 & 2 \end{vmatrix}.$$

Then, to solve for x replace the x coefficients in D by the quantities on the right-hand sides of the equations, write a new determinant, and finally divide by D:

$$x = \frac{\begin{vmatrix} 6 & -2 & 3 \\ -2 & -1 & -1 \\ 2 & -3 & 2 \end{vmatrix}}{\begin{vmatrix} 1 & -2 & 3 \\ 3 & -1 & -1 \\ 2 & -3 & 2 \end{vmatrix}}.$$

To evaluate a determinant of any size we use the *Laplace expansion in minors*. For example, this theorem gives for a three-by-three determinant

$$\begin{vmatrix} a_{11} & a_{12} & a_{13} \\ a_{21} & a_{22} & a_{23} \\ a_{31} & a_{32} & a_{33} \end{vmatrix} = (+1)a_{11} \begin{vmatrix} a_{22} & a_{23} \\ a_{32} & a_{33} \end{vmatrix}$$

$$+ (-1)a_{12} \begin{vmatrix} a_{21} & a_{23} \\ a_{31} & a_{33} \end{vmatrix} + (+1)a_{13} \begin{vmatrix} a_{21} & a_{22} \\ a_{31} & a_{32} \end{vmatrix}$$

followed by the prescription

$$\begin{vmatrix} a_{22} & a_{23} \\ a_{32} & a_{33} \end{vmatrix} = a_{22}a_{33} - a_{23}a_{32}$$

and so forth. Note the alternation of signs in front of the multipliers in the expansion above. Alternatively, three-by-three determinants may be evaluated by the mnemonic shown below in which the sum of all counterclockwise products is subtracted from the sum of all clockwise products.

$$\begin{vmatrix} a_{11} & a_{12} & a_{13} \\ a_{21} & a_{22} & a_{23} \\ a_{31} & a_{32} & a_{33} \end{vmatrix} = \begin{bmatrix} a_{11}a_{22}a_{33} + \\ a_{12}a_{23}a_{31} + \\ a_{13}a_{32}a_{21} \end{bmatrix} - \begin{bmatrix} a_{13}a_{22}a_{31} + \\ a_{12}a_{21}a_{33} + \\ a_{11}a_{32}a_{23} \end{bmatrix}$$

                 Clockwise   Counterclockwise

This mnemonic, however, does not apply to higher-order determinants.

Example 2. In the simple molecular orbital theory of cyclobutadiene (C_4H_4), the following determinant must be expanded.

$$\begin{vmatrix} x & 1 & 0 & 1 \\ 1 & x & 1 & 0 \\ 0 & 1 & x & 1 \\ 1 & 0 & 1 & x \end{vmatrix}.$$

Express this determinant as a polynomial in x.

Answer. A Laplace expansion across the top row gives

$$(x)\begin{vmatrix} x & 1 & 0 \\ 1 & x & 1 \\ 0 & 1 & x \end{vmatrix} - (1)\begin{vmatrix} 1 & 1 & 0 \\ 0 & x & 1 \\ 1 & 1 & x \end{vmatrix} + 0 - (1)\begin{vmatrix} 1 & x & 1 \\ 0 & 1 & x \\ 1 & 0 & 1 \end{vmatrix}$$

and if we now expand each of the three-by-three determinants by the clockwise–counterclockwise mnemonic, we get

$$x(x^3 + 0 + 0 - 0 - x - x) - (x^2 + 1 + 0 - 0 - 0 - 1)$$

$$- (1 + x^2 + 0 - 1 - 0 - 0).$$

Finally, after collecting like terms one obtains $x^4 - 4x^2$.

If we now return to our original problem, we find that $x = -10/D = 1$ and similarly,

$$y = \frac{\begin{vmatrix} 1 & 6 & 3 \\ 3 & -2 & -1 \\ 2 & 2 & 2 \end{vmatrix}}{D} = 2.$$

Finally, by substitution we have $z = 3$. Note that when $D = 0$ a finite solution is not possible. This happens, for example, when the equations are not consistent or are not independent. Thus for the set of equations

$$x - 2y + 3z = 6$$

$$3x - y - z = -2$$

$$4x - 3y + 2z = a$$

we have as the system determinant

$$D = \begin{vmatrix} 1 & -2 & 3 \\ 3 & -1 & -1 \\ 4 & -3 & 2 \end{vmatrix}$$

$$= -2 + 8 - 27 + 12 + 12 - 3$$

$$= 0.$$

Addition of the first two equations reveals that when $a = 4$ the equations are not all independent, and when a is anything else the equations are inconsistent.

Other properties of determinants that are useful are the following:

1. If all elements of a row or column are multiplied by C, the value of the determinant is multiplied by C.

2. The value of a determinant is *not* changed if the elements of any row (or column) are multiplied by C and are added to the corresponding elements of another row (or column).

3. If a determinant has two identical rows or columns its value is zero.

4. If two rows (or columns) of a determinant are interchanged, the sign of the determinant is changed but the magnitude remains the same.

3 EQUATIONS OF THE SECOND DEGREE; IMAGINARIES

The general equation of the second degree may be written as

$$Ax^2 + Bxy + Cy^2 + Dx + Ey + F = 0.$$

The graph of such a function depends on various possible relations between the coefficients.

Circle	$B = 0, A = C$
Parabola or two parallel or coincident lines	$B^2 - 4AC = 0$
Ellipse	$B^2 - 4AC < 0, A \neq C$
Hyperbola or two intersecting lines	$B^2 - 4AC > 0$

The various geometric possibilities listed above are collectively referred to as the *conic sections*, and the relations to the right may be looked upon as algebraic definitions of the conic sections.

When you first encountered these geometric forms in school, however, you were probably introduced to them by way of their geometric definitions. Thus a circle is the locus of all points equidistant from a given fixed point, and an ellipse is the locus of all points the sum of whose distances from two given fixed points, called the *foci*, is constant. Or again, a parabola is the locus of a point P which moves so that the ratio of its distance from a fixed point, called the *focus*, and from a fixed line, called the *directrix*, is unity (see Figure 1.8). The focal chord passing through F and parallel to the directrix is referred to as the *latus rectum*.

Often the geometric definitions of the conic sections are more useful, but you should also learn to recognize their algebraic counterparts. Thus the conditions for the circle allow the second-degree equation to be written in the form

$$(x - h)^2 + (y - k)^2 = r^2$$

where r is the radius of the circle and (h, k) is its center or origin.

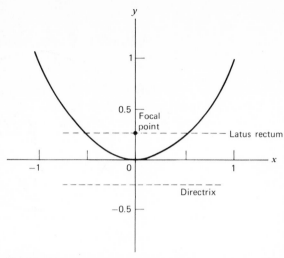

Fig. 1.8 The parabola.

Useful trigonometric identities can frequently be proved with the aid of the conic sections. If we take our graph (Figure 1.9) of the circle of radius r and center (h,k), then from simple geometry it is not hard to see that

$$\text{area } OCB = \text{area } ACB - \text{area } AOB$$

$$\tfrac{1}{2}r^2\sin 2\theta = \tfrac{1}{2}(2r)(2r\sin\theta)\sin(\tfrac{1}{2}\pi - \theta) - \tfrac{1}{2}(2r\cos\theta)(r\sin\theta)$$

$$\sin 2\theta = 2\sin\theta\cos\theta.$$

Inspection of the equations used to define polar coordinates shows that, in general,

$$\sin^2\theta + \cos^2\theta = 1$$

so that combination of this with the above result gives

$$\cos 2\theta = 2\cos^2\theta - 1$$

$$= \cos^2\theta - \sin^2\theta.$$

It is from results such as this that the "half-angle formulas" are derived. Thus the equation above may also be written as

$$\cos\tfrac{1}{2}\theta = \sqrt{\frac{1+\cos\theta}{2}} \ .$$

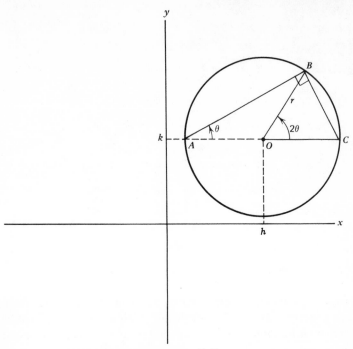

Fig. 1.9 A circle of radius r and center at (h,k).

More generally, it can be shown that

$$\sin(\theta \pm \phi) = \sin\theta\cos\phi \pm \cos\theta\sin\phi$$

$$\cos(\theta \pm \phi) = \cos\theta\cos\phi \mp \sin\theta\sin\phi.$$

Other important relations that you should remember, and that are stated with reference to the triangle in Figure 1.10, are the *law of sines* and the *law of cosines*:

Law of sines: $\dfrac{\sin a}{A} = \dfrac{\sin b}{B} = \dfrac{\sin c}{C}$

Law of cosines: $C^2 = A^2 + B^2 - 2AB\cos c.$

If y is regarded as the dependent variable, then the general second-degree equation can be written as

$$Cy^2 + (Bx + E)y + (Ax^2 + Dx + F) = 0$$

or

$$ay^2 + by + c = 0$$

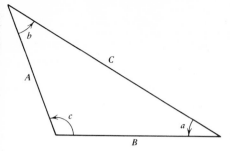

Fig. 1.10 The laws of sines and of cosines.

where $a \equiv C$, $b = f(x)$, and $c = g(x)$.[6] Then, on rearrangement, this becomes

$$y^2 + \left(\frac{b}{a}\right)y = \frac{-c}{a}$$

$$y^2 + \left(\frac{b}{a}\right)y + \frac{b^2}{4a^2} = \frac{b^2}{4a^2} - \frac{c}{a}$$

$$\left(y + \frac{b}{2a}\right)\left(y + \frac{b}{2a}\right) = \left[\sqrt{\frac{b^2 - 4ac}{4a^2}}\right]^2 .$$

Hence on taking the square root of both sides one has the familiar *quadratic formula*:

$$\boxed{y = \frac{-b \pm \sqrt{b^2 - 4ac}}{2a}} .$$

Another way to approach the solution to the quadratic equation has the advantage of suggesting a line of attack on equations of the third degree. Consideration of the binomial expansion of $(y + 1)^n$ shows that in an equation of the nth degree

$$y^n + a_1 y^{n-1} + a_2 y^{n-2} + \cdots + a_n = 0$$

the term of degree $n - 1$ can always be removed by making the substitution $y = u - (a_1/n)$. Thus in the equation $ay^2 + by + c = 0$, that we may write as

$$y^2 + \left(\frac{b}{a}\right)y + \frac{c}{a} = 0,$$

let $y = u - (b/2a)$. Substitution and rearrangement then yield

$$u^2 = \frac{1}{4}\left(\frac{b}{a}\right)^2 - \frac{c}{a} ;$$

[6]The symbol $\equiv$ means "is identically equivalent to."

hence

$$u = \pm \frac{\sqrt{b^2 - 4ac}}{2a} .$$

From this the original quadratic formula can be recovered easily.

When $b^2 - 4ac < 0$, there can be no graph in the real plane. Mathematicians extended the range of algebra by inventing *complex numbers*: functions of the quantity $i = \sqrt{-1}$, subject to the law that $i^2 = -1$. Quantities of the form bi are referred to as pure imaginaries, and the mixed quantities $a + bi$ are said to be complex. Solutions to an equation such as

$$x^2 + x + 1 = 0$$

may thus be expressed after applying the quadratic formula as

$$x = -\tfrac{1}{2} \pm \tfrac{1}{2} i \sqrt{3} .$$

4   FUNCTIONS OF A COMPLEX VARIABLE

From the above it would seem that we have introduced complex numbers[7] in a purely algebraic way. There is a geometric way in which complex numbers can be viewed that serves to bring out their close association (but not identity) with vectors. It was Hamilton who in 1837 pointed out that in $x + iy$, the iy cannot really be added to x. The use of the plus sign is a historical accident, and a complex number is to be throught of as nothing more than an ordered pair (x, y) of real numbers which describes the location of a point in a plane. Thus point A in Figure 1.11 is $4 + 2i$. With it we may associate a length, namely, the length of the segment OA. We say that $4 + 2i$ has *modulus* $r = \sqrt{20}$. It also has *amplitude* $\theta = \tan^{-1} \tfrac{1}{2}$, and thus any complex number z may also be expressed in the form

$$z = r(\cos\theta + i\sin\theta)$$

or, more concisely, just $z = r\,\mathrm{Cis}\,\theta$.

A consistent way of performing addition and subtraction of complex numbers is suggested by Figure 1.11, namely, in the same way as addition

---

[7]The Italian mathematician Rafaello Bombelli in his *Algebra* (1572) carried on where Hindu and Arab algebraists left off by elevating $\sqrt{-1}$ to the rank of a number and defining arithmetic operations on it. The geometric interpretation of complex numbers is usually credited to Caspar Wessel (1745–1818), a Norwegian surveyor, and independently to the Swiss–French mathematician Jean Robert Argand (1768–1822). See W. W. Rouse Ball, *A Short Account of the History of Mathematics*, 4th ed., Macmillan, London, 1927.

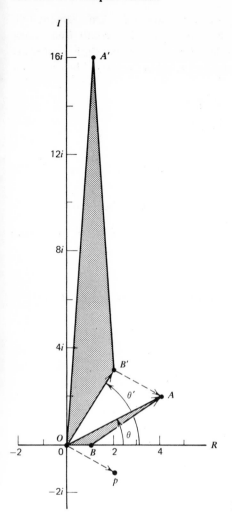

Fig. 1.11 The Argand plane.

and subtraction of displacements or directed line segments. Thus if $A = (4, 2)$ and $B' = (2, 3)$, then $OA - OB' = B'A$, and this identifies a line segment OP, where $P = (4 - 2, 2 - 3)$, or the point $(2, -1)$. For two complex numbers $z_1 = x + yi$ and $z_2 = x' + y'i$, we accordingly define the operations of addition and subtraction as follows:

$$z_1 \pm z_2 = \{ x \pm x' + (y \pm y')i \}.$$

Multiplication is more interesting because here we introduce quite naturally the requirement that $i^2 = -1$. Consider the triangle OAB, where B

$=(1,0)$, and suppose we wish to multiply OA and OB'. On segment OB' construct triangle $OA'B'$ so that it is similar to OAB (recall from plane geometry that two triangles are similar if their corresponding angles are equal or if the ratios of their corresponding sides are equal). Then we have $OA/OA' = OB/OB'$, or

$$OA \cdot OB' = OB \cdot OA'$$
$$= OA'$$

since the length of OB is one.

In terms of the polar coordinates of the points A, B', and A', we may write this as

$$(r\cos\theta, r\sin\theta) \cdot (r'\cos\theta', r'\sin\theta') = \{ rr'\cos(\theta + \theta'), rr'\sin(\theta + \theta') \}.$$

If we use the relations given in Section 1.3 for the sine and cosine of the sum of two angles, this becomes

$$(r\cos\theta, r\sin\theta) \cdot (r'\cos\theta', r'\sin\theta') =$$
$$\{ rr'\cos\theta\cos\theta' - rr'\sin\theta\sin\theta', rr'\sin\theta\cos\theta' + rr'\cos\theta\sin\theta' \}$$

or

$$(x, y) \cdot (x', y') = (xx' - yy', yx' + xy').$$

However, if two complex numbers $z_1 = x + yi$ and $z_2 = x' + y'i$ are treated as ordinary binomials and are multiplied,

$$(x + yi) \cdot (x' + y'i) = \{ xx' + yy'i^2 + (yx' + xy')i \},$$

then in order for this result to be consistent with that given above, we must stipulate that i^2 is to be replaced by -1. This definition of multiplication of complex numbers leads to associativity, commutativity, and distributivity (see Section 1.1), all of which are highly desirable. The operations of addition and multiplication are also closed; that is, the addition or multiplication of two complex numbers does not yield a new kind of number. Further, it is not hard to see that a complex number $z = x + yi$ is zero only when $x = y = 0$, and that two complex numbers are equal when their real parts are equal and their imaginary parts are equal.

At this point we may anticipate two comparisons of complex numbers with other quantities. First, although addition of two complex numbers is in essence the same as that of addition of two vectors, multiplication is not. For example, the product of two complex numbers can never be zero unless at least one of them is identically zero. In contrast, the dot or scalar product of two vectors can be zero even if neither is a null vector. Second, whereas real numbers can be ordered, that is, arranged in an ascending or descending order, complex numbers cannot. There is no meaning attached to the statement $z_1 > z_2$. Their moduli, which by definition are real numbers, can be ordered, however.

A function of a complex variable is one where the independent variable is a complex number $z = x + yi$. For example, consider the function

$$f(z) = z^n$$

where n is any integer. Suppose for concreteness that $n = 2$. Then we have

$$f(z) = r(\cos\theta + i\sin\theta) \times r(\cos\theta + i\sin\theta)$$

$$= r^2\{\cos^2\theta - \sin^2\theta + (2\sin\theta\cos\theta)i\}$$

$$= r^2(\cos 2\theta + i\sin 2\theta)$$

from relations given earlier. Next, suppose that $n = 3$. Then we have in a similar manner

$$f(z) = r^2(\cos 2\theta + i\sin 2\theta) \times r(\cos\theta + i\sin\theta)$$

$$= r^3\{\cos 2\theta\cos\theta - \sin 2\theta\sin\theta + (\sin 2\theta\cos\theta + \cos 2\theta\sin\theta)i\}$$

$$= r^3(\cos 3\theta + i\sin 3\theta).$$

Thirdly, suppose that $n = -1$. In this case we can write

$$f(z) = z^{-1}$$

$$= \frac{1}{r}\frac{1}{\cos\theta + i\sin\theta}$$

$$= \frac{1}{r}\frac{\cos\theta - i\sin\theta}{\cos^2\theta + \sin^2\theta}$$

$$= \frac{1}{r}(\cos\theta - i\sin\theta)$$

$$= r^{-1}\{\cos(-\theta) + i\sin(-\theta)\}.$$

The general result can be stated in the form of the following theorem.

Theorem 1 (de Moivre's Theorem[8]). *If* $f(z) = z^n$ *and n is any integer, then*

$$f(z) = r^n \operatorname{Cis} n\theta$$

and if n is a nonintegral rational number, then one of the values of $f(z)$ *is* r^n *Cis* $n\theta$.

To see the reason for the particular form of the latter part of the theorem, consider the problem of solving the equation $z^n = a$. For generality, let

[8]After the French-born mathematician Abraham de Moivre (1667–1754).

$a = R(\cos\theta + i\sin\theta)$; then the problem has the form

$$r^n(\cos n\theta + i\sin n\theta) = R(\cos\theta + i\sin\theta).$$

If we equate reals with reals and imaginary parts with imaginary parts, we have

$$r^n\cos n\theta = R\cos\theta \qquad\qquad r^n\sin n\theta = R\sin\theta$$

and if we set $r = R^{1/n}$, then we have the two equations

$$\cos n\theta = \cos\theta \qquad\qquad \sin n\theta = \sin\theta.$$

These will be satisfied whenever $n\theta = \phi \pm 2\pi m$, where m is a non-negative integer. Thus

$$\theta = \frac{\phi}{n} \pm 2\pi\left(\frac{m}{n}\right)$$

with m taking values $0, 1, 2, \ldots, (n-1)$, and the solution to the original problem is therefore

$$z = \sqrt[n]{R}\left\{\cos\left(\frac{\phi + 2\pi m}{n}\right) + i\sin\left(\frac{\phi + 2\pi m}{n}\right)\right\}.$$

It is customary to designate the *principal value* of $\sqrt[n]{a}$ as the case when $m = 0$ and the angle ϕ is limited to a range of 2π, say, from $-\pi$ to $+\pi$ or 0 to 2π.

$$\sqrt[n]{a} = \sqrt[n]{R}\left(\cos\frac{\phi}{n} + i\sin\frac{\phi}{n}\right)$$

$$= \sqrt[n]{R}\,\text{Cis}\,\frac{\phi}{n}$$

As another common example of a function of a complex variable, take the case of $f(z) = e^z$. Now two properties of real exponents are

$$(1)\ e^a e^b = e^{a+b}$$
$$(2)\ e^0 = 1.$$

If we wish e^z to preserve these properties also, then it is necessary for $e^z = e^x \cdot e^{yi}$. We now *define* e^{yi} to be Cis y; then if z is real (i.e., $y = 0$), the expression e^z reduces to e^x, and if $z_1 = x + yi$ and $z_2 = x' + y'i$ are two complex numbers, one can show by means of the trigonometric relations given earlier that algebraic rule (1) above holds for exponents which are complex (this is not hard to show; try it!).

$$e^{z_1} \times e^{z_2} = \exp(z_1 + z_2).$$

Some special cases of e^z are worth noting.

x	y	e^z
0	$2\pi n$	1
1	0	e
0	π	-1
0	$\frac{1}{2}\pi$	i

For finite x and y, the function e^z can never be zero.

The discussion above shows that we now have still another way to represent complex numbers, namely, in the form $z = re^{i\theta}$. In this form the operations of multiplication and division are particularly easy.

$$\frac{z_1}{z_2} = \frac{re^{i\theta}}{r'e^{i\theta'}} = \frac{r}{r'}\exp[i(\theta - \theta')].$$

The table above shows that if the amplitude θ is of the form $\theta = \phi \pm 2\pi n$, then the complex numbers $re^{i\theta}$ and $re^{i\phi}$ are identical for all integral n. If now we inquire about the natural logarithm of z, we see that it is not uniquely determined.

$$\ln z = \ln r + i\phi \pm 2\pi n i$$

As before, we designate the principal value of this function, written Log z, as the case where $n = 0$ and $-\pi < \phi \leqslant \pi$:

$$\text{Log}\, z = \ln r + i\phi.$$

This definition of the logarithm of a complex number allows us to handle still other possibilities. Thus for a complex number raised to a power that is also complex, we write

$$z^w = e^{w\,\text{Log}\, z}$$

$$= e^{w\ln r}e^{iw\phi}.$$

Finally, we turn to trigonometric functions of a complex variable. Since by definition one has

$$e^{yi} = \cos y + i\sin y$$

it is natural to define the cosine and sine of a complex number in a similar way.

$$e^{zi} = \cos z + i\sin z$$

If the sign of the exponent is negative, then this would become

$$e^{-zi} = \cos(-z) + i\sin(-z)$$

$$= \cos z - i\sin z$$

by analogy with the behavior of the sine and cosine of real arguments. Now if these two equations are added and subtracted, respectively, we get

$$\cos z = \frac{e^{zi} + e^{-zi}}{2}$$

$$\sin z = \frac{e^{zi} - e^{-zi}}{2i}.$$

As you will see in Chapter 3, these equations bear an intimate relationship to hyperbolic trigonometric functions.

Example 3. Find the following for $z = 1 + i$:

$$(1) \quad \sqrt{z} \qquad (2) \quad e^z \qquad (3) \quad \cos z.$$

Answer. By reference to Figure 1.11 one can see that z can be written as $\sqrt{2}\ (\cos\frac{1}{4}\pi + i \sin\frac{1}{4}\pi)$.

(1) $\sqrt{z} = (\sqrt{2}\ )^{\frac{1}{2}}\mathrm{Cis}\dfrac{\pi}{8}$

$\qquad \cong 1.19\left(\cos\dfrac{\pi}{8} + i\sin\dfrac{\pi}{8}\right)$

$\qquad = 1.10 + 0.45i$

(2) $e^z = e^1 e^i$

$\qquad = e\,\mathrm{Cis}\,1$

$\qquad = e(\cos 1 + i\sin 1)$

$\qquad \cong 1.47 + 2.38i$

(3) $\cos z = \frac{1}{2}\left(e^{i-1} + e^{-i+1}\right)$

$\qquad = \frac{1}{2}(\cos 1 + i\sin 1)e^{-1} + \frac{1}{2}(\cos 1 - i\sin 1)e^{1}$

$\qquad = \dfrac{(e^2 + 1)\cos 1}{2e} + \dfrac{(1 - e^2)\sin 1}{2e}i$

$\qquad \cong 0.83 - 0.99i$

There is nothing imaginary about imaginary numbers; they are as real a concept as the so-called real numbers. The term is admittedly unfortunate, and to help remove some of the mystery surrounding imaginary numbers, the American mathematician Arnold Dresden (1882–1954) suggested that they be called *normal numbers* because in the Argand diagram the imaginary axis is normal (i.e., perpendicular) to the real axis. This suggestion is rendered more plausible by the following physical interpretation. A directed line segment four units long, for example, and pointing along the positive real axis, is transformed upon multiplication by i into a new directed line segment of identical length but perpendicular to the first. In other words, multiplication by i is equivalent to a rotation by 90° in the plane of any vector. See if you can show from Figure 1.11 that in the more general case a multiplication by $\cos\theta + i\sin\theta$ is equivalent to a rotation in the plane by θ degrees of any directed line segment. In Chapter 6 we will see that this operation has its counterpart in matrix terminology.

5   THE GENERAL CUBIC; THE BINOMIAL THEOREM

Occasionally one has to solve an equation of the third degree in one independent variable. A number of approaches are available; one procedure is outlined below. Let the equation be written as

$$ax^3 + 3bx^2 + 3cx + d = 0.$$

Substitute $x = (1/a)(z - b)$ to give

$$z^3 + 3Hz + G = 0$$

where $H = ac - b^2$ and $G = a^2d - 3abc + 2b^3$. Now assume a solution to this equation of the form

$$z = \sqrt[3]{p} + \sqrt[3]{q}\;.$$

If this is cubed and rearranged, there results the identity

$$z^3 - 3\sqrt[3]{p}\,\sqrt[3]{q}\left(\sqrt[3]{p} + \sqrt[3]{q}\right) - (p + q) = 0$$

or

$$z^3 - 3\sqrt[3]{p}\,\sqrt[3]{q}\,z - (p + q) = 0$$

and hence by comparison with the equation above in H and G,

$$H = -\sqrt[3]{pq}$$

$$G = -(p + q).$$

Elimination of q from these two equations gives the quadratic equation

$$p^2 + pG - H^3 = 0.$$

What has been accomplished so far, by means of a clever substitution and by assuming a form for the answer, is to show that the solution of the original third-degree equation can be made to hinge upon the solution of an equation of lower degree, namely, a quadratic equation. This auxiliary equation, which must be solved before the solution to the original one can be written down, is sometimes referred to as the *resolvent*.

We can now solve for p in the quadratic equation above by means of the quadratic formula developed previously.

$$p = \frac{1}{2}\left(-G + \sqrt{G^2 + 4H^3} \right)$$

$$\sqrt[3]{q} = \frac{-H}{\sqrt[3]{p}}$$

Therefore, it follows that z may be expressed as

$$z = \frac{1}{2}\ \sqrt[3]{4}\ \left(-G + \sqrt{G^2 + 4H^3} \right)^{1/3} - \frac{H\ \sqrt[3]{2}}{\left(-G + \sqrt{G^2 + 4H^3} \right)^{1/3}},$$

and finally, this gives

$$x = \frac{1}{a}\left[\frac{1}{2}\sqrt[3]{4}\ \left(-G + \sqrt{G^2 + 4H^3} \right)^{1/3} - \frac{H\ \sqrt[3]{2}}{\left(-G + \sqrt{G^2 + 4H^3} \right)^{1/3}} - b \right].$$

The above result is an exact result for any third-degree equation in the same way that the quadratic formula is an exact result for any second-degree equation. It is not advisable that one memorize the above formula. Since a number has three cube roots, there will be three possible values for x. In the next chapter you will learn of an alternative and approximate algebraic method of dealing with equations of degree higher than two. The above exact method of solution of the general cubic is apparently due to the Venetian mathematics professor Niccolo Fontana (1500–1557; nicknamed Tartaglia, "the stammerer"), but the procedure was wheedled out of him by the Italian "bad boy of mathematics," Girolamo Cardano (1501–1576; sometimes called the "gambling scholar" because of his authorship in ca. 1526 of a mathematical treatise called *Manual on Games of Chance*), and published in his book *Ars Magna*.[9] Some books today still refer to the method as Cardan's solution of the cubic.

There is an exact formula due to the Italian mathematician Ludovico Ferrari (1522–1565) that can be used for the solution of the general fourth-degree (quartic) equation, but you should not be bamboozled into supposing that, in principle, any algebraic equation can be solved in closed form. An important theorem (known sometimes as *Abel's theorem*) says that this, in fact, is not generally possible for equations of degree five or higher. Transcendental equations such as $\tan x = x$ also cannot, in general, be solved in closed form. However, any equation is susceptible to approximate treatment by graphical means. The following example should be studied carefully.

Example 4. Show that $x^3 - x + 2 = 0$ has only one real root.

Answer. Rewrite the equation as $x^3 = x - 2$ and then set $y = x^3$ and $z = x - 2$. The desired solution is when $y = z$, so we plot y and z versus x on the same set of Cartesian axes. From Figure 1.12 it is clear that the two curves have only one point in common—near $x = -1.5$ (a more exact value is -1.522). How would you obtain the other two roots?

It might be remarked that there is an extremely general theorem which states that any nonconstant polynomial equation has at least one root (even though we may not be able to obtain that root in closed form). This statement is known as the *fundamental theorem of algebra* and it was first proved by the great German mathematician Karl Friedrich Gauss (1777–1855) in 1799.[10] The theorem is generally proved today with the aid of statements from the powerful field of complex variables, so that many people actually regard it as one of the basic theorems in the theory of functions of a complex variable rather than one of algebra.

From the fundamental theorem of algebra one can go on to show, in general, that a nonconstant polynomial of degree n has n roots. There is a pretty result that can be obtained regarding these n roots, namely, if $x^n + c_1 x^{n-1} + c_2 x^{n-2} + \cdots + c_n = 0$, then $-c_1$ is the sum of the n roots, c_2 is the sum of all products of the roots taken two at a time, $-c_3$ is the sum of all products of the roots taken three at a time, etc. Thus if x_1, x_2, and x_3 satisfy

[9]See E. E. Kramer, *The Nature and Growth of Modern Mathematics*, Hawthorn Books, New York, 1970, pp. 96–97, 292 for this and other interesting historical material. See also O. Ore, *Cardano—The Gambling Scholar*, Dover, New York, 1965.
[10]What can one say about this great figure? He is the Napoleon of mathematics. He is the perpetrator of half that is great and nearly all that is inspired in mathematics. For biographical detail see G. W. Dunnington, *Carl Friedrich Gauss: Titan of Science*, Exposition Press, New York, 1955.

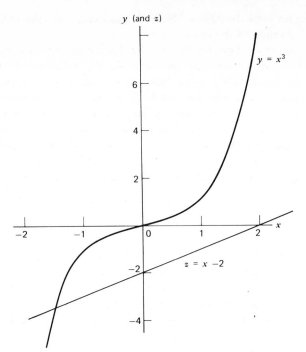

Fig. 1.12 Graphical solution of $x^3 - x + 2 = 0$.

the cubic equation

$$ax^3 + bx + c = 0,$$

then from the statements above one has the three relations

$$x_1 + x_2 + x_3 = 0$$

$$x_1 x_2 + x_1 x_3 + x_2 x_3 = \frac{b}{a}$$

$$x_1 x_2 x_3 = -\frac{c}{a}.$$

Clearly, any of these three relations could be used in a practical sense to check the accuracy of the results of solution of a particular cubic.

In the solution of the general cubic at the start of this section it was necessary to raise a binomial to the third power. In the general case for any positive integral power the *binomial theorem* gives

$$(x + y)^n = x^n + nx^{n-1}y + \frac{n(n-1)x^{n-2}y^2}{2!} + \cdots + y^n$$

or expressed more compactly

$$(x+y)^n = \sum_{r=0}^{n} \binom{n}{r} x^{n-r} y^r$$

where

$$\binom{n}{r} = {}_rC_n = \frac{n!}{r!(n-r)!}$$

$$= \text{a binomial coefficient.}$$

The ${}_rC_n$'s are important in statistics because they are the number of combinations of n distinct things taken r at a time. This is to be distinguished from the notion of permutations in which not only the groupings but also the arrangement of objects within each grouping are to be considered. Thus the number of combinations of four things taken three at a time might be represented as ABC, ABD, BCD, and ACD; there is no distinction between ABC and ACB, for example. Now the number of ways that r objects can be arranged in a line is evidently $r!$ Therefore, the number of permutations of n distinct things taken r at a time will always be $r!$ larger than the number of combinations.

$$_rP_n = r!\,{}_rC_n$$

In the example above there would be 24 permutations: ABC, ACB, BAC, BCA, CAB, CBA; ABD, ADB, BAD, BDA, DAB, DBA; BCD, and so on.

The binomial theorem, of course, is more useful than just a means of calculating statistical combinations, and we have more to say about it in Chapter 4. Incidentally, another way to remember the ${}_rC_n$'s is by means of Pascal's triangle (after the French mathematician and philosopher Blaise Pascal, 1623–1662), shown in Figure 1.13, and the recursion relationship below:

$$\binom{n}{r} + \binom{n}{r+1} = \binom{n+1}{r+1}$$

or

$$_rC_n + {}_{(r+1)}C_n = {}_{(r+1)}C_{(n+1)}.$$

The form of the binomial theorem provides an algorithm for extracting by hand the square root of a number; you perhaps may have learned this process in school. A similar but slightly lengthier process can be worked out for extraction of cube root by hand. Details are given in the book by Merritt listed in the Annotated Bibliography.

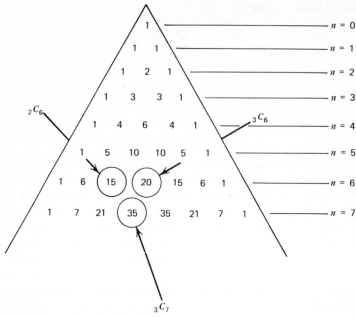

Fig. 1.13 Pascal's triangle.

6 ARITHMETIC AND GEOMETRIC SERIES

The terms of the binomial theorem constitute a *series*; this series, however, is not a simple series. Two types of series of a more elementary nature are the arithmetic and the geometric series.

Arithmetic: $a_0 + (a_0 + d) + (a_0 + 2d) + (a_0 + 3d) + \cdots +$

There is a common difference d between any two consecutive terms of an arithmetic series. Two properties of an arithmetic series that one would be interested in are its nth term and its sum after the first n terms. These can be seen by inspection.

$$n\text{th term} = a_0 + (n-1)d$$

$$\text{sum of first } n \text{ terms} = a_0 + (a_0 + d) + \cdots + \{a_0 + (n-1)d\}$$

$$= na_0 + d(1 + 2 + \cdots + n - 1)$$

$$= na_0 + d \sum_{i=1}^{n-1} i.$$

Here we have used the usual sigma notation to indicate a series summation; the index i takes integral values from 1 to $n-1$. We now need a formula for the sum of a given number of positive integers. From algebra this is known to be

$$\sum_{i=1}^{n} i = \frac{n(n+1)}{2}$$

so that for the problem above we have

$$\text{sum of first } n \text{ terms} = na_0 + d\left[\frac{(n-1)(n)}{2} \right]$$

$$= n\left[a_0 + \tfrac{1}{2}d(n-1) \right].$$

As n increases without bound, so will the sum.

Geometric: $a_0 + ra_0 + r^2a_0 + r^3a_0 + \cdots +$

Here, there is a common ratio r between any two consecutive terms. Again, we may inquire about the nth term and the sum of the first n terms.

$$n\text{th term} = r^{n-1}a_0$$

$$\text{sum of first } n \text{ terms} = a_0 + ra_0 + r^2a_0 + \cdots + r^{n-1}a_0$$

$$= S_n$$

This is not easily seen by inspection. Let us multiply S_n by r:

$$rS_n = ra_0 + r^2a_0 + r^3a_0 + \cdots + r^na_0.$$

If S_n is now subtracted from this, we get

$$rS_n - S_n = S_n(r-1)$$

$$= r^{n-1}a_0(r-1) - a_0$$

or

$$\boxed{S_n = \frac{a_0(r^{n-1}-1)}{r-1}}.$$

If $|r| \geqslant 1$, then S_n will increase without bound with n. However, if $|r| < 1$, the series will still have a finite sum as n increases without limit because r^{n-1} approaches zero as n increases without limit. This yields the result

$$\text{sum of an infinite geometric series} = \frac{a_0}{1-r}.$$

Two examples of this that you should verify on your own are the following:

$$1 - \tfrac{1}{2} + \tfrac{1}{4} - \tfrac{1}{8} + \tfrac{1}{16} - \cdots + = \tfrac{2}{3}$$

$$\sin^2\theta + \sin^4\theta + \sin^6\theta + \cdots + = \tan^2\theta.$$

Much more material on infinite series will be presented in Chapter 4.

For further reading in algebra as well as in geometry and trigonometry at an elementary level, you are urged to consult any of the manuals in the Barnes & Noble College Outline Series that are listed in the Annotated Bibliography. A great deal of interesting material at a more advanced level may also be found in Volume I of the famous work by Burnside and Panton. Extensive literature references are not made at the ends of each chapter of this book; however, you should begin to develop the habit of pursuing outside reading as a complement to your in-class assignments. The Annotated Bibliography should serve as a valuable listing of where to go for further reading on troublesome points or on topics only briefly mentioned here.

EXERCISES

Working exercises is a necessary part of your study for the following reasons: it will direct your study properly, and it should show, after you have finished a chapter, whether you have grasped the essentials. Work as many problems as you can; study sessions with other students are a good idea. Seek help for problems that give you trouble. Problems marked * are intended to be hard; those with **, very hard.

1. Functions that one normally encounters in chemistry involve arguments that can span a continuous spectrum of values. Does the definition of a function permit cases where the argument can be selected from a discrete or countable collection of elements? In Moseley's periodic law—the properties of the elements are a periodic function of their atomic number—do you see any objection to the use of the word "function"?

2. Suppose that you have a mathematical system with all the properties itemized in Section 1.1. The zero element is *defined* to be that element having the property $a + 0 = 0 + a = a$. By considering the expression $a(a + 0)$, convince yourself that the zero must also have the property $a \cdot 0 = 0 \cdot a = 0$.

3. What does $y^2 - 4y + x = 0$ become when the origin is translated to the point $(4, 2)$ and the directions of the axes remain unchanged?

4. On the same set of coordinate axes make qualitative plots of $y = \exp(x^2)$ and of $y = x^6$. As x increases which of these two functions increases faster? From another pair of plots determine whether $y = \exp(-x^2)$ or $y = x^{-6}$ approaches zero more closely as x increases. Formulate a generalization from these two examples.

5. The harmonic oscillator is an idealistic physical model that is much used in chemistry. When it is treated quantum mechanically, a set of wave functions describing its behavior can be obtained. One of these is

$$\psi_1 = A x \exp(-a x^2)$$

where A and a are merely constants. In view of your answers to Exercise 4, make a quick, qualitative sketch of ψ_1 for positive and negative values of x without actually doing any laborious calculations.

6. On the Nivlek temperature scale (named after the obscure German chemist Umwen den Nivlek) $78°N$ corresponds to $87°$ on the Celsius scale, and $13°N$ corresponds to $35°C$. What is absolute zero on the Nivlek scale?

7. The Langevin function, $L(x)$, figured prominently in Peter Debye's theory of the dipole moment. The function is defined as

$$L(x) = \coth x - \frac{1}{x}$$

where $\coth x$ stands for the hyperbolic cotangent of x. We take up hyperbolic functions a little later, but for the moment simply know that values of the hyperbolic cotangent can be looked up in mathematics tables. For experience in graphing obtain a plot of the Langevin function for the interval $0 < x \leqslant 5$. How does $L(x)$ seem to be related to x for small values of the argument? Same question for large values (say, $x > 3$) of the argument. Armed with this knowledge and supposing that tables were not available, what might you do if you wanted a quick estimate of $L(2)$?

8. Debye derived the following equation relating to a gaseous sample of a pure substance:

$$\frac{\varepsilon - 1}{\varepsilon + 2} \frac{M}{\rho} = \frac{N_0}{\varepsilon_0}\left(\alpha + \frac{\mu^2}{3kT}\right)$$

where $\varepsilon =$ the dielectric constant, $M =$ molecular weight, $\rho =$ density of the gas, N_0 = Avogadro's number, α = the molecular polarizability, μ = the molecular dipole moment, and ε_0 = the permittivity of free space $(8.854 \times 10^{-12} \, \mathrm{F\,m^{-1}})$. By making measurements of density and dielectric constant, how could you obtain both the polarizability α and the dipole moment μ?

9. A certain 100-liter distilled water tank on the roof of a freshman chemistry laboratory can be filled exactly 2 days by one still and in 36 hours by another still. Normal bench use is such that the tank could be emptied in $4\frac{1}{2}$ days. If both stills commence simultaneously to fill the empty tank and also normal use in the laboratory begins, in how many hours will the tank be two-thirds full?

10. Balance the following chemical equations by algebraic means:

(a) $\qquad$ $I_2 + Ca(OH)_2 \rightarrow CaI_2 + Ca(IO_3)_2 + H_2O$

(b) $\qquad$ $Cr_2O_7^{2-} + H^+ + CH_3CH_2OH \rightarrow CH_3CHO + H_2O + Cr^{3+}$.

11. Let V_1 ml of a solution containing m_0 g of a substance be extracted once with V_2 ml of a given immiscible solvent, and let m_1 be the mass of substance remaining in the first solution. The *distribution coefficient* of the substance for the two-solvent system is defined to be

$$K = \frac{m_1/V_1}{(m_0 - m_1)/V_2}.$$

At 25°C a solution of 5.00 g of mercuric chloride in 100 ml of water is prepared. This is then extracted three times successively with 75-ml portions of ether, and it is found that only 0.241 g of salt still remains in the aqueous phase. What is the value of $K_{H_2O/ether}$ for this salt?

12. A solution of perchloric acid is made by dissolving 0.12 μmole of pure perchloric acid in enough water to make a liter of solution. What will be the pH of this solution? Be careful of your assumptions here; you may find it helpful to first consider the case where the amount of perchloric acid used is 0.1 μmole.

13. Some simple enzyme-catalyzed reactions of a substrate S can be characterized by the *Michaelis–Menton equation*:

$$v = \frac{v_{max}[S]}{K + [S]}$$

where v is the rate of the reaction and v_{max} and K are constants to be determined. This equation is not convenient, however, because a plot of rate versus substrate concentration would not be linear. Show how to transform this equation into a form which can lead to a linear plot. Note: there is more than one way to do this; you may stumble upon the type of plot known as a *Lineweaver–Burke plot*, or 'some alternative form. From your plot how will you extract K?

14. Consider the following equilibrium: $A \overset{K}{\rightleftharpoons} 2B$. From mass action considerations we can express the equilibrium constant as

$$K = \frac{[B]^2}{[A]}.$$

Now let the equilibrium be rewritten as $2A \overset{K'}{\rightleftharpoons} 4B$. In this case the equilibrium constant is apparently

$$K' = \frac{[B]^4}{[A]^2}.$$

Clearly, $K' = K^2$, and so it looks as if a given system could be characterized by more than one equilibrium constant. By considering a $1\ M$ solution of A in each of the two cases, show, however, that this redefining of the chemical process with its attendant change in the value of the equilibrium constant does not really alter the physical description of the system.

15. Polymer preparations generally result in mixtures of molecules with different molecular weights. The "molecular weight" of the polymeric sample, therefore, can have more than one meaning:

$$\overline{M}_n = \frac{\text{number-average}}{\text{molecular weight}} = \frac{\sum\limits_i M_i n_i}{\sum\limits_i n_i}$$

where n_i = the number of molecules of the ith kind;

$$\overline{M}_w = \frac{\text{weight-average}}{\text{molecular weight}} = \frac{\sum\limits_i M_i w_i}{\sum\limits_i w_i}$$

where w_i = the weight (mass) of material with molecular weight M_i.

Values of $\overline{M}_n$ are obtained from osmotic pressure (a colligative property) measurements, whereas $\overline{M}_w$ values are obtained from light-scattering measurements. Assume a particular sample of polyethylene to contain only units of molecular weight 5000, 10,000, and 12,000. If $\overline{M}_n = 8340$ and $\overline{M}_w = 9480$, find the mole fraction of each type of polymer.

16. Assume that a reaction obeys the Arrhenius equation describing the temperature dependence of the reaction rate constant k:

$$k = A \exp\left(-E_a/RT\right)$$

and assume further that the *pre-exponential factor A* is essentially temperature independent. If a reaction is carried out at any of several temperatures close to room temperature, what would be a rough value of the *activation energy* E_a if a 10-degree increase in the temperature doubles the reaction rate?

17. The secular determinant

$$\begin{vmatrix} x & 1 & 0 \\ 1 & x & 1 \\ 0 & 1 & x \end{vmatrix} = 0$$

must be solved in order to find the π energies of the allyl cation, anion, or free radical. The variable x is $(\alpha - E)/\beta$, and α and β are quantities referred to as the *Coulomb integral* and *resonance integral*, respectively. Find the permitted values of E as a function of α and β.

18. You have the following system of linear equations:

$$2x + y + 2z + w = 3$$

$$-y - 7z - w = 7$$

$$3y + 4z - 3w = 5$$

$$2y + z + 2w = -2.$$

Apply Cramer's rule for determinants and show how you would calculate y. Also show that the following system determinant is actually equivalent to a single 3×3 determinant:

$$\begin{vmatrix} 2 & 1 & 2 & 1 \\ 0 & -1 & -7 & -1 \\ 0 & 3 & 4 & -3 \\ 0 & 2 & 1 & 2 \end{vmatrix}.$$

19. A point moves in such a way that its distance from $(3, 2)$ is always the same as its distance from the line $x = -4$. Find an expression that describes the functional behavior of this point. How would such a function look when graphed? What is the slope of the graphed figure at $x = -\frac{1}{2}$?

20. Solve the following equations for x:

   (a) $$10^x + 10^{-x} = 3$$

   (b) $$x(x+1)^3 = 3x(x^2+x) - (1-x).$$

21. What conditions must be true in order for the expression $ax^2 - bx + c$ to be a perfect square?

22. Using only the identities $\sin 2\theta = 2\sin\theta\cos\theta$ and $\sin^2\theta + \cos^2\theta = 1$, plus any needed definitions, derive expressions for the following:

   (a) $\sin\frac{1}{2}\theta$ as a function of $\sin\theta$, only

   (b) $\csc 2\theta + \cot 2\theta$ as some function of θ.

23. A new cyclotron in Europe is designed in the form of a circle with two tangent entry arms. The arms are 2 miles long and the circular arc AB contained between the arms is also 2 miles long. What is the diameter d in feet of the circular path that a particle in this cyclotron would travel?

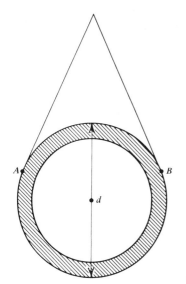

Fig. 1.14 A cyclotron.

24. Consider the two complex numbers $z_1 = 2\sqrt{3}\ e^{i\pi/6}$ and $z_2 = \sqrt{3}\ e^{-i\pi/3}$. Locate each of these numbers on an Argand diagram. Now add z_1 and z_2 algebraically and see if this agrees with what you would get by adding the displacements on the Argand diagram.

25. Find the following:

    (a) $\sqrt{3 + 2i}$

    (b) $e^{i\pi} + 1$

    (c) $\mathrm{Log}(i^i)$

    (d) the three cube roots of -1.

26. Complex numbers appear in developments of the theory of dielectrics where one is dealing with a periodic electric field, $E = E_0 e^{i\omega t}$. One is interested in knowing how the dielectric constant ε' varies with the frequency ω. An approximate theory for a dilute solution of polar molecules gives the equation

$$\varepsilon' - n^2 = \frac{N_0\rho}{M\varepsilon_0}\ \frac{\mu^2}{3kT}\ \frac{1}{1 + i\omega\tau}$$

where n = the refractive index, N_0 = Avogadro's number, ρ = density of the solution, M = molecular weight, ε_0 = the permittivity of free space, μ = the molecular dipole moment, and τ = a relaxation time. Since the right side is complex, it is reasonable to express ε' as $\varepsilon_0' + i\varepsilon_1'$. The physical quantity which is measured is ε_0'; work out what this is in terms of the other quantities.

27. The *complex conjugate* of a quantity is a new quantity formed from the old by making the changes $+i$ to $-i$ and $-i$ to $+i$ wherever the former occur in the original quantity. If Q is the original quantity, then its complex conjugate is notated $\overline{Q}$, or as Q^*. Now look at Example 3, (3) in the text again. What is $\overline{\cos z}$? Is this the same as $\cos\overline{z}$?

28. Assume that at $600°C$ the equilibrium

$$2SO_3 \rightleftharpoons 2SO_2 + O_2$$

has an equilibrium constant of 0.0276 atm, and that all three gases behave like ideal gases. If 8.00 g of SO_3 is injected into an evacuated flask of constant volume, how many grams of molecular oxygen will be present in the equilibrium mixture?

29. If $(x + x^{-1})^2 = 3$, evaluate the quantity $x^3 + x^{-3}$. If $x + x^{-1} = 1$, evaluate the quantity $x^7 + x^{-7}$.

30. Which contains more terms: the general polynomial of third degree in seven variables, that is, $(x+y+z+t+u+v+w)^3$, or the general polynomial of seventh degree in three variables?

31. By reference to Pascal's triangle determine how many different ways (combinations) four molecules can be selected from seven molecules (assumed to be distinguishable) for occupancy of some energy level. Verify your answer by writing out the possibilities.

32. Verify the two infinite geometric series presented near the end of Section 1.6. Is the trigonometric series valid for $\theta = 90°$?

33. The mean square distance, $\overline{h^2}$, from end to end of a freely rotating polymeric chair of σ links, each of length l, is given by

$$\overline{h^2} = \sigma l^2 (1 + 2\cos\theta + 2\cos^2\theta + 2\cos^3\theta + \cdots +)$$

where θ is the interlink angle. Write a compact expression for $\overline{h^2}$. Note: we have used an upper bar to indicate a quantity which has been averaged. Context will usually make it clear whether such notation is intended to mean "averaged quantity" or "complex conjugate" (Exercise 27). Some authors use the symbol $\langle\ \rangle$ to denote "averaged quantity" and some use both this symbol and the bar in the same work.

34.* Pauling found that the fractional ionic character in a bond in a diatomic molecule $A - B$, as inferred from its dipole moment, could be represented empirically by the function

$$\text{ionic character} = 1 - \exp\left\{ -\frac{1}{4}(x_A - x_B)^2 \right\}$$

where x_A and x_B are the values of the Pauling electronegativities. Make a graph of this function. Given that the dipole moment of hydrogen chloride is 1.084 D, estimate with the aid of your graph the $H - Cl$ bond distance and compare with the experimental value of 1.27 $\mathring{A}$.

35.* According to Irving Langmuir the adsorption of a gas by a solid consists of molecules condensing and evaporating from a monolayer surface of the solid. Let f equal the fraction of a surface covered by gas molecules at a given time. Then the rate of condensation of gas is $k_1(1-f)P$, where k_1 is a rate constant and P is the gas pressure. Show that at equilibrium one has the *Langmuir adsorption isotherm*:

$$f = \frac{aP}{1 + aP}$$

where a is a constant.

36.* Langmuir obtained the following data for the adsorption of methane on mica at $-183°C$ [*J. Am. Chem. Soc.*, **40**, 1361 (1918)].

Table 1.1   **Adsorption Data for Methane**

P (atm)	2.7	5.1	7.9	12.6	17.1	25.5	44.6
Vol CH_4 (reduced to STP) (mm^3)	30.6	43.7	52.7	60.6	71.2	82.2	90.2

(*a*) What simple relationship exists between f (see preceding exercise), the volume V of gas adsorbed, and the monolayer capacity V_{max} of the solid surface?

(*b*) By an appropriate graphical plot show that the above data follow a Langmuir adsorption isotherm.

37.* A rather neat application of the properties of determinants occurs in the construction of many-electron wave functions for atoms and molecules. Individual electrons are assumed to be describable by the product of a function of the spatial coordinates times a spin function. For molecules the function of the spatial coordinates is any one of the molecular orbitals; the spin function can be either the function designated as α (corresponding to "spin up") or the function β (corresponding to "spin down"). Thus if electron number 1 is to have spin β and is to be located in molecular orbital 2, we write the complete one-electron function as

$$\psi_2(1)\beta(1).$$

John C. Slater showed that acceptable many-electron wave functions can be constructed by forming a determinant in a certain way of many terms like the one above. The so-called *Slater determinant* for a four-electron molecule (e.g., lithium hydride) has the form

$$\Psi = \frac{\sqrt{6}}{12} \begin{vmatrix} \psi_1(1)\alpha(1) & \psi_1(1)\beta(1) & \psi_2(1)\alpha(1) & \psi_2(1)\beta(1) \\ \psi_1(2)\alpha(2) & \psi_1(2)\beta(2) & \psi_2(2)\alpha(2) & \psi_2(2)\beta(2) \\ \psi_1(3)\alpha(3) & \psi_1(3)\beta(3) & \psi_2(3)\alpha(3) & \psi_2(3)\beta(3) \\ \psi_1(4)\alpha(4) & \psi_1(4)\beta(4) & \psi_2(4)\alpha(4) & \psi_2(4)\beta(4) \end{vmatrix}.$$

To see how the determinant is constructed, observe that any given column contains the same molecular orbital–spin function product, and that in this one puts successively each of the electrons. Alternatively, each row is restricted to a particular electron and this is put successively into each of the molecular orbital–spin function combinations under consideration. What would happen to this determinant if one tried to describe a physical system with two electrons in the same orbital and having the same spin? Is this consistent with the Pauli exclusion principle?

38.* According to the *Law of Corresponding States* an appropriately scaled pressure should be a universal function of a reduced volume and a reduced temperature. Let us test this notion by examining the properties of coexistent liquid–gas systems. In Table 1.2 are given equilibrium vapor pressure data for three fluids.

Table 1.2   Some Vapor Pressure Data

Fluid	Temperature (°C)					
	1 mm	10 mm	40 mm	100 mm	400 mm	760 mm
O_2		−210.6	−204.1	−198.8	−188.8	−183.0
CS_2	−73.8	−44.7	−22.5	−5.10	+28.0	+46.5
C_2H_4	−168.3	−153.2	−141.3	−131.8	−113.9	−103.7

For each substance make a plot of ln (P/P_c) versus (T_c/T), where P_c and T_c are the critical pressure and critical temperature (in degrees Kelvin!).

Table 1.3   Some Critical Data

Fluid	$T_c(°C)$	$P_c(atm)$
O_2	−118.4	50.1
CS_2	279	78.0
C_2H_4	9.9	50.5

Investigate whether nearly the same function satisfactorily describes all three plots.

39.* Given only that in some base log 2 = 0.607 and log 3 = 0.959, find a good value for log 5.

40.* Early workers found that Bragg's law did not yield the same value of λ in the different orders of reflection of a monochromatic beam from a crystal. The explanation was that X rays are refracted upon penetrating a crystal. From Snell's law (see Exercises at the end of Chapter 2) the refractive index of the solid, η, is given by

$$\eta = \frac{\lambda}{\lambda'} = \frac{\sin \theta}{\sin \theta'} \,.$$

Show that Bragg's law can be written in the usual way (as a function of λ and θ) times a correction factor which takes into account the refraction that occurs upon entering the crystal.

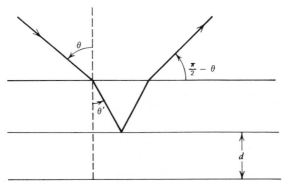

Fig. 1.15   Refraction in a crystal.

41.* J. N. Brønsted and K. J. Pedersen showed that for many reactions catalyzed by bases there is a relationship between the rate of the reaction and the strength of the base:

$$k = GK_b{}^a.$$

Here, G and a are parameters that depend upon the nature of the substrate, the solvent, the temperature, etc. The base-catalyzed hydrolysis of ethyl dichloroacetate was studied by W. P. Jencks and J. Carriuolo [*J. Am. Chem. Soc.*, **83**, 1743 (1961)].

$$\underset{\text{}}{\text{Cl}_2\text{CH}-\overset{\displaystyle \text{O}}{\overset{\|}{\text{C}}}-\text{OCH}_2\text{CH}_3} \underset{\text{base}}{\overset{\text{H}_2\text{O}}{\longrightarrow}} \text{Cl}_2\text{CH}-\overset{\displaystyle \text{O}}{\overset{\|}{\text{C}}}-\text{OH}+\text{CH}_3\text{CH}_2\text{OH}$$

Table 1.4   Rate Data for the Hydrolysis of Ethyl
Dichloroacetate

Base	Rate constant, k (liter mole^{-1} min^{-1})	Basicity constant, K_b
H_2O	5.3×10^{-6}	1.82×10^{-16}
HCO_2^-	1.9×10^{-3}	5.65×10^{-11}
$CH_3CO_2^-$	3.0×10^{-3}	5.62×10^{-10}
Pyridine	1.2×10^{-2}	1.78×10^{-9}
4-Picoline	1.7×10^{-2}	1.05×10^{-8}
Imidazole	8.2×10^{-2}	8.91×10^{-8}
OH^-	5.3×10^4	5.50×10^1

Investigate how well these data conform to the Brønsted relation, and estimate a value for the exponent a.

42.[*] A mechanical model for a diatomic molecule that is often used is that of the *rigid rotor*. It may be viewed as a sort of teeter-totter with lever arms r_1 and r_2 about the center of mass O, so that $m_1 r_1 = m_2 r_2$. The mass of this system is, of course, $m_1 + m_2$, but in many problems it is more convenient to use what is called the *reduced mass*, defined as

$$\mu = \frac{m_1 m_2}{m_1 + m_2}.$$

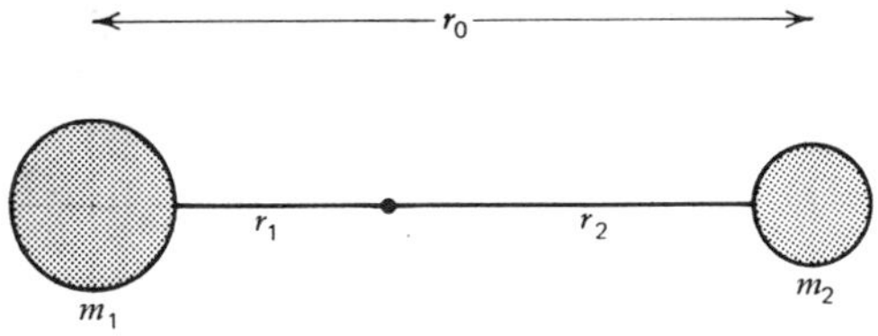

Fig. 1.16   The rigid rotor.

For example, the *moment of inertia*, I, of the molecule about its center of mass is

$$I = m_1 r_1{}^2 + m_2 r_2{}^2.$$

Write I as a function of μ and r_0.

43.[*] Refer to a standard text that gives a picture of a hexagonal close-packed unit cell (for example, see J. V. Quagliano and L. M. Vallarino, *Chemistry*, 3rd ed., Prentice-Hall, Englewood Cliffs, N. J., 1969, p. 181). Assume that the spheres in the cell touch, and calculate the percentage of space in the cell that is wasted (i.e., empty).

44.* Prove or disprove the following trigonometric relation:

$$\sec x + \tan x = \tan\left(\tfrac{1}{4}\pi + \tfrac{1}{2}x\right).$$

45.** Sums of powers of integers are often needed in applied work. Derive a formula for the sum of the squares of the first n positive integers. Hint: look at differences in the cubes of the integers. Then from your formula derive another formula for the sum of the squares of the first n positive odd integers.

[Note: of interest in relation to this problem is the fact that in a recent article there was derived a recursion relationship between the sums of nth powers and sums of lower powers.

$$S(n,r) = \frac{n(n+1)^r - \sum_{j=0}^{r-2} \binom{r}{j} S(n,j+1)}{(r+1)}$$

where

$$S(n,r) = \sum_{i=1}^{n} i^r.$$

See M. Lentner, *Am. Stat,* **27**, 87 (1973).]

46.** An analysis first given by Arthur Compton in 1923 was instrumental in demonstrating the particlelike nature of electromagnetic radiation. A photon of frequency ν strikes an electron (assumed "at rest") of energy $m_0 c^2$ (according to special relativity). The photon is scattered and the electron recoils as shown in Figure 1.17. As a result of the scattering, the electron now has a total energy of $m_0 c^2 [1 - (v^2/c^2)]^{-1/2}$. Now write the following three equations:

(*a*)   conservation of energy;   .
(*b*)   conservation of x momentum;
(*c*)   conservation of y momentum.

From these equations deduce an expression for the difference $\lambda' - \lambda$; thus show that the theory predicts (and experiment confirms) that the scattered radiation should be of longer wavelength than the incident radiation and also independent of the nature of the scattering material. In addition, show that the two scattering angles are related to each

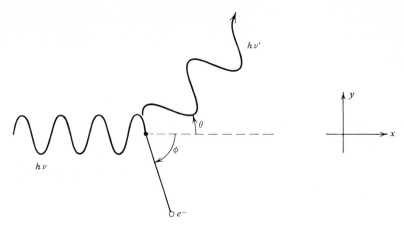

Fig. 1.17 Compton scattering.

other by the expression

$$\cot\phi = (1 + \varepsilon)\tan \tfrac{1}{2}\theta$$

where $\varepsilon = h\nu / m_0 c^2$.

47.** After considering the technique involved in the derivation of the quadratic formula and in the general solution to the cubic, see if you can devise an algorithm for solving the general quartic which hinges upon the prior solution of one or more equations of degree less than four. Test your algorithm on the equation

$$x^4 + 4x^3 + x^2 + x + 1 = 0$$

and obtain a real root for it.

Differentiation

1   REVIEW: MAXIMA AND MINIMA; IMPLICIT DIFFERENTIATION

In Chapter 1 we restricted ourselves to some elementary ideas from algebra and geometry. We now leave those areas and enter the world of the calculus (note the use of the article "the"; the word "calculus" can be used in other ways). It goes without saying that the calculus is so much an everyday part and tool of the physical sciences that no student can afford not to be proficient in it. The approach in this and succeeding chapters is to strike a median between a thoroughly rigorous treatment in which proofs of all important statements are supplied and a treatment which gives formulas and results in quantity but no feeling or understanding. In order to provide this understanding it is necessary that the language become more precise than that of the preceding chapter; this means, primarily, reacquainting yourself with the notion of a limit.

> *"No, no! the adventures first,"* said the Gryphon in an impatient tone: *"explanations take such a dreadful time."*
>
> CHAS. LUTWIDGE DODGSON

Let us begin, then, by first reviewing some basic ideas from the differential calculus. Suppose $f(x)$ is a continuous, single-valued function of x. The *derivative* of $f(x)$ is defined as the following limit, provided the limit exists and is finite:

$$y = f(x)$$

$$\frac{dy}{dx} = \lim_{h \to 0} \frac{f(x+h) - f(x)}{h}.$$

Other notations besides dy/dx for the derivative are $df(x)/dx$, $f'(x)$, and y'; in some applications $\dot{y}$ means the derivative with respect to time.

We might say a few words at this point by way of review about the term "continuous." You probably remember this as meaning qualitatively something akin to "smoothness." To be more precise, we say that a function $f(x)$ is *continuous at the point* $x = a$ if and only if the following are satisfied:

(a) $f(x)$ is defined at $x = a$;

(b) $\lim_{x \to a} f(x)$ exists, is finite, and is the same whether a is approached from the left or the right;

(c) the limit in (b) is, in fact, $f(a)$.

A way of compressing these statements is to say that $f(x)$ is continuous at $x = a$ if and only if

$$\lim_{h \to 0} [f(a+h) - f(a)] = 0$$

and this you see is, in effect, the numerator of the definition of the derivative at $x = a$. However, the existence of this limit does not automatically guarantee that

$$\lim_{h \to 0} \frac{f(x+h) - f(x)}{h}$$

for $x = a$, say, will also exist, In other words, continuity is a necessary condition for the derivative to exist, but it does not ensure that it will exist. Most functions describing some aspect of Nature are continuous, and most of these are differentiable as well, but this is something that, in general, has to be checked.

The geometrical interpretation of the derivative is that of a tangent to a curve. In Figure 2.1 as point P' moves along the curve $y = f(x)$ and approaches point P, the slope of the secant drawn through P and P' ultimately approaches the slope of the tangent drawn to the curve at point P. The slope at this point is the value of dy/dx at that point.

The derivatives of various functions have been tabulated and usually can be found in any standard textbook on the calculus; they may also be found in reference sources such as the mathematical section of the *Handbook of Chemistry and Physics*. This section is also published independently in expanded form as *Handbook of Tables for Mathematics*; see the Annotated Bibliography for a more complete reference. Some selected derivatives are presented in Table 2.1. The last entry in the table is the famous *chain rule*; it tells you how to treat functions of functions. Note also the difference between $\arcsin ax$ or $\sin^{-1} ax$, and the reciprocal of $\sin ax$ or $(\sin ax)^{-1}$.

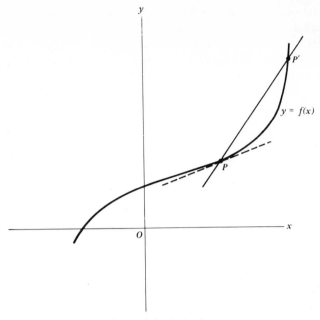

Fig. 2.1 Geometrical picture of the derivative.

Table 2.1 Some Selected Derivatives

$f(x)$	$f'(x)$	$f(x)$	$f'(x)$
$g(x)h(x)$	$g(x)h'(x) + h(x)g'(x)$	$\sin ax$	$a \cos ax$
e^{ax}	ae^{ax}	$\ln ax$	$\dfrac{1}{x}$
$\cosh ax$	$a \sinh ax$	$\sin^{-1}ax$	$a(1 - a^2x^2)^{-1/2}$
$(\sin ax)^{-1}$	$-a \csc ax \cot ax$	$g\{h(x)\}$	$\dfrac{dg(h)}{dh(x)} \cdot \dfrac{dh(x)}{dx}$

Although the derivative is notated dy/dx, no meaning has been ascribed yet to the quantities dy and dx. Our inclination is to suppose that they are very, very small changes in y and x, but this is unsatisfactory. Suppose we have the curve $y = f(x)$ and two points A and B on it (see Figure 2.2), where $A = (x_0, y_0)$ and $B = (x_0 + \delta x, y_0 + \delta y)$, where δx denotes a small change in x.

Then if B is close to A we have the approximate relationship $\delta y = (dy/dx)_{x=x_0} \delta x$. However, if C is a point at $(x_0 + dx, y_0 + dy)$ on the tangent at A, then the relationship $dy = (dy/dx)_{x=x_0} dx$ is exact. Thus the equation dy

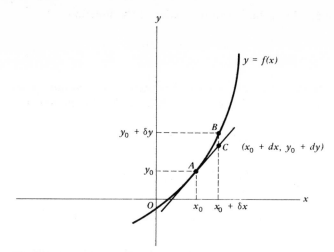

Fig. 2.2 A curve and its tangent.

$= f'(x)dx$ is a relation between two neighboring points on a tangent and not on the original curve. The relation between increments can be written as $\delta y = (f'(x) + \varepsilon)\delta x$, where ε tends to zero with δx.

A theorem of great practical use in the differential calculus is a result first derived by Leibniz[1] for the repeated differentiation of a product. Consider the expression $y = uv$, where u and v are both functions of x. One differentiation gives $y' = uv' + vu'$; a second differentiation gives $y'' = uv'' + 2u'v' + vu''$. This begins to resemble in some way the expansion of a binomial by the binomial theorem. There is, indeed, a close similarity and we state without proof the following theorem (proof can be established by induction).

Theorem 2 (Leibniz' Rule). *If* u(x) *and* v(x) *are functions of* x, *each of which possesses derivatives up to order* n, *then the product* uv *does also and its* nth *derivative is given by*

$$\frac{d^n}{dx^n}(uv) = \frac{d^n u}{dx^n} \cdot v + \binom{n}{1}\frac{d^{n-1}u}{dx^{n-1}} \cdot \frac{dv}{dx} + \binom{n}{2}\frac{d^{n-2}u}{dx^{n-2}} \cdot \frac{d^2 v}{dx^2} + \cdots + u \cdot \frac{d^n v}{dx^n}$$

where the coefficients are the binomial coefficients (see Section 1.5).

To illustrate the theorem let us consider the following example.

[1]Gottfried Wilhelm von Leibniz (1646–1716), co-inventor of the calculus with Newton, and otherwise philosopher, lawyer, and diplomat, has been described by Bertrand Russell as the last Renaissance man of modern times.

Example 5. Find the fourth derivative of the function

$$y = e^{-x} \sin x.$$

Answer. Both e^{-x} and $\sin x$ have derivatives up to infinite order. If we let $u(x) = e^{-x}$ and $v(x) = \sin x$, then one has by induction

$$\frac{d^n u}{dx^n} = (-1)^n e^{-x}$$

$$\frac{d^n v}{dx^n} = (-1)^{\frac{1}{2}n} \sin x \qquad \text{for even } n$$

$$= (-1)^{\frac{1}{2}n - \frac{1}{2}} \cos x \qquad \text{for odd } n.$$

From this $d^4 y / dx^4$ can be written down immediately as

$$\frac{d^4 y}{dx^4} = \binom{4}{0} e^{-x} \sin x + \binom{4}{1} e^{-x} \cos x - \binom{4}{2} e^{-x} \sin x$$

$$- \binom{4}{3} e^{-x} \cos x + \binom{4}{4} e^{-x} \sin x$$

$$= \boxed{-4e^{-x} \sin x}.$$

If a curve shows a relative maximum or minimum at some point, then it follows that $dy/dx = 0$ there.[2] The best way to decide whether the point is a maximum or a minimum is to sketch a portion of the curve near that point. Alternatively, one can work out the second derivative of the function and evaluate it at the point in question. Then, if the first derivative is zero at the point, the following three possible cases can arise:

$$\frac{d^2 y}{dx^2}\bigg|_{x = x_0} = \begin{cases} - & \text{a relative maximum} \\ 0 & \text{the test fails} \\ + & \text{a relative minimum.} \end{cases}$$

Figure 2.3(a) shows, for example, that as x approaches x_0 from the left, that is, as x increases in the direction of the critical point, the slope (which is the first derivative) decreases. A decreasing slope means that the derivative

[2]This is somewhat incomplete. A better statement is the following: if a function $f(x)$ has a maximum or minimum value on an interval at the point x_0 of the interval, then x_0 is either an end point of the interval or a *critical value*, where by a critical value we mean a point such that $f'(x_0)$ does not exist (as a finite quantity) or $f'(x_0) = 0$.

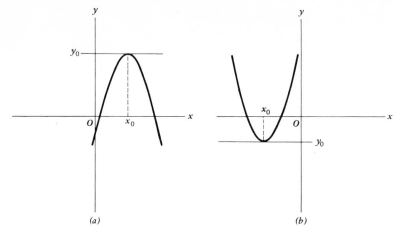

Fig. 2.3   Relative maximum and minimum of a function.

of the slope (which is the second derivative of the original function) must be negative. Note that for $f''(x_0) = 0$ we do not simply say that the point is an inflection point. Thus $y = x^3$ has a zero-valued second derivative at $x = 0$ (which is an inflection point), but $y = x^4$ has a minimum at $x = 0$ even though the second derivative is zero there in this case also.

Example 6.   Find the radius of the Bohr orbit for the most stable state of a hydrogenic atom.

Answer.   An electron moving about a nucleus of charge $+Ze$ in a circular orbit (see Figure 2.4) has angular momentum

$$l = mvr$$

$$= \frac{nh}{2\pi}$$

according to Bohr's quantization hypothesis. Hence $v = nh/2\pi mr$ and

$$E_{\text{total}} = KE + PE$$

$$= \tfrac{1}{2}m\left(\frac{nh}{2\pi mr}\right)^2 - \frac{Ze^2}{r}$$

$$= \frac{n^2 h^2}{8\pi^2 m r^2} - \frac{Ze^2}{r}.$$

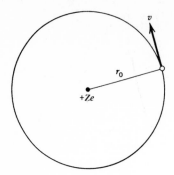

Fig. 2.4 A hydrogenic atom.

We now minimize the total energy by setting its first derivative equal to zero.

$$\frac{dE}{dr} = \frac{-n^2h^3}{4\pi^2mr^3} + \frac{Ze^2}{r^2} = 0$$

Therefore

$$r = r_0 = \boxed{\frac{n^2h^2}{4\pi^2Zme^2}} = 0.529 \,\overset{\circ}{A} \qquad \text{if } Z = 1 \text{ and } n = 1.$$

We have to check to see if the expression for r is really a minimum.

$$\frac{d^2E}{dr^2} = \frac{3n^2h^2}{4\pi^2mr^4} - \frac{2Ze^2}{r^3}$$

$$= 64(Ze^2)^4\left(\frac{\pi^2m}{n^2h^2}\right)^3 \qquad \text{at } r = r_0$$

$$> 0$$

All terms in the expression for d^2E/dr^2 are positive, so the energy is a minimum.

Another application of differentiation is in the evaluation of indeterminate limits. This makes use of the famous theorem of l'Hôpital (after

Guillaume François Antoine de l'Hôpital, 1661–1704) which we state here without proof (the proof is very long).[3]

Theorem 3. *If* f(x) *and* g(x) *are differentiable functions and* $g'(x) \neq 0$ *in a neighborhood around* $x = a$, *and if* lim f(x) = lim g(x) = 0 *or* ∞ *as* $x \rightarrow a$, *and*

$$\lim_{x \to a} \frac{f'(x)}{g'(x)} = L,$$

then also

$$\lim_{x \to a} \frac{f(x)}{g(x)} = L.$$

A tricky but interesting example occurs in the treatment of what is called the *Einstein crystal*. An Einstein crystal is a stable collection of N_0 (Avogadro's number) particles which oscillate about their mean positions with a certain characteristic fundamental frequency ν_0. By analogy with a vibrating violin string, Einstein assumed that overtone frequencies (integral multiples of ν_0) were also possible but no others. The energies of the particles were thus quantized (see Figure 2.5); some have energy $\varepsilon = h\nu_0$, some 2ε, some 3ε, etc.

The next step is to determine how many particles are in each level; to this end Einstein supposed that the Boltzmann distribution law (see Example 14) applied. According to this law one has

$$n_1 = n_0 e^{-\varepsilon/kT}$$

$$n_2 = n_0 e^{-2\varepsilon/kT}$$

$$n_3 = n_0 e^{-3\varepsilon/kT}$$

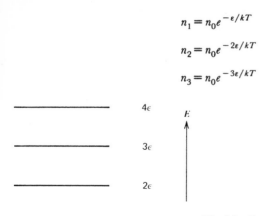

Fig. 2.5 Energy levels of an Einstein crystal.

[3]On page 383 of the book by M. Kline, *Mathematical Thought from Ancient to Modern Times*, Oxford University Press, New York, 1972, it is stated that the theorem was produced by Johann Bernoulli (1667–1748), and that later it was incorporated by his pupil l'Hôpital into an influential book on the calculus, the *Analyse des infiniments petits* (1694).

and so forth. These equations plus the conservation relation

$$n_0 + n_1 + n_2 + n_3 + \cdots + = N_0$$

allow one to work out the total molar energy of the crystal as

$$E = \frac{3N_0\varepsilon}{e^{\varepsilon/kT} - 1}.$$

Example 7. To what does the heat capacity of an Einstein crystal approach at high temperatures?

Answer.   The heat capacity at constant volume, C_v, is dE/dT and from the above this is given by

$$C_v = \frac{3N_0\varepsilon^2}{k} \frac{e^{\varepsilon/kT}}{\left[T(e^{\varepsilon/kT} - 1) \right]^2}.$$

Let $\varepsilon/kT = u$; then C_v becomes

$$C_v = (3N_0 k) \frac{u^2 e^u}{(e^u - 1)^2}$$

and as $T \to \infty$, then $u \to 0$ so that the expression for C_v is of the form $0/0$. Application of Theorem 3 to this gives

$$C_v = \lim_{u \to 0} (3N_0 k) \frac{u^2 + 2u}{2(e^u - 1)}$$

which is still of the form $0/0$! A second differentiation finally resolves the problem.

$$C_v = \lim_{u \to 0} (3N_0 k) \frac{2u + 2}{2e^u}$$

$$= \boxed{3N_0 k \,(\text{or } 3R\,)}$$

The result above says that the molar heat capacity of a monatomic *solid* should be close to $3R$ or $3 \times 1.987 = 5.96$ cal deg^{-1} at high temperatures. For many solids room temperature is already "high." Table 2.2 gives some representative data.

Table 2.2 Some Heat Capacity Data[a]

Solid	Temperature (°C)	Heat Capacity (cal $mole^{-1}deg^{-1}$)
Al	25	5.80
Au	25	6.07
Na	25	6.62
Os	25	5.90
Te	25	6.14

[a]Data are actually for constant pressure and are taken from R. C. Weast (ed.), *Handbook of Chemistry and Physics*, 54th ed., Chemical Rubber Co., Cleveland, 1973, pp. D-144 and D-145. Typically, values of C_v for solids are less than C_p by about 0.1 cal $mole^{-1}deg^{-1}$.

These data support very well the empirical generalization first stated by the French scientists Pierre Dulong (1785–1838) and Alexis Petit (1791–1820) in 1819, namely, that the molar heat capacity of a solid element is about 6 cal deg^{-1}. The *Law of Dulong and Petit* was extended by H. Kopp and others to include compounds, and thus to account for the fact that the heat capacities of several halides ($BaCl_2$, PbI_2, $HgCl_2$) were all observed to lie between 18 and 19 cal $mole^{-1}deg^{-1}$.

We conclude this section with an illustration of how to obtain the derivative of a function in cases where it is difficult or impossible to solve explicitly for the dependent variable. The technique is known as *implicit differentiation*, and it may be seen to be a consequence of the chain rule presented in Table 2.1. Consider, for example, the equation $y^3 + yx - 2x^2 = 7$. This equation expresses a complicated relationship between x and y since y occurs to the third power. One could take this equation and solve for y in terms of x using the method outlined in Section 1.5.

$$y = \tfrac{1}{2} \sqrt[3]{4} \left[7 + 2x^2 + \sqrt{49 + 28x^2 + 4x^4 + \frac{4}{27}x^3} \right]^{1/3}$$

$$- \frac{x\sqrt[3]{2}}{3\left[7 + 2x^2 + \sqrt{49 + 28x^2 + 4x^4 + \frac{4}{27}x^3} \right]^{1/3}}$$

$$= f(x)$$

This could then be differentiated straightforwardly, but obviously with a considerable amount of labor, to obtain the derivative dy/dx. It is simpler to look upon the dependent variable y as a function of x and to rewrite the original equation in the form

$$F(x) + xf(x) - 2x^2 = 7$$

where the function $F(x)$ is a composite function (function of a function), $F(x) = g[f(x)]$, and $g(x) = x^3$.

Example 8.   For $y^3 + yx - 2x^2 = 7$ evaluate the derivative dy/dx at the point $(4,3)$.

Answer.   If $g(x) = x^3$, then $g'(x) = 3x^2$ and application of the chain rule to $F(x)$ leads to the equation

$$3[f(x)]^2 f'(x) + xf'(x) + f(x) - 4x = 0.$$

If we now solve this for $f'(x)$ and recall that $f'(x) = dy/dx$, we get

$$\frac{dy}{dx} = \frac{4x - y}{3y^2 + x}\bigg|_{\substack{x=4 \\ y=3}}$$

$$= \boxed{\frac{13}{31}}.$$

2   THE NEWTON–RAPHSON METHOD

A very useful application of the derivative is to the solution of higher-order algebraic equations or of transcendental equations such as $x - \sin x = 0$. Suppose $y = f(x)$ has a real root at $x = a_0$. Let us select an approximate value for this root, say $x = a_1$, so that $f(a_1) \cong 0$. Then from Figure 2.6 it would appear that a_2 is a better root, where

$$a_2 = a_1 - \frac{f(a_1)}{f'(a_1)}.$$

This result follows directly from the geometry of the situation.

$$AB = AC - BC$$

$$(a_2 - a_0) = (a_1 - a_0) - \frac{PC}{\tan\theta}$$

$$a_2 = a_1 - \frac{f(a_1)}{f'(a_1)}$$

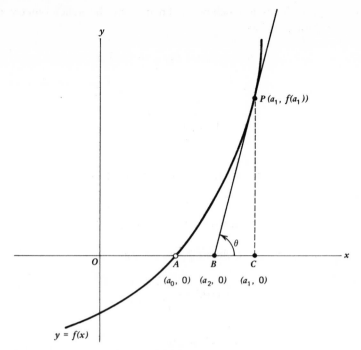

Fig. 2.6   Geometrical basis of the Newton–Raphson method.

After evaluating a_2, one can then use this root to generate a new root a_3, and so on until successive iterations converge closely on an answer. This process was conceived in a more primitive form by Newton,[4] and then improved by Raphson[5] to that used now. Some caution in its use is needed, however. If a_1 is poorly picked, that is, if it is too far away from the correct root, for example, the approximations may appear to diverge. In this case pick another a_1 and begin anew.

Example 9.   At $298°K$ the equilibrium constant for the chemical reaction

$$2OF_2 \rightleftharpoons O_2 + 2F_2$$

is 0.410 atm. If OF_2 is introduced into a vessel at $298°K$ and at time $t = 0$ it has a pressure of 1 atm, what will be the final total pressure?

[4] Sir Isaac Newton (1642–1726), of course, physicist and co-inventor of the calculus, and one of the greatest intellects of all time.
[5] Joseph Raphson (1648–1715).

Answer. Assume ideal gas behavior. Then from the stoichiometry of the reaction one has

$$2OF_2 \rightleftharpoons O_2 + 2F_2$$
$$1-2p \qquad p \qquad 2p$$

$$\frac{4p^3}{(1-2p)^2} = 0.410,$$

or

$$y = 4p^3 - 1.640p^2 + 1.640p - 0.410 = 0$$

and

$$y' = 12p^2 - 3.280p + 1.640.$$

As a first guess we choose $p_1 = 0.50$ atm.

$$p_2 = 0.50 - \frac{y(0.50)}{y'(0.50)}$$

$$= 0.34 \text{ atm}$$

$$p_3 = 0.34 - \frac{y(0.34)}{y'(0.34)}$$

$$= 0.28 \text{ atm}$$

$$p_4 = 0.28 - \frac{y(0.28)}{y'(0.28)}$$

$$= 0.27 \text{ atm}$$

This is already very near to convergence. As a check we note that $y(0.27) = -0.008$, which is quite close to zero. Hence the final total pressure will be

$$P = 3p_4 + (1 - 2p_4)$$

$$= \boxed{1.27 \text{ atm}}.$$

3   PARTIAL DIFFERENTIATION

Because few quantities in science depend upon the variation of just a single quantity, a knowledge of partial differentiation is of great importance. Suppose that $z = f(x,y)$ is a function of two real variables. Then, if the limits

$$\lim_{h \to 0} \frac{f(x+h,y) - f(x,y)}{h} \qquad \lim_{k \to 0} \frac{f(x,y+k) - f(x,y)}{k}$$

exist for all values of x and y in question, we call these limits the *partial derivatives* of $f(x,y)$ with respect to x or y, and we employ the notation $\partial f(x,y)/\partial x$, $\partial f(x,y)/\partial y$ or $\partial z/\partial x$, $\partial z/\partial y$. Nothing more than ordinary differentiation is really implied, except that we presume the variables x and y to be independent.

The geometrical meaning of $\partial f(x,y)/\partial x$, for example, is that of a tangent to a surface in a particular plane, namely, the xz plane. This is illustrated in Figure 2.7. The concept of the partial derivative can obviously be extended to functions of still more than two variables, but in these cases easy geometrical visualization is precluded.

We may extend the concept of differentiation still one step further by asking for the derivative of a function $u = u(x,y,z)$, say, in some particular direction. Suppose P in Figure 2.8 is some point at which $u(x,y,z)$ is defined and differentiable, and P' is a similar point nearby. As P' approaches P along the line segment PP', then $u(P')$ will approach $u(P)$ and we say that

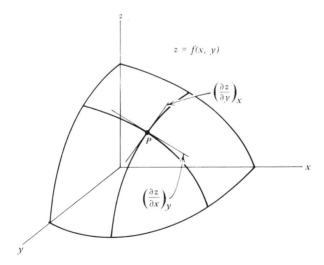

Fig. 2.7   Partial derivatives.

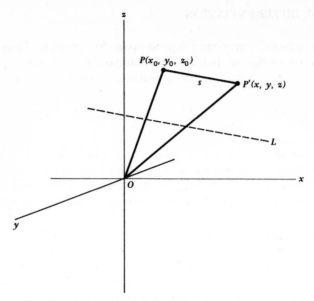

Fig. 2.8 The directional derivative.

the *directional derivative* of $u(x,y,z)$ at the point P and in the direction specified by the line L is given by

$$\frac{du}{ds} = \lim_{s\to 0} \frac{u(P')-u(P)}{s}$$

where the point P' is selected so that PP' is parallel to L. The partial derivatives are clearly special cases of this; if L, for example, is the x axis, then the y and z coordinates of point P' remain constant as P' approaches P, and the directional derivative as so defined becomes just

$$\frac{du}{ds} = \left(\frac{\partial u}{\partial x}\right)_{y,z}.$$

The physical picture of a directional derivative is still the same as that of an ordinary derivative, namely, the slope of a tangent line as in Figure 2.7. For a function $u = u(x,y,z)$, however, the surface is a four-dimensional surface (which we cannot draw) and the tangent line in general would not lie in any of the coordinate planes. We consider the directional derivative again in Chapter 6 when we take up the gradient of a function.

One difference between functions of one variable and functions of two variables must be observed. In the former one usually has

$$\frac{dy}{dx} = \frac{1}{dx/dy}$$

but this may not be so in the case of the latter if the partial derivatives are computed in a particular way. For example, consider the case of cylindrical polar coordinates (see Section 1.1).

$$x = r\cos\theta \qquad\qquad r = \sqrt{x^2 + y^2}$$

$$y = r\sin\theta \qquad\qquad \theta = \tan^{-1}\left(\frac{y}{x}\right)$$

$$\frac{\partial x}{\partial r} = \cos\theta = \frac{x}{r} \qquad \frac{\partial r}{\partial x} = \frac{x}{\sqrt{x^2 + y^2}} = \frac{x}{r}$$

$$\frac{\partial y}{\partial\theta} = r\cos\theta = x \qquad \frac{\partial\theta}{\partial y} = \frac{1/x}{1 + (y/x)^2} = \frac{x}{r^2}.$$

These results seem to say that $\partial x/\partial r = \partial r/\partial x$ and $\partial y/\partial\theta = r^2\partial\theta/\partial y$. The reason that these statements are not nonsense is that in the conjugate cases different quantities are being held constant. Thus when we obtain $\partial x/\partial r$ we assume that θ is being kept constant, but when we obtain $\partial r/\partial x$ we assume that y is kept constant. To make this clear we usually indicate the variables held constant by means of a subscript on the derivative:

$$\left(\frac{\partial x}{\partial r}\right)_\theta = \cos\theta \qquad \left(\frac{\partial\theta}{\partial y}\right)_x = \frac{x}{r^2}.$$

As an exercise, you might verify that $(\partial r/\partial x)_\theta$ is, indeed, the expected reciprocal of $(\partial x/\partial r)_\theta$.

A useful relation connecting partial derivatives of functions of two variables is the following: if the partial derivatives $\partial f(x,y)/\partial x$ and $\partial f(x,y)/\partial y$ exist in some region and the mixed second partial derivative of the first exists and is continuous, then the mixed second partial derivative of the second will also exist and be identical to the first.

$$\frac{\partial}{\partial x}\left(\frac{\partial f(x,y)}{\partial y}\right) = \frac{\partial}{\partial y}\left(\frac{\partial f(x,y)}{\partial x}\right).$$

this means
x is held
constant

this means
y is held
constant

These conditions are so general that nearly any two-variable function in applications will satisfy the equality. Discussion of this important relation can be found in various texts.[6] One consequence of the equality above, which is easily seen, is that if $u(x,y)$ and $v(x,y)$ satisfy the *Cauchy–Riemann equations*

$$\frac{\partial u}{\partial x} = \frac{\partial v}{\partial y} \qquad \frac{\partial u}{\partial y} = \frac{-\partial v}{\partial x},$$

then $u(x,y)$ and $v(x,y)$ will satisfy the equations

$$\frac{\partial^2 u}{\partial x^2} + \frac{\partial^2 u}{\partial y^2} = 0 \qquad \frac{\partial^2 v}{\partial x^2} + \frac{\partial^2 v}{\partial y^2} = 0.$$

Either of these equations is referred to as *Laplace's equation*; it occurs very frequently in physical applications.

When x and y may both be regarded as functions of some common parameter or variable t, then the derivative of $f(x,y)$ with respect to t calls for an extension of the chain rule given in Table 2.1. The result is the theorem of the total differential.

Theorem 4. *If* f(x, y) *is a function of two variables, and* x, y *are restricted to motion on some curve*

$$x = g(t) \qquad y = h(t)$$

with continuous derivatives g′(t) *and* h′(t), *then*

$$\frac{df(x,y)}{dt} = \left(\frac{\partial f(x,y)}{\partial x} \right)_y \frac{dx}{dt} + \left(\frac{\partial f(x,y)}{\partial y} \right)_x \frac{dy}{dt}.$$

The result can be extended to functions of more than two variables. Here, $df(x,y)$ is called the *total differential*, and we can write more generally

$$df(x,y) = \left(\frac{\partial f(x,y)}{\partial x} \right)_y dx + \left(\frac{\partial f(x,y)}{\partial y} \right)_x dy$$

[6]See, for example, J. M. H. Olmsted, *Advanced Calculus*, Appleton-Century Crofts, New York, 1961, pp. 262–264.

which is of the form $P\,dx + Q\,dy$. If x and y are themselves functions of more than one variable t, u, v,..., then a typical result is the following:

$$\frac{\partial f(x,y)}{\partial t} = \frac{\partial f(x,y)}{\partial x}\frac{\partial x}{\partial t} + \frac{\partial f(x,y)}{\partial y}\frac{\partial y}{\partial t}.$$

If it happens that an expression $P\,dx + Q\,dy$ is the differential of a function of two variables, then the expression is said to be an *exact differential*. It follows that in such a case

$$P = \left(\frac{\partial f(x,y)}{\partial x}\right)_y, \quad Q = \left(\frac{\partial f(x,y)}{\partial y}\right)_x$$

and therefore we have the *reciprocity relation*

$$\left(\frac{\partial P}{\partial y}\right)_x = \left(\frac{\partial Q}{\partial x}\right)_y$$

in view of the identity given earlier for mixed second-order partial derivatives. The reciprocity relation is utilized in thermodynamics because quantities such as dE, dH, dS, and dG are exact differentials. This will become clearer when we take up the topic of line integrals in the next chapter. Before working out an example that involves partial derivatives and the reciprocity relation, let us at this point make a slight digression into the general field of thermodynamics.

DIGRESSION INTO THERMODYNAMICS

Classical thermodynamics is concerned with the measurement and the interpretation of work (w) and heat changes (q) in macroscopic chemical systems, and in the changes in certain specially defined quantities which include internal energy, E, enthalpy, H, entropy, S, Helmholtz free energy, A, and Gibbs free energy, G. Internal energy and entropy are defined by way of the first two laws of thermodynamics; the other quantities are defined as shown below in Table 2.3, but their definitions do not have the status of laws.

Table 2.3   Some Thermodynamic Relations

Laws

$\Delta E = q + w$ First law

$dS = dq_{rev} / T$ Second law

$S(0°K) = 0$ for a well-ordered crystal   Third law

Definitions

$H = E + PV$ $dw = -P\, dV$ $\dfrac{1}{V}\left(\dfrac{\partial V}{\partial T}\right)_P = \alpha$

$A = E - TS$ $\left(\dfrac{\partial H}{\partial T}\right)_p = C_p$

$G = H - TS$ $\left(\dfrac{\partial E}{\partial T}\right)_V = C_V$ $\dfrac{-1}{V}\left(\dfrac{\partial V}{\partial P}\right)_T = \beta$

Differential Forms

$dE = T\,dS - P\,dV$ $dA = -S\,dT - P\,dV$

$dH = T\,dS - V\,dP$ $dG = -S\,dT - V\,dP$

Maxwell Relations

$\left(\dfrac{\partial S}{\partial V}\right)_T = \left(\dfrac{\partial P}{\partial T}\right)_V = \dfrac{\alpha}{\beta}$ $\left(\dfrac{\partial V}{\partial S}\right)_P = \left(\dfrac{\partial T}{\partial P}\right)_S$

$\left(\dfrac{\partial S}{\partial P}\right)_T = -\left(\dfrac{\partial V}{\partial T}\right)_P = -\alpha V$ $\left(\dfrac{\partial P}{\partial S}\right)_V = -\left(\dfrac{\partial T}{\partial V}\right)_S$

Refer to this table whenever you do derivations. An experimental quantity of great importance is the *heat capacity*. It is loosely defined as the heat required to raise the temperature of one mole of substance 1°C.

$$C = \frac{q}{\Delta T}$$

This is unsatisfactory for two reasons: (*1*) it does not make it clear how the heat is to be added, and (*2*) the heat capacity is known experimentally to be dependent upon the temperature, so that it is better to express C as a derivative. The addition of heat can be carried out in two distinct ways:

Reversibly and at constant volume	Reversibly and at constant pressure
At constant volume the first and second laws of thermodynamics reduce to	At constant pressure the definition of enthalpy and the second law of thermodynamics reduce to
$dE = dq = T\,dS.$	$dH = dq = T\,dS.$
$\therefore\ C_v = \left(\dfrac{\partial E}{\partial T}\right)_V = T\left(\dfrac{\partial S}{\partial T}\right)_V$	$\therefore\ C_P = \left(\dfrac{\partial H}{\partial T}\right)_P = T\left(\dfrac{\partial S}{\partial T}\right)_P$

These equations show the obvious relationship between the elusive quantity entropy and the experimentally measurable quantity heat capacity. Note also that heat capacity and entropy have the same units.

The quantity α in Table 2.3 is the *coefficient of thermal (cubic) expansion*; it tells how fast per unit volume the volume of a substance increases with the temperature at constant pressure. The quantity β is the *isothermal compressibility*, and it tells how fast per unit volume the volume of a substance decreases as the pressure on it increases at constant temperature. Both these quantities are readily measurable.

From the definitions of H, A, and G many useful identities can be obtained. For example, the definition of the Helmholtz free energy, A, can be expressed as

$$dA = (dq + dw) - (T\,dS + S\,dT).$$

For a reversible process the second law of thermodynamics allows us to equate dq and $T\,dS$. Let us further suppose that the only kind of work involved is that of expansion (pressure–volume work). We can then write

$$dA = -P\,dV - SdT.$$

The differential expressions for dE, dH, and dG in Table 2.3 can be obtained similarly. These expressions are useful in two ways. First, to use dA as an example, this expression suggests that in a given problem where volume (V) or temperature (T) is held constant, the Helmholtz function could be useful. We will illustrate this point with an example, shortly. The four differential forms in Table 2.3 may be summarized, then, by saying

> E is useful for constant S or V
> H is useful for constant S or P
> A is useful for constant T or V
> G is useful for constant T or P

Second, again using dA as an example, we put to advantage the idea that dA is an exact differential. The reciprocity relation then supplies us with the identity

$$-\left(\frac{\partial P}{\partial T}\right)_V = -\left(\frac{\partial S}{\partial V}\right)_T$$

and this is the first of the four *Maxwell relations*; the others can be derived similarly. They are useful for replacing one partial derivative by another in derivations.

A word about thermodynamic derivations—many thermodynamic derivations start with a statement in which some thermodynamic property of a substance is expressed as a function of two variables, seemingly chosen at random. This is not magic, and there is nothing illegitimate in what is being done because in the absence of external fields, effects of gravity, etc., the equation of state of a definite amount of a pure substance is a functional relationship among just three variables. Hence if any two are specified, the third is known in principle. Mathematically, this means that so long as there is no loss or gain of matter, any of the first-order partial derivatives need contain only one subscript, and hence a property of the substance such as its internal energy can be expressed in terms of any two parameters regarded as independent of each other.

Example 10. How much does the internal energy of a van der Waals gas increase when the volume increases from V_1 to V_2 at constant temperature?

Answer. Since T is to be held constant and V is the variable of differentiation, we suppose that the Helmholtz free energy may be useful:

$$A = E - TS$$

$$\left(\frac{\partial A}{\partial V}\right)_T = \left(\frac{\partial E}{\partial V}\right)_T - T\left(\frac{\partial S}{\partial V}\right)_T.$$

From the differential forms in Table 2.3 we see that the first partial derivative in the equation above is just $-P$, and from the Maxwell relations the third partial derivative is equivalent to $(\partial P/\partial T)_V$. Therefore, we have

$$\left(\frac{\partial E}{\partial V}\right)_T = T\left(\frac{\partial P}{\partial T}\right)_V - P$$

and this puts everything in terms of the measurable quantities P, T, and V. For a van der Waals gas the equation of state is

$$\left(P + \frac{n^2 a}{V^2}\right)(V - nb) = nRT$$

from which it is easy to calculate that

$$P = \frac{nRT}{V - nb} - \frac{an^2}{V^2}$$

and hence $(\partial P/\partial T)_V = nR/(V - nb)$. Insertion of these two expressions into the internal energy equation above gives

$$\left(\frac{\partial E}{\partial V}\right)_T = T\left(\frac{nR}{V - nb}\right) - \left[\frac{nRT}{V - nb} - \frac{n^2 a}{V^2}\right]$$

$$= \frac{n^2 a}{V^2}.$$

Finally, to find the internal energy change we integrate between the limits V_1 and V_2 to give

$$\Delta E = \int_{V_1}^{V_2} \frac{n^2 a}{V^2} dV$$

$$= \boxed{n^2 a \left(\frac{V_2 - V_1}{V_1 V_2} \right)} .$$

To get a feel for the answer consider 1 mole ($n = 1$) of carbon dioxide gas for which the van der Waals a constant is 3.59 liters^{2}atm mole^{-2}. If a sample of this gas is expanded from 5 to 10 liters, then the change in internal energy becomes

$$\Delta E = 3.59 \text{ liter}^2 \text{ atm} \left(\frac{5 \text{ liter}}{50 \text{ liter}^2} \right)$$

$$= 0.359 \text{ liter atm}$$

$$= 0.359 \text{ liter atm} \times 24.2 \text{ cal/liter atm}$$

$$= 8.69 \text{ cal.}$$

Another common line of attack on derivations in thermodynamics makes use of specially defined quantities referred to as *Jacobians*.[7] These are nothing more than determinants of partial derivatives:

$$\frac{\partial (x,y)}{\partial (u,v)} = \begin{vmatrix} \dfrac{\partial x}{\partial u} & \dfrac{\partial x}{\partial v} \\ \dfrac{\partial y}{\partial u} & \dfrac{\partial y}{\partial v} \end{vmatrix}$$

$$\frac{\partial (x,y,z)}{\partial (u,v,w)} = \begin{vmatrix} \dfrac{\partial x}{\partial u} & \dfrac{\partial x}{\partial v} & \dfrac{\partial x}{\partial w} \\ \dfrac{\partial y}{\partial u} & \dfrac{\partial y}{\partial v} & \dfrac{\partial y}{\partial w} \\ \dfrac{\partial z}{\partial u} & \dfrac{\partial z}{\partial v} & \dfrac{\partial z}{\partial w} \end{vmatrix} .$$

Jacobians have the interesting property that they obey a rule somewhat similar to the chain rule of ordinary calculus. Thus if x and y are functions

[7] After the Prussian mathematician Carl Gustav Jacob Jacobi (1804–1851); see E. T. Bell, *Men of Mathematics*, Simon & Schuster, New York, 1960, Chapter 18.

of u and v, and these in turn are functions of the independent variables a and b,

$$x = x(u,v) \quad u = u(a,b)$$
$$y = y(u,v) \quad v = v(a,b)$$

then the following relation holds:

$$\frac{\partial(x,y)}{\partial(u,v)} \cdot \frac{\partial(u,v)}{\partial(a,b)} = \frac{\partial(x,y)}{\partial(a,b)}.$$

In the special case of $y = v$, the Jacobian $\partial(x,y)/\partial(u,v)$ reduces to $(\partial x/\partial u)_y$. Hence one has the identity

$$\left(\frac{\partial x}{\partial u}\right)_y = \frac{\left[\dfrac{\partial(x,y)}{\partial(a,b)}\right]}{\left[\dfrac{\partial(u,y)}{\partial(a,b)}\right]}$$

and in using this relation for problems in thermodynamics the variables a and b are to be identified with some pair of independent thermodynamic quantities such as temperature (T) and pressure (P). Thus, as an example, if $x = T$, $y = H$ (enthalpy), and $u = P$, one has

$$\left(\frac{\partial T}{\partial P}\right)_H = \frac{\begin{vmatrix} \dfrac{\partial T}{\partial T} & \dfrac{\partial T}{\partial P} \\ \dfrac{\partial H}{\partial T} & \dfrac{\partial H}{\partial P} \end{vmatrix}}{\begin{vmatrix} \dfrac{\partial P}{\partial T} & \dfrac{\partial P}{\partial P} \\ \dfrac{\partial H}{\partial T} & \dfrac{\partial H}{\partial P} \end{vmatrix}} = -\frac{\left(\dfrac{\partial H}{\partial P}\right)_T}{\left(\dfrac{\partial H}{\partial T}\right)_P}.$$

The quantity on the left is a famous quantity called the *Joule–Thomson coefficient*, μ_H; the denominator of the fraction on the right is just the heat capacity at constant pressure, C_p. The above result then may also be written as

$$\mu_H C_p + \left(\frac{\partial H}{\partial P}\right)_T = 0$$

and this relation is valid for any substance, in general. Additional manipulations allow the partial derivative above to be replaced by a combination of well-defined experimental quantities.

One more example of a slightly more complicated nature will illustrate the scope of the method.

Example 11. C_v is more difficult to measure than C_p; if the former is desired, show how it can be obtained from the latter.

Answer. In view of the close affinity between heat capacity and entropy, it seems logical to let $x = S$ in the Jacobian expression. If $y = V$, $u = a = T$, and $b = P$, then we get

$$\left(\frac{\partial S}{\partial T} \right)_V = \begin{vmatrix} \dfrac{\partial S}{\partial T} & \dfrac{\partial S}{\partial P} \\ \dfrac{\partial V}{\partial T} & \dfrac{\partial V}{\partial P} \end{vmatrix} \div \begin{vmatrix} 1 & 0 \\ \dfrac{\partial V}{\partial T} & \dfrac{\partial V}{\partial P} \end{vmatrix}$$

$$= \left(\frac{\partial S}{\partial T} \right)_p - \frac{\left(\dfrac{\partial S}{\partial P} \right)_T \left(\dfrac{\partial V}{\partial T} \right)_p}{\left(\dfrac{\partial V}{\partial P} \right)_T}$$

$$= \left(\frac{\partial S}{\partial T} \right)_p - \left(\frac{\partial S}{\partial V} \right)_T \left(\frac{\partial V}{\partial T} \right)_p,$$

and multiplication of both sides by T, recalling the relation between entropy and heat capacity given earlier, yields

$$C_v = C_p - T \left(\frac{\partial S}{\partial V} \right)_T \left(\frac{\partial V}{\partial T} \right)_p.$$

The first derivative on the right may be seen to be equivalent to $(\partial P / \partial T)_v$ by referring to the Maxwell relations in Table 2.3. Reference in that table to the definitions of coefficient of thermal expansion (α) and isothermal compressibility (β) finally allow the equation above to be written as

$$\boxed{C_v = C_p - \frac{\alpha^2 T V}{\beta}}.$$

This equation is exact, regardless of whether the substance is a gas, liquid, or solid. The difference between the two heat capacities is thus expressible in terms of four experimentally measurable quantities.

From this example above it is seen that the method of Jacobians is clearly of general utility.[8] However, it should be pointed out that generally any thermodynamic derivation can be accomplished by other means without resort to this sophisticated technique, and the beginning student might well be advised to obtain familiarity with the other methods first before going on to employ Jacobians regularly.

4 METHOD OF LAGRANGIAN MULTIPLIERS

Another application of partial differentiation arises in the solution of maxima–minima problems involving functions of two variables. If $f(x,y)$ is a function of two variables, then $f(a,b)$ is said to be a maximum or a minimum according as $f(a+h, b+k)$ is less or greater than $f(a,b)$ for h, k very small.

Theorem 5.   *An essential condition for a maximum or a minimum is that*

$$\left[\left(\frac{\partial f}{\partial x}\right)_y\right]_{\substack{x=a \\ y=b}} = \left[\left(\frac{\partial f}{\partial y}\right)_x\right]_{\substack{x=a \\ y=b}} = 0.$$

To determine which we use Lagrange's condition:

$$Maximum: \quad \left(\frac{\partial^2 f}{\partial x^2}\right)_{\substack{x=a \\ y=b}} \text{ and } \left(\frac{\partial^2 f}{\partial y^2}\right)_{\substack{x=a \\ y=b}} \text{ are both} < 0$$

$$\text{and} \left[\left(\frac{\partial^2 f}{\partial x^2}\right)\left(\frac{\partial^2 f}{\partial y^2}\right) - \left(\frac{\partial^2 f}{\partial x\, dy}\right)^2\right]_{\substack{x=a \\ y=b}} > 0$$

$$Minimum: \quad \left(\frac{\partial^2 f}{\partial x^2}\right)_{\substack{x=a \\ y=b}} \text{ and } \left(\frac{\partial^2 f}{\partial y^2}\right)_{\substack{x=a \\ y=b}} \text{ are both} > 0$$

$$\text{and} \left[\left(\frac{\partial^2 f}{\partial x^2}\right)\left(\frac{\partial^2 f}{\partial y^2}\right) - \left(\frac{\partial^2 f}{\partial x\, \partial y}\right)^2\right]_{\substack{x=a \\ y=b}} > 0.$$

If the difference of the partial derivatives in the brackets above is negative, then we have neither a maximum nor a minimum, and if it is equal to zero the test is inconclusive.

[8]A collection of thermodynamic formulas useful for working out partial derivatives is given in P. W. Bridgman, *Phys. Rev.*, **3**, 273 (1914), and a discussion of the use of Jacobians is given in A. N. Shaw, *Phil. Trans. Roy. Soc. (London)*, **A234**, 299 (1935).

Example 12.   Investigate $f(x,y) = x^3y^2(1 - x - y)$ for a relative maximum or minimum.

Answer.

$$\left(\frac{\partial f}{\partial x}\right)_y = x^3y^2(-1) + (1 - x - y)(3x^2y^2) = 0$$

$$\left(\frac{\partial f}{\partial y}\right)_x = x^3y^2(-1) + (1 - x - y)(2x^3y) = 0$$

If these are solved, one gets $x = \frac{1}{2}$ and $y = \frac{1}{3}$.

$$\left(\frac{\partial^2 f}{\partial x^2}\right)_{\frac{1}{2},\frac{1}{3}} = \left[-3x^2y^2 + 6xy^2(1 - x - y) - 3x^2y^2 \right]_{\frac{1}{2},\frac{1}{3}} = -\frac{1}{9}$$

$$\left(\frac{\partial^2 f}{\partial y^2}\right)_{\frac{1}{2},\frac{1}{3}} = \left[-2x^3y + 2x^3(1 - x - y) - 2x^3y \right]_{\frac{1}{2},\frac{1}{3}} = -\frac{1}{8}$$

$$\left(\frac{\partial^2 f}{\partial x \partial y}\right)_{\frac{1}{2},\frac{1}{3}} = \left[-2x^3y + 6x^2y(1 - x - y) - 3x^2y^2 \right]_{\frac{1}{2},\frac{1}{3}} = -\frac{1}{12}$$

$$\left[\left(\frac{\partial^2 f}{\partial x^2}\right)\left(\frac{\partial^2 f}{\partial y^2}\right) - \left(\frac{\partial^2 f}{\partial x \partial y}\right)^2 \right]_{\frac{1}{2},\frac{1}{3}} = -\frac{1}{144}$$

Hence this is indicative of a maximum and $f(\frac{1}{2},\frac{1}{3}) = \frac{1}{432}$. It should be emphasized again that as in the calculus of one variable, the maximum obtained is not necessarily an absolute maximum but only a relative maximum. Thus in the example above the point $x = -1$, $y = 3$ leads to $f(x,y) = 9$, which is clearly larger than $f(\frac{1}{2},\frac{1}{3})$, but for points on the surface close to $x = \frac{1}{2}, y = \frac{1}{3}$ the value $\frac{1}{432}$ is a relative maximum.

The interesting situations in chemistry that arise usually involve cases where there are one or more constraints imposed on the system. This limits the domains of x and y in which one can hunt for a maximum or minimum.

Example 13.   Maximize $x^m y^n z^p$ subject to the constraint $x + y + z = a$.

Answer.   Let $f(x,y,z) = x^m y^n z^p$, and $g(x,y,z) = x + y + z = a$. Instead of substituting $g(x,y,z)$ into $f(x,y,z)$ we note that the partial derivatives of $f(x,y,z)$ are zero by hypothesis, and $dg(x,y,z) = 0$ since a is a constant. Now form the new function

$$F(x,y,z) = x^m y^n z^p + \lambda(x + y + z)$$

where λ is an arbitrary constant referred to as a *Lagrangian multiplier*. We next obtain the three partial derivatives.

$$\left(\frac{\partial F}{\partial x}\right)_{y,z} = mx^{m-1}y^n z^p + \lambda = 0$$

$$\left(\frac{\partial F}{\partial y}\right)_{x,z} = nx^m y^{n-1} z^p + \lambda = 0$$

$$\left(\frac{\partial F}{\partial z}\right)_{x,y} = px^m y^n z^{p-1} + \lambda = 0$$

From the first two equations it follows that $x = my/n$, and from the bottom two equations one has $z = py/n$. Therefore,

$$\frac{my}{n} + y + \frac{py}{n} = a$$

and from this one finds $y = an/(m + n + p)$. Since x and z can be related to y, one has finally

$$\boxed{f(x,y,z)_{\max} = \left(\frac{a}{m+n+p}\right)^{m+n+p} m^m n^n p^p \ .}$$

In complicated situations this method involves far less labor than substitution followed by taking derivatives. The procedure illustrated above was first worked out and described by the French–Italian mathematician Joseph-Louis Lagrange (1736–1813) in Volume 1 of his famous work, *Mécanique Analytique*.

Ordinarily one is not interested in the value of a Lagrangian multiplier, but in one application in statistical mechanics it turns out to be important.

Example 14.   Derive the Boltzmann distribution law.

Answer.   From algebra the number of ways (W) of distributing N distinguishable objects among k compartments with n_1 in the first compartment, n_2 in the second, etc., is given by

$$W = \frac{N!}{n_1! n_2! \cdots n_k!} \ .$$

Suppose now that there are N molecules and k energy levels. If N is very large the equilibrium distribution will resemble closely the most probable distribution. To find the latter we maximize W, or more conveniently, $\ln W$.

$$\ln W = f(n_1, n_2, \dots, n_k)$$

$$= \ln(N!) - \sum_k \ln(n_k!)$$

We have two restraints on the system:

$$n_1 + n_2 + \cdots + n_k = N = g(n_1, n_2, \dots, n_k)$$

$$n_1 \varepsilon_1 + n_2 \varepsilon_2 + \cdots + n_k \varepsilon_k = E = h(n_1, n_2, \dots, n_k).$$

Now form the new function

$$F(n_1, n_2, \dots, n_k) = \ln(N!) - \sum_k \ln(n_k!) + \lambda g + \gamma h$$

where λ and γ are two Lagrangian multipliers. The function F is to be differentiated with respect to each of the n_k's. A typical result is the following:

$$\frac{\partial F}{\partial n_1} = -\frac{\partial}{\partial n_1}\big[\ln(n_1!)\big] + \lambda + \gamma \varepsilon_1 = 0.$$

For large x, typically greater than 10^3, the logarithm of the factorial of x can be closely approximated by

$$\ln(x!) \cong x \ln x - x,$$

a result known as *Stirling's formula* (to be discussed in Chapter 4). If we use this in the above equation, there results

$$\frac{\partial F}{\partial n_1} = \frac{\partial}{\partial n_1}(n_1 - n_1 \ln n_1) + \lambda + \gamma \varepsilon_1 = 0$$

$$= -\ln n_1 + \lambda + \gamma \varepsilon_1.$$

Therefore, $n_1 = e^\lambda \exp(\gamma \varepsilon_1)$ and similar equations hold for all the other n_k's. From $n_1 + n_2 + \cdots + n_k = N$

$$e^\lambda \big[\exp(\gamma \varepsilon_1) + \exp(\gamma \varepsilon_2) + \cdots + \exp(\gamma \varepsilon_k)\big] = N$$

we get on solving for e^{λ}:

$$e^{\lambda} = \frac{N}{\sum_{k} \exp(\gamma \varepsilon_k)}.$$

The summation in the denominator is sometimes symbolized Z and is called the *molecular partition function*. Thermodynamic reasoning on the side shows that the multiplier γ is to be identified with $-1/kT$. This gives, then,

$$n_j = \frac{N}{Z} \exp(-\varepsilon_j/kT)$$

and finally,

$$\boxed{\frac{n_j}{n_i} = \exp\left[\frac{-(\varepsilon_j - \varepsilon_i)}{kT}\right]}.$$

This is the relation that was discussed just before Example 7.[9]

The molecular partition function, Z, sometimes also called the *sum over states*, is an important quantity in statistical thermodynamics since thermodynamic quantities such as the entropy and the free energy can be related to the partition function. Therefore if energy level data are available from various spectroscopic measurements, then thermodynamic properties can be calculated. For example, if we take the logarithm of Z and then find the partial derivative with respect to the temperature, we find that

$$\frac{\partial \ln Z}{\partial T} = \frac{\sum \exp(-\varepsilon_i/kT)\varepsilon_i/kT^2}{\sum \exp(-\varepsilon_i/kT)}.$$

However, if we consider the average energy, $\bar{\varepsilon}$, of the particles in the system

$$\bar{\varepsilon} = \frac{E}{N} = \frac{\sum \varepsilon_i n_i}{\sum n_i}$$

$$= \frac{\sum \varepsilon_i \exp(-\varepsilon_i/kT)}{\sum \exp(-\varepsilon_i/kT)}$$

[9]It is interesting that the Boltzmann distribution law can also be derived without the use of Lagrangian multipliers and of Stirling's approximation. See F. T. Wall, "Alternative Derivations of the Statistical Mechanical Distribution Laws," *Proc. Natl. Acad. Sci.*, **68**, 1720 (1971).

from a previous equation, then it is clear from these two equations that the internal energy of the system is given by

$$E = NkT^2 \left(\frac{\partial \ln Z}{\partial T} \right)_V.$$

5 DIFFERENTIATION OF AN INDEFINITE INTEGRAL

A problem that occasionally arises is that of differentiation of a function defined by an integral. This occurs for example in theories of the heat capacity. A common case is when the upper and lower limits on the integral are finite constants. Then, one has

$$\frac{d}{dy} \int_a^b f(x,y)\,dx = \int_a^b \frac{\partial f(x,y)}{\partial y}\,dx$$

under the very general conditions that $f(x,y)$ and the partial derivative $\partial f(x,y)/\partial y$ are both continuous functions of x and y in some region of interest. Since both the concept of a derivative and an integral involve a limit (albeit of two different kinds), you should appreciate that this is an important statement about interchanging the order in which these two limits are taken. The case where a or b or both are infinite is more difficult to deal with and involves the idea of *uniform convergence*, a topic not taken up in this book. For the present, we assume that the equality applies here also.

A more general situation is when a and/or b is a function of the single variable y. The following theorem then applies.

Theorem 6 (Leibniz' Theorem). *If* a(y) *and* b(y) *are differentiable on some interval and if* ∂ f(x,y)$/\partial$y *is continuous for all* y *in this interval and for* a(y) *and* b(y), *then one has*

$$\frac{d}{dy} \int_{a(y)}^{b(y)} f(x,y)\,dx = \int_{a(y)}^{b(y)} \frac{\partial f(x,y)}{\partial y}\,dx + f(b,y)\frac{db(y)}{dy} - f(a,y)\frac{da(y)}{dy}.$$

This result is not hard to see. Let $I(y,a,b)$ denote the integral $\int_{a(y)}^{b(y)} f(x,y)\,dx$; that is, we look upon I as a function of three variables with, however, a and b actually being functions of the third. Let $F(x,y)$ be the indefinite integral $\int f(x,y)\,dx$; it has the property, of course, that $dF(x,y)/dx = f(x,y)$. We now write the total derivative of $I(y,a,b)$ with respect to y, making use of

Theorem 4:

$$\frac{dI}{dy} = \frac{\partial I}{\partial y} + \frac{\partial I}{\partial a}\frac{\partial a}{\partial y} + \frac{\partial I}{\partial b}\frac{\partial b}{\partial y}$$

$$= \int_{a(y)}^{b(y)} \frac{\partial f(x,y)}{\partial y}dx + \frac{da}{dy}\frac{\partial}{\partial a}[F(b,y) - F(a,y)]$$

$$+ \frac{db}{dy}\frac{\partial}{\partial b}[F(b,y) - F(a,y)].$$

Theorem 6 follows since the derivative of $F(b,y)$ with respect to a is zero, and likewise for the derivative of $F(a,y)$ with respect to b.

Example 15. Find $F'(T)$ if $F(T)$ is given by the integral

$$F(T) = \int_{1}^{T} \frac{\exp(-u^2 T)}{u} du.$$

Answer. Attempts to integrate with respect to u before differentiating lead only to frustration. From Theorem 6 we have directly

$$\frac{d}{dT}\int_{1}^{T}\frac{\exp(-u^2 T)}{u}du = \int_{1}^{T}\frac{-u^2\exp(-u^2 T)}{u}du + \frac{\exp(-T^3)}{T}\frac{dT}{dT} - 0$$

$$= \frac{1}{2T}\int_{1}^{T}\exp(-u^2 T)(-2uT\,du) + \frac{\exp(-T_3)}{T}$$

$$= \boxed{\frac{1}{2T}\left[3\exp(-T^3) - e^{-T}\right]}.$$

6* DIFFERENTIATION OF FUNCTIONS OF A COMPLEX VARIABLE

In Section 1.4 we introduced the idea of a complex number $z = x + yi$, and the notion of a function of a complex variable

$$w = f(z)$$

where, if for each value of z in a set S of complex numbers, the unique value of a second complex number w is prescribed, then w is said to be a function of the complex variable z on the set S. Nothing new in this interpretation is implied over that suggested by Figure 1.1. Further, a function $w = f(z)$ is said to be continuous at a point z_0 if exactly the same set of conditions given in Section 2.1 is satisfied, namely,

(a) $f(z_0)$ is defined;

(b) $\lim_{z \to z_0} f(z)$ exists and is independent of the direction of approach to z_0;

(c) the limit is, in fact, $f(z_0)$.

From these statements you would be led to the speculation that the definition of the derivative $f'(z)$ should be identical in form to that of the derivative of a real-valued function of a real variable x—and you would be right!

$$f'(z_0) = \lim_{\Delta z \to 0} \frac{f(z_0 + \Delta z) - f(z_0)}{\Delta z}$$

However, there is one important difference. The limit involved in the definition of $f'(z)$ is a two-dimensional one, involving as it were, the variables x and y in the definition $z = x + yi$. This means that in some cases the limit of a function at a particular point z_0 may not be *uniquely* defined. When this occurs, condition (b) required for continuity is being violated and hence by the rules of the game, the derivative cannot be said to exist there. The simple argument given below can be used to show that $w = e^{z}$ has a derivative almost nowhere, whereas $w = z^2$ has a derivative everywhere.

Suppose $f(z) = u(x,y) + iv(x,y)$, and that it has a derivative $f'(z) = s + it$ at the point $z_0 = x_0 + y_0 i$. The derivative at the point z_0 may be written as follows:

$$\left(\frac{df(z)}{dz} \right)_{z = z_0} = f'(z_0) = \lim_{\Delta z \to 0} \frac{\begin{Bmatrix} u(x_0 + \Delta x, y_0 + \Delta y) - u(x_0, y_0) \end{Bmatrix} + i \begin{Bmatrix} v(x_0 + \Delta x, y_0 + \Delta y) - v(y_0, y_0) \end{Bmatrix}}{\Delta x + i \Delta y}$$

$$= s + it.$$

Now the idea is to let Δz approach zero two different ways, in one case along a direction parallel to the real axis (see Figure 2.9a), and in the second case along a direction parallel to the imaginary axis (see Figure 2.9b).

Consider first the approach along a direction parallel to the real axis. This means that as $z \to z_0$ the imaginary part of the complex variable z does not change, that is, $\Delta y = 0$. Then, since two complex numbers are equal only if their real parts are equal and their imaginary parts are equal, we can write

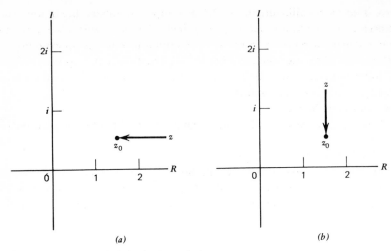

Fig. 2.9   Finding a limit in the Argand plane.

the following two equations:

$$\lim_{\Delta x \to 0} \frac{u(x_0+\Delta x,y_0)-u(x_0,y_0)}{\Delta x} = s$$

$$i \lim_{\Delta x \to 0} \frac{v(x_0+\Delta x,y_0)-v(x_0,y_0)}{\Delta x} = it.$$

But these limits are nothing more than just partial derivatives (recall Figure 2.6) of two functions of two variables.

$$\left(\frac{\partial u}{\partial x}\right)_y = s \qquad \left(\frac{\partial v}{\partial x}\right)_y = t$$

Next consider approach along a direction parallel to the imaginary axis. Here $\Delta x = 0$, so that now the following two equations can be written:

$$\lim_{\Delta y \to 0} \frac{v(x_0,y_0+\Delta y)-v(x_0,y_0)}{\Delta y} = s$$

$$\frac{1}{i} \lim_{\Delta y \to 0} \frac{u(x_0,y_0+\Delta y)-u(x_0,y_0)}{\Delta y} = it.$$

These limits are again partial derivatives.

$$\left(\frac{\partial v}{\partial y}\right)_x = s \qquad \left(\frac{\partial u}{\partial y}\right)_x = -t$$

Hence among the four partial derivatives there exist the following two equalities:

$$\frac{\partial u}{\partial x} = \frac{\partial v}{\partial y} \qquad \frac{\partial u}{\partial y} = -\frac{\partial v}{\partial x}$$

These relations are the Cauchy–Riemann conditions, that were mentioned earlier in another connection, and these conditions plus the continuity of the four partial derivatives are sufficient to ensure the existence of the derivative $f'(z_0)$ at the point $z = z_0$.

What this boils down to is that if you have a function of a complex variable $f(z) = u(x,y) + iv(x,y)$, then the derivative (with respect to $z = x + yi$, remember) is given by either of the two expressions

$$f'(z) = \begin{cases} \dfrac{\partial u}{\partial x} + i\dfrac{\partial v}{\partial x} \\ \quad \text{or} \\ \dfrac{\partial v}{\partial y} - i\dfrac{\partial u}{\partial y} \end{cases}$$

provided that these two expressions are identical and the derivatives are continuous.

Example 16. Investigate the two functions of a complex variable $f(z) = z^2$ and $f(z) = e^{\bar{z}}$ for the existence of a derivative.

Answer. (*a*) The function $f(z) = z^2$ may be written as

$$f(z) = (x + yi)^2$$
$$= (x^2 - y^2) + 2xyi.$$

From this one has

$$\frac{\partial u}{\partial x} + i\frac{\partial v}{\partial x} = 2x + 2yi$$

and

$$\frac{\partial v}{\partial y} - i\frac{\partial u}{\partial y} = 2x - i(-2y)$$

and since these two expressions are identical, either represents the derivative at any point (x,y) in the Argand plane.

(b) The function $f(z) = e^{\bar{z}}$ may be written as

$$f(z) = \exp(\overline{x+yi})$$
$$= \exp(x-yi).$$

The bar, you recall, is a shorthand notation for complex conjugate, which means change the sign of i wherever it occurs. From material in Chapter 1, $f(z)$ can further be written as

$$f(z) = e^x(\cos-y + i\sin-y)$$
$$= e^x\cos y - ie^x\sin y.$$

From this one has the two equations

$$\frac{\partial u}{\partial x} + i\frac{\partial v}{\partial x} = e^x\cos y - ie^x\sin y$$

and

$$\frac{\partial v}{\partial y} - i\frac{\partial u}{\partial y} = e^x\cos y + ie^x\sin y.$$

These will be equal only when $\sin y = 0$, which occurs at $y = \pm n\pi$. Hence $f(z) = \exp(\bar{z})$ is nowhere differentiable except along the real x axis and along lines parallel to this and at a distance $\pm n\pi$ from it (Figure 2.10).

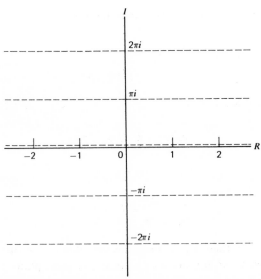

Fig. 2.10 Regions of differentiability of $f(z) = e^{\bar{z}}$.

EXERCISES

1. Find the derivative dy/dx for the following:

    (a) $y = \sqrt{1 + \tan x}$ (d) $y = \cot^{-1}(\csc x)$

    (b) $x = y \ln xy$ (e) $y = \exp(x^x)$

    (c) $y = \ln(x^2 e^x)$ (f) $y = \dfrac{2e^g - 1}{1 - g^2}$; $g = \cos^2 2x$.

2. Differentiate $\sec^{-1}[1/(2x^2 - 1)]$ with respect to $\sqrt{1 - x^2}$.

3. According to Poiseuille's law, if a liquid of viscosity coefficient η is pushed through a tube of radius R and length L by a driving pressure P, then after a period of time t a volume V will have been delivered, where

$$V = \frac{PR^4 t}{8 \eta L} .$$

    This type of experiment is actually used to measure η. Suppose in such an experiment the error in R is aR, the error in V is bV, and the error in P is cP (a, b, c all very small). What will be the error in η?

4. Make a graph of the function $y = |x|$ for positive x, negative x, and $x = 0$. Does $\lim_{x \to 0} f(x)$ exist? Is the function continuous at $x = 0$? Does the function have a derivative at $x = 0$?

5. Differentiate the differential equation

$$x^2 \frac{d^2 y}{dx^2} + x \frac{dy}{dx} + y = 0$$

    n times with respect to x. Assume that y has derivatives through order $n + 2$. You will meet this kind of exercise again in Chapter 7 where the associated Legendre differential equation is obtained from the important Legendre differential equation by means of several differentiations.

6. According to Maxwell the number of molecules having a speed between v and $v + dv$ is given by

$$n(v)dv = 4 \pi N_0 \left(\frac{m}{2 \pi k T} \right)^{3/2} \exp\left(\frac{-mv^2}{2kT} \right) v^2 \, dv.$$

    What will be the most likely speed for methane molecules in a sample at $100°C$?

7. Show that $\tan 3\theta \cot 2\theta$ must lie outside the interval bounded by $\frac{1}{9}$ and by $\frac{3}{2}$.

8. Electron spin resonance (esr) signals generally follow the equation of a Lorentz curve:

$$g(w) = \frac{T}{\pi} \frac{1}{1 + T^2(w - w_0)^2}$$

where w is the radiation frequency, w_0 is some reference frequency (a constant), and T is a constant referred to as a *relaxation time*. On conventional spectrometers the signals are plotted as the derivative $dg(w)/d(w - w_0)$.

(a) Make a representative plot of $dg(w)/d(w - w_0)$ versus $(w - w_0)$ to see what the shape is like. For this you may let $T = \pi$; note that $(w - w_0)$ can be both positive and negative. Take $(w - w_0)$ in multiples of $1/\pi$.

(b) A certain free radical in solution is found to have a peak-to-trough separation [like that noted in part (a)] of 1.4×10^5 sec^{-1}. From this datum evaluate the relaxation time T.

9. The very interesting looking curve called the *folium of Descartes* has the equation

$$x^3 + y^3 = 3axy.$$

Make a rough plot of this curve. Find the value of x which leads to a relative maximum in y.

10. Another very interesting curve, one of the few which is named after a woman, is the so-called *witch of Agnesi*:

$$xy^2 = 4a^2(2a - y).$$

Make a rough plot of this curve. The curve has two inflection points; locate them. This curve was first discussed in 1748 by Maria Gaetana Agnesi, who at that time was a professor of mathematics in Bologna.

11. If a plot of pressure versus volume is made for a gaseous substance at several temperatures, the *critical point* can be located at that (P, V, T) locus where a point of inflection occurs. Using the van der Waals equation of state find expressions for P_c, V_c, and T_c, and then evaluate them for CO_2 given that $a = 3.59$ liters^{2}atm mole^{-2} and $b = 0.0427$ liter mole^{-1}. Compare with experiment.

12. Find the limits:

$$\lim_{x \to 0} \left(\frac{a}{x} - \cot \frac{x}{a} \right); \quad \lim_{x \to \infty} \frac{\sin x}{x} .$$

13. In 1943 J. G. Kirkwood derived a remarkable theoretical equation for calculating the dielectric constant, ε, of a pure liquid. As applied to water the equation takes the form

$$\frac{\varepsilon - 1}{3} = \frac{4 \pi N_0 \varepsilon}{V(2\varepsilon + 1)} \frac{\left(1 + z \cos^2 \frac{1}{2}\theta \right) \mu_0^2}{3kT \left[1 - \frac{2\alpha z \cos^2 \frac{1}{2}\theta}{a^3} \right]}$$

where $V =$ the molar volume of water, $\theta =$ the HOH bond angle, $\mu_0 =$ the dipole moment, $\alpha =$ the polarizability, $z =$ the coordination number, and $a =$ the distance between nearest neighbors. By using implicit differentiation evaluate how fast the dielectric constant is changing at 25° C; take $z = 4.5$, $a = 2.92$ Å, and look up values for other quantities.

14. Suppose that in a mixture of reacting substances, the concentration of B builds up according to the law

$$[B] = [B]_\infty (1 - e^{-2t})$$

while the concentration of A depletes at a rate

$$[A] = \frac{[A]_0}{1 + 6t} .$$

If for simplicity we assume that the initial concentration of A, that is, $[A]_0$, is equal to the concentration of B at the end of the reaction, $[B]_\infty$, at what intermediate time will the instantaneous concentrations of A and B be identical?

15. From material given in Table 2.3 and at the end of Section 2.4, show by a compact formula how the heat capacity at constant volume is related to the molecular partition function.

16. In one approximate formulation of the dependence of the reaction rate constant k on temperature, one has the relation

$$k = A \exp \left\{ \frac{T\Delta S - \Delta H}{RT} \right\}$$

where A is a temperature-dependent frequency factor, and ΔS and ΔH are the activation entropy and enthalpy, respectively. If it can be assumed that

$$T\left(\frac{\partial \Delta S}{\partial T}\right)_P = \left(\frac{\partial \Delta H}{\partial T}\right)_P,$$

then show that

$$\left(\frac{\partial k}{\partial T}\right)_P = k\left[\frac{1}{A}\left(\frac{\partial A}{\partial T}\right)_P + \frac{\Delta H}{RT^2}\right].$$

17. Verify, as suggested in Section 2.3, that the two partial derivatives $(\partial r/\partial x)_\theta$ and $(\partial x/\partial r)_\theta$ are, indeed, reciprocals.

18. Derive expressions for the coefficient of thermal expansion and the isothermal compressibility for a van der Waals gas (refer to Table 2.3 and to Example 11). Next, find a compact expression for the difference $C_P - C_V$ for 1 mole of a van der Waals gas; what does this expression reduce to in the case of an ideal gas?
     (Bonus: for extra credit show that $C_P - C_V$ for the van der Waals gas can be written as R times the quantity one plus a small correction factor, and that this correction factor is approximately $2a/PV^2$. Then estimate the heat capacity difference for ethane at STP; this gas has $a = 5.49$ liters^{2}atm mole^{-2}.)

19. The *compressibility factor*, Z, (not to be confused with the partition function) of a gas is defined to be PV/RT. Verify that the coefficient of thermal expansion of a gas is given by

$$\alpha = \frac{1}{T} + \left(\frac{\partial \ln Z}{\partial T}\right)_P.$$

20. Starting from the definition of dG and the stipulation that the only kind of work involved is PV work, prove the relation

$$\left(\frac{\partial G}{\partial T}\right)_P = -S.$$

(*a*) Next, verify that if f is a function of T, then

$$T^2\left[\frac{\partial (f/T)}{\partial T}\right] = f - T\left(\frac{\partial f}{\partial T}\right).$$

(*b*) Combine the results of the first two parts of this problem to prove the important relation

$$\left[\frac{\partial (G/T)}{\partial (1/T)} \right]_P = H.$$

This relation is known as the *Gibbs–Helmholtz equation*. Its importance lies in the fact that it tells how the temperature dependence of the free energy change of a reaction is related to the enthalpy change.

21. Is $(y^3 - 3x^2y^2)dx - (3xy^2 + x^3)dy$ an exact differential? Explain.

22. Starting from the definition of enthalpy and the definitions of the heat capacities at constant volume and constant pressure, prove that for 1 mole of an ideal gas $C_p - C_v = R$. Next, starting with the differential form of the first law of thermodynamics, $dE = dw + dq$, the stipulation that the only kind of work done is PV work, and the definition of an ideal gas as one where E is a function only of the Kelvin temperature, show that for an adiabatic process (no heat exchange) carried out on an ideal gas one has

$$PV^\gamma = \text{constant}$$

where $\gamma = C_p/C_v$. Remember that PV work is $dw = -P\,dV$.

23. In the simple molecular orbital treatment of the hydrogen molecule-ion, H_2^+, the energy of the ground-state molecular orbital

$$\psi_{MO} = c_1 \lambda_{1s_1} + c_2 \lambda_{1s_2}$$

takes the following form:

$$E = \left(c_1^2 + c_2^2 \right) H_{11} + 2c_1 c_2 H_{12}.$$

The terms H_{11} and H_{12} are the Coulomb and resonance integrals, respectively, and are the same kind of quantities as were designated α and β in Exercise 17 of Chapter 1. What necessary condition must be placed on the c's in order for the energy to assume a maximum or a minimum value? Take H_{11} and H_{12} to be constant.

24. How would you describe the role that temperature plays in the Boltzmann distribution law? Suppose for some physical system 1 mole of particles is in a particular energy level; how many particles should you expect to find in this same system in a level 1 kcal higher if the temperature is $-200°C$?

25. In a plane triangle with internal angles a, b, and c, find the maximum value of $\cos a \cos b \cos c$.

26. Instead of supposing as Einstein did that atoms in a monatomic crystal vibrate with only one fundamental frequency, Debye picked a model with a spectrum of vibrational frequencies running from 0 to ν_{max}. The internal energy in this case turns out to be

$$E = \frac{9N_0 h}{\nu_{max}^3} \int_0^{\nu_{max}} \frac{\nu^3 d\nu}{[\exp(h\nu/kT)-1]}.$$

Express the heat capacity C_v as an integral, but do not attempt to evaluate the integral (that comes later!).

27. After first evaluating the integral

$$\int_0^\infty \frac{dx}{x^2 + y^2}$$

use this result to work out the related integral

$$\int_0^\infty \frac{dx}{x^4 + 2x^2 y^2 + y^4}.$$

In both cases assume that y is not a function of x.

28. Investigate each of the following to see if it possesses a derivative anywhere:

$(a)\ f(z) = \bar{z}$ $(c)\ f(z) = \text{Log}\, z$

$(b)\ f(z) = |z|^2$ $(d)\ f(z) = \sin z.$

29. *Elliptic coordinates* (α, β) are defined by the relation

$$x + iy = c \cosh(\alpha + i\beta)$$

where $0 \leqslant \alpha < \infty$ and $-\pi < \beta < \pi$. Show that the square of the line element

$$(ds)^2 = (dx)^2 + (dy)^2$$

in elliptic coordinates is given by the expression

$$(ds)^2 = c^2(\cosh^2\alpha - \cos^2\beta)(d\alpha)^2 + (d\beta)^2.$$

Although we have not yet taken up hyperbolic functions (see Chapter

3), you may at this point accept the following relations:

$$\cosh u = \tfrac{1}{2}(e^u + e^{-u}) \qquad \sinh u = \tfrac{1}{2}(e^u - e^{-u})$$

$$\cosh^2 u - \sinh^2 u = 1.$$

30.* Define the function $y_n = {}^{2n-1}\sqrt{x}$ for all real x; graph the function that y_n tends to as $n \to \infty$. The result is called a *step function*, or also the *signum function*, notated $y = \operatorname{sgn} x$. What does the limit of the derivative dy_n/dx as $n \to \infty$ look like? This result is referred to as the *Dirac delta function* (more on this unusual function is presented in Chapter 7). What can you say about the derivative of $y = \operatorname{sgn} x$?

31.* Data taken from the reference work Landolt–Börnstein for the molar heat capacity at constant volume of diatomic nitrogen as a function of temperature are given in Table 2.4.

Table 2.4 Heat Capacity Data for N_2

$T(°K)$	450	500	600	700	800	900	1000
$C_v(\text{cal deg}^{-1})$	5.04	5.08	5.21	5.35	5.52	5.66	5.83

If we assume that there is a relationship of the form $C_v = aT + b$, find best values for a and b. (Hint: what function should you minimize?) Use your $aT + b$ expression to calculate a few C_v values and compare with results in the table. What do these comparisons tell you mathematically?

32.* An artificial, one-dimensional potential energy barrier that is sometimes employed in theoretical work is the *Eckart potential*:

$$V(x) = \frac{Au}{(1+u)^2} + \frac{Bu}{(1+u)}$$

$$u = e^{bx}$$

where A, B, and b are adjustable constants. Make a very rough sketch of $V(x)$ in order to ascertain the general shape; what difference is produced when B is changed from a positive to a negative number? By differentiation determine where $V(x)$ has its maximum value; what is this maximum value? Now be specific and let $A = 70$ kcal, $B = -5$ kcal, and $b = 3/a_0$ ($a_0 =$ the Bohr radius). Make a careful plot of $V(x)$ with $b = 1/a_0$ so as to see the effect of varying this parameter.

33.* Discuss any problems associated with finding the limit

$$\lim_{n \to \infty} \frac{e^n}{n!}.$$

34.* Suggest two reasons why the Boltzmann distribution law of Example 14 should not be accurate for a total population of only six molecules, say. Consider the simple energy level diagram shown, and suppose that six molecules are to be distributed among these levels so as to give a total energy of $10kT$. On the basis of simple statistics, calculate the average populations of each level. Compare this with what you would get using the Boltzmann distribution law, and show that if the latter is made to fit either the correct number of total molecules or the correct total energy, then the number of molecules in the ground level is greatly overestimated. Think about the reason for this result.

$$\underline{\hspace{3cm}} \quad \varepsilon_3 = 5kT$$

$$\underline{\hspace{3cm}} \quad \varepsilon_2 = 3kT$$

$$\underline{\hspace{3cm}} \quad \varepsilon_1 = kT$$

35.* Molecules with a dipole moment μ are placed in an electric field of strength E. When one of these molecules is aligned with the field, its potential energy is $-\mu E$; when opposed to the field it is $+\mu E$. If we assume that these are the only two positions permitted, show that at a temperature T the average potential energy of a molecule will be $-\mu E \tanh(\mu E / kT)$. In this expression tanh stands for the hyperbolic tangent and is defined, as one might expect, by $\tanh u = \sinh u / \cosh u$ (see Exercise 29).

36.* Propagation of a sound wave through a gas is very nearly an adiabatic process. It can be shown that the velocity of such a wave through a gas at a pressure P and a density ρ is given by

$$v = \left[\left(\frac{\partial P}{\partial \rho} \right)_S \right]^{\frac{1}{2}}.$$

Is it clear here that constant S (entropy) means the same thing as an adiabatic process? On the basis of your result in Exercise 22, show that the velocity of sound through an ideal gas is

$$v = \left(\frac{C_p RT}{C_v MW} \right)^{\frac{1}{2}}.$$

Use this to calculate the velocity of sound in argon at 0°C, and compare with the experimental value of 308 m sec^{-1}. Do the same calculation for dry air at 0°C; here, $C_p = 0.2399$ cal g^{-1}deg^{-1} and $C_v = 0.1710$ cal g^{-1}deg^{-1}. Compare with the well-known experimental value of 1087 ft sec^{-1}.

37.* In a region of space containing a continuous distribution of charge, the electrostatic potential $\psi(r)$, which has units of energy per charge, must satisfy at any point an important relation known as *Poisson's equation*.[10]

$$\nabla^2\psi(r) = \frac{-\rho}{\varepsilon_0}$$

In this equation ρ is the charge density, which in general is a function of position from some arbitrary origin, ε_0 is the electric permittivity of free space, and ∇^2 is the partial derivative operator

$$\nabla^2 = \frac{\partial^2}{\partial x^2} + \frac{\partial^2}{\partial y^2} + \frac{\partial^2}{\partial z^2}$$

referred to as the *Laplacian*. The charge density has units of charge per volume, and in regions where there are no free charges, Poisson's equation reduces to Laplace's equation (recall material in Section 2.3). Poisson's equation applies, for example, to the region surrounding some ion in a solution of an electrolyte, and for this the equation is modified to include the dielectric constant ε of the solvent.

$$\nabla^2\psi(r) = \frac{-\rho}{\varepsilon\varepsilon_0}$$

In their study of electrolyte solutions P. Debye and E. Hückel solved the Poisson equation

$$\nabla^2\psi(r) = \kappa^2\psi(r)$$

$\kappa = $ a collection of constants

to give for the electrostatic potential

$$\psi(r) = \frac{Ae^{-\kappa r}}{r} + \frac{Be^{\kappa r}}{r},$$

[10]After Siméon Denis Poisson (1781–1840), a French mathematician who worked in several areas in physics. For interesting comments see S. Bochner, *The Role of Mathematics in the Rise of Science*, Princeton University Press, Princeton, N. J., 1966.

where A and B are constants. Show by substitution that this expression is, indeed, a solution to the Poisson equation.

38.* By an appropriate substitution of variables in the Jacobian expression given in the text, derive the useful result

$$\left(\frac{\partial E}{\partial V}\right)_P = C_p \left(\frac{\partial T}{\partial V}\right)_P - P.$$

39.* A beam of light is to travel from the fixed point P to the fixed point Q across a phase boundary at O in a minimum length of time. (Figure 2.11). In the upper region the speed of light is c/η_1, where η_1 is the index of refraction there. In the lower region the speed is c/η_2. Use the method of Lagrangian multipliers to show that

$$\eta_1 \sin \theta_1 = \eta_2 \sin \theta_2.$$

This relation is known as *Snell's law* [after the Dutch mathematician Willebrord Snell (1580–1626)]; you used this law in Exercise 40* of Chapter 1.

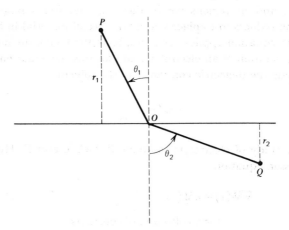

Fig. 2.11   Refraction.

40.* In Exercise 23 you wrote some simple equations which were necessary conditions for the energy of the ground-state molecular orbital in H_2^+ to be a maximum or a minimum. These equations can be found in any book on molecular orbital theory, but there is one point that is not usually discussed. We would like to test our results to see whether they correspond mathematically to a maximum for E or a minimum. Now at the equilibrium bond distance for H_2^+ the integrals H_{11} and H_{12} can be evaluated; they are found to follow the inequalities

$$H_{11} < H_{12} < 0.$$

The integral H_{11} is, roughly speaking, the energy of the electron in the field of one of the nuclei; the integral H_{12} is roughly the energy of the electron in the field of both nuclei. Application of Lagrange's condition shows that the results of Exercise 23 are an energy maximum (show this), whereas physical reasoning says that this must be an energy minimum. Can you think of a reason why Lagrange's test gives an "incorrect" result?

41.* Much importance is made of the fact that dw and dq are inexact differentials (that is, when either is integrated between two fixed limits, the value of the integral depends on the choice of path—more on this in Chapter 3), but that their sum, which is dE in the first law of thermodynamics, is an exact differential. We can demonstrate that dw, for example, is inexact. Consider a pure substance that is undergoing a reversible compression or expansion, and to keep the situation simple, assume there is no change of phase. Now write dV as a total differential in terms of the variables P and T. Form the expression for dw and attempt to impose exactness on it by means of the reciprocity relation. Show that this leads to a zero coefficient of thermal expansion, which is simply not true experimentally.

42.** Let us explore the directional derivative in more detail than was given in Section 2.3. Consider two fixed points in space, P and Q, with coordinates (x_1, y_1, z_1) and (x_2, y_2, z_2), respectively. In contrast to a line in a plane (two-dimensional space), a line in three-dimensional space requires *two* equations to describe it. If P' is any point on the line through P and Q, then from similar triangles (see Figure 2.12) we may write these two equations as

$$\frac{x - x_1}{x_2 - x_1} = \frac{y - y_1}{y_2 - y_1} = \frac{z - z_1}{z_2 - z_1}.$$

From the figure one can also relate these ratios to the distance s, and thus as point P' approaches point P as in Figure 2.8, one can describe this process in terms of the single variable s. Now to take an hypothetical example, suppose that the temperature in a beaker of some fluid that is being heated is given at any instant by the equation $T = x^2 - y^2 + 4z^2 + 273$. We want to find the directional derivative at the point $(1, 2, 3)$ and in the direction of the line L pointing from $(1, 1, 1)$ to $(-2, 0, 3)$. Use Theorem 4 to write dT/ds as a total derivative, work

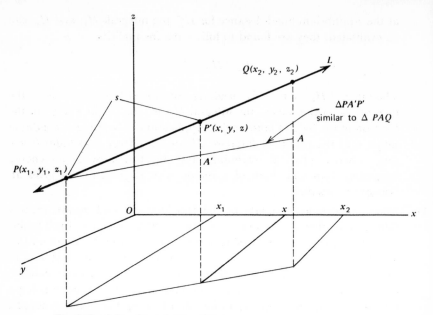

Fig. 2.12 A line through two points.

out the partial derivatives from your equations relating x, y, and z to s, and show that the value of the directional derivative at $(1, 2, 3)$ is $+23\sqrt{14}/7$.

43.** One way of defining *parabolic coordinates* (α, β) is by the relation

$$x + yi = \tfrac{1}{2}c(\alpha + i\beta)^2$$
$$-\infty < \alpha < \infty$$
$$0 \leqslant \beta < \infty$$

Show that the Laplacian ∇^2 (with only x and y derivatives) is equal to

$$\frac{1}{c^2(\alpha^2 + \beta^2)}\left(\frac{\partial^2}{\partial \alpha^2} + \frac{\partial^2}{\partial \beta^2}\right).$$

44.** Verify the statement made in Section 2.3 that Jacobians obey a "chain-rule" type of relation:

$$\frac{\partial(x,y)}{\partial(u,v)} \cdot \frac{\partial(u,v)}{\partial(a,b)} = \frac{\partial(x,y)}{\partial(a,b)}.$$

45.** In 1884 Boltzmann found by thermodynamic arguments that the change in entropy of a system of enclosed blackbody radiation is given by

$$dS = \frac{1}{T}dE + \frac{1}{3}\frac{\psi}{T}dV$$

where ψ, the energy density $(\psi = E/V)$, is a function of the temperature, only. Make use of the fact that dS is an exact differential and show that ψ depends on the fourth power of the temperature. Incidentally, quantum theory originated in Planck's investigation of this same problem. He showed that the proportionality constant in the T^4 relation above is $8\pi^5 k^4/15c^3h^3$; evaluate this and work out the units.

THREE

Techniques of Integration

1 REVIEW OF ELEMENTARY TRICKS

Chapter 2 focused exclusively on the ramifications of the derivative; this chapter focuses exclusively on the ramifications of the integral. The basic problem that we have to solve may be stated as follows: given a function $f(x)$, determine another function $F(x)$ such that $F'(x)=f(x)$. The solution to this problem breaks down into three parts:

(a) Does such a function $F(x)$ exist?

Generally, if $f(x)$ is continuous, then there is a function $F(x)$ such that $F'(x)=f(x)$.

(b) Does more than one such function exist?

If $F(x)$ is one such function, then so is $G(x) = F(x)+c$.

(c) How do we find an expression for such a function?

This question is not the same as question (a). The operation of forming $F(x)$ from $f(x)$ is called *integration*. Since we have standard forms for the derivatives, one way is to put $f(x)$ into one such form.

"I have answered three questions, and that is enough,"
Said his father; "don't give yourself airs!
Do you think I can listen all day to such stuff?
Be off, or I'll kick you down stairs!"

CHAS. LUTWIDGE DODGSON

It is interesting to reflect philosophically on the fact that although differentiation and integration are in some sense opposite procedures, the latter is by far the "richer" process. There are more difficulties, more pitfalls, and more theorems relating to integration than to differentiation, and this really ought to suggest that fundamentally the two are *not* precisely opposite processes. The derivative as we saw in the last chapter is the limit of the *ratio* of two small quantities; the integral is the limit of a *sum* as Leibniz conceived it and this, in fact, is why he chose a stylized Σ as his symbol for the integral.

$$F(x) = \int f(x)\,dx$$

Leibniz' original conception has since been expanded and refined many times. We now look at a modern and precise definition of the integral.

Suppose we have some curve $y = f(x)$. Let the abscissa in the region $[a, b]$ be divided into an arbitrary number of subdivisions, not necessarily of equal width, and let ζ_k be an arbitrary point in the interval $[x_k, x_{k+1}]$. We underscore that this selection of a point is to be purely arbitrary, but in order to help us visualize the picture, let us take two special cases: in the first case (see Figure 3.1a) let ζ_r be that point on the interval $[x_r, x_{r+1}]$ that gives $f(\zeta_r)$ its least value there, and in the second case (see Figure 3.1b) let ζ_s be that point on the interval $[x_s, x_{s+1}]$ that gives $f(\zeta_s)$ its greatest value there. Except possibly near turning points of the curve these special points will generally be one or the other of the two end points of their respective intervals.

Now for these two cases let us find the total area of all the rectangles having $x_{r+1} - x_r$ as base and $f(\zeta_r)$ as the altitude in the one case, and those having $x_{s+1} - x_s$ as base and $f(\zeta_s)$ as the altitude in the other case. We can

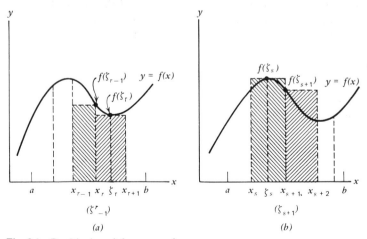

Fig. 3.1 Partitioning of the area under a curve.

write the two total areas as the sums $\sum_r f(\zeta_r)(x_{r+1} - x_r)$ and $\sum_s f(\zeta_s)(x_{s+1} - x_s)$. Clearly these sums do not quite equal the area under the curve, but if we make the size of the subdivisions of the abscissa smaller and smaller, the amount of area that is contained either above the curve or under the curve, and that represents our error in the area, becomes smaller and smaller. More precisely, we want to take the limits of the two sums above as $(x_{r+1} - x_r)$ and $(x_{s+1} - x_s)$ approach zero. If these two limits are identical and equal to $S(a, b)$, and furthermore are independent of the mode of subdivision of the abscissae, then we say that $S(a, b)$ is the *definite integral* $\int_a^b f(x)dx$ of the function $f(x)$ between the limits a and b. Since the definite integral is not supposed to depend on the mode of subdivision we can express it as a function of just the two end points.

$$F(b) - F(a) = \int_a^b f(x)\,dx.$$

The definite integral has thus been presented (in the traditional way) as an area under a curve, and for applications this is undoubtedly the most useful way of looking at it. Notice that by restricting ourselves to only those ζ_k that maximize or minimize $f(\zeta_k)$ in the intervals $[x_k, x_{k+1}]$, it becomes possible to actually follow through on the algebra outlined above and to show that the definite integral of $f(x) = x^2$, for example, is $\frac{1}{3}(b^3 - a^3)$ as inferred from the equality of the lower and upper sums. If the ζ_k are arbitrary as in the strict definition, direct calculation is more or less impossible and the definition then becomes useful only as an abstract, theoretical tool for problems in analysis. For the sort of continuous, well-behaved functions that you are most likely to encounter, it will not be necessary to test every point in an interval to see if the limits of the sums are equal. In some applications such as in the Fourier integral (see Section 4.5) we form our sums in a particular way, with the understanding, of course, that this is rather sloppy and that a more rigorous analysis should be carried out. In spite of the fact that this is not often done when one is more interested in the applications, it is nice to have the more accurate background material.

Sometimes it is necessary to have the integral in the form of a function. We may define the *indefinite integral* as follows:

$$F(x) = \int f(x)\,dx = F(a) + \int_a^x f(t)\,dt.$$

An important theorem assures us that the definite integral $F(b) - F(a)$ will exist if $y = f(x)$ is continuous in the region $[a, b]$. This, however, does not mean that we will necessarily be able to write down the indefinite integral $F(x)$ as a closed expression. An example for which this cannot be done is the integral $\int \exp(-x^2)\,dx$.

It would appear that we have given two different definitions of the integral. If the function $f(x)$ has the indefinite integral $F(x)$, then one definition of $F(x)$ is

$$\frac{d}{dx}F(x) = f(x).$$

The other way of defining the integral, that was given above, is to say that it is the common limit of two sums, $S(a,b)$. We have to actually show that the function $F(x)$, having the property that its derivative is $f(x)$, and the sum $S(a,x)$, with the right end point b of the integration interval being left unspecified, are related by the equality

$$S(a,x) = F(x) - F(a).$$

The proof, not given here, involves showing that the derivative of the left side of this equation is $f(x)$. The equivalence of the two definitions of the integral follows and provides us with the justification for using a table of derivatives to carry out an integration.

Incidentally, the definite integral just outlined in the last few paragraphs is called the *Riemann integral* (after G. F. B. Riemann, 1826–1866, one of the co-founders of non-Euclidean geometry). However, integration can be defined so as to encompass more general conditions and functions. This leads to what are called *Stieltjes* and *Lebesgue* (after Thomas Jan Stieltjes, 1856–1894, and Henri Lebesgue, 1875–1941) *integrals*. The interested reader is referred to material in Chapter 8 of the book by M. M. Nicolson (see Annotated Bibliography) for an interesting introduction.[1]

There are two special cases of the Riemann integral that deserve comment; both types are very common in applications. First, if the range of integration is infinite, the Riemann definition is not directly applicable. This

---

[1] The mathematically sophisticated reader who is intrigued by the concept of integration may find the article E. J. McShane, "A Unified Theory of Integration," *Am. Math. Mon.*, **80**, 349 (1973) interesting.

Additional caveats, discussions of theory, and a collection of tricks may be found in Part 9, "Integration," of the very worthwhile book by T. M. Apostol et al., *Selected Papers on Calculus*, Mathematical Association of America, Inc., 1969.

case is known as an *infinite integral*, and it is defined to be the limit of an indefinite integral:

$$\int_a^\infty f(x)\,dx = \lim_{\varepsilon \to \infty} \int_a^\varepsilon f(x)\,dx$$

$$\int_{-\infty}^\infty f(x)\,dx = \lim_{\delta \to -\infty} \left[\lim_{\varepsilon \to \infty} \int_\delta^\varepsilon f(x)\,dx \right].$$

Second, if the integrand is infinitely discontinuous at some point in the range, we have an *improper integral*. Thus if the integrand is undefined (infinite) at some point c, $a \leqslant c \leqslant b$, then we take the integral to be the following limit:

$$\int_a^b f(x)\,dx = \lim_{\varepsilon \to 0} \int_a^{c-\varepsilon} f(x)\,dx + \lim_{\varepsilon \to 0} \int_{c+\varepsilon}^b f(x)\,dx.$$

Let us now look at just three common methods for integrating common, well-behaved functions before going on to less well-known tricks.

Partial Fractions

There are three different cases falling under this heading.

CASE 1.   DENOMINATOR FACTORABLE

Example 17.   Perform the integration

$$\int \frac{2x+9}{(2x+1)^2}\,dx.$$

Answer.   The integrand can be split into the sum of two fractions.

$$\frac{2x+9}{(2x+1)^2} = \frac{2x+1}{(2x+1)^2} + \frac{8}{(2x+1)^2}$$

$$= \frac{1}{2x+1} + \frac{8}{(2x+1)^2}$$

Hence

$$I = \int \frac{2x+9}{(2x+1)^2} \, dx$$

$$= \int \frac{dx}{2x+1} + 4 \int \frac{d(2x+1)}{(2x+1)^2}$$

$$= \boxed{\tfrac{1}{2}\ln(2x+1) - \frac{4}{2x+1} + c} \, .$$

CASE 2. DENOMINATOR UNFACTORABLE, BUT NUMERATOR THE DIFFERENTIAL OF THE DENOMINATOR

Example 18. Perform the integration

$$\int \frac{(2x+13)\,dx}{x^2+14x+47} \, .$$

Answer. If the numerator were $2x+14$, it would be the derivative of the denominator. Hence

$$I = \int \frac{(2x+13)\,dx}{x^2+14x+47}$$

$$= \int \frac{d(x^2+14x+47)}{x^2+14x+47} - \int \frac{dx}{x^2+14x+47}$$

$$= \boxed{\ln(x^2+14x+47) - \int \frac{dx}{x^2+14x+47} + c} \, .$$

CASE 3. DENOMINATOR UNFACTORABLE

Example 19. Perform the integration

$$\int \frac{dx}{x^2+14x+47} \, .$$

Answer. This case can be seen to fit one of the standard forms given in Table 3.1.

Table 3.1   Some Common Integrals

$f(x)$	$\int f(x)\,dx$
1. $\dfrac{1}{x^2+a^2}$	$\dfrac{1}{a}\tan^{-1}\left(\dfrac{x}{a}\right)$
2. $\dfrac{1}{a^2-x^2}$	$\begin{cases}\dfrac{1}{a}\tanh^{-1}\left(\dfrac{x}{a}\right)\\[2mm]\dfrac{1}{2a}\ln\left(\dfrac{x+a}{a-x}\right)\end{cases}$
3. $\dfrac{1}{x^2-a^2}$	$\begin{cases}-\dfrac{1}{a}\coth^{-1}\left(\dfrac{x}{a}\right)\\[2mm]\dfrac{1}{2a}\ln\left(\dfrac{x-a}{x+a}\right)\end{cases}$

For the purposes of Example 19, we make use of integral 3 of Table 3.1.

$$I=\int \frac{dx}{x^2+14x+47}$$

$$=\int \frac{d(x+7)}{(x+7)^2-\left(\sqrt{2}\,\right)^2}$$

$$\boxed{\;=\tfrac{1}{4}\sqrt{2}\,\ln\left(\frac{x+7-\sqrt{2}}{x+7+\sqrt{2}}\right)+c\;}$$

Substitution

No general rule can be given as to what substitution to make. Typical substitutions are simple algebraic ones such as $x=u^{-2}$ or trigonometric ones such as $x=\tan u$.

Example 20.   Perform the integration

$$\int \frac{dx}{x^2-a^2}\,.$$

Answer.   We look for a trigonometric substitution that will make the denominator an identity. Let $x = a \coth u$. Then one has

$$I = \int \frac{dx}{x^2 - a^2}$$

$$= \int \frac{-a \operatorname{csch}^2 u \, du}{a^2 \coth^2 u - a^2}$$

$$= \frac{-1}{a} \int du \qquad \text{since } \coth^2 u - \operatorname{csch}^2 u = 1$$

$$= \frac{-u}{a}$$

$$\boxed{= \frac{-1}{a} \coth^{-1}\left(\frac{x}{a}\right) + c} \, .$$

To show the equivalence between this answer and the logarithmic expression given previously in Table 3.1, suppose that $y = \coth^{-1} z$. This also implies

$$z = \coth y$$

$$= \frac{\cosh y}{\sinh y}$$

$$= \frac{e^y + e^{-y}}{e^y - e^{-y}} \, .$$

If we solve this for y, we get

$$e^{2y} = \frac{z+1}{z-1}$$

$$y = \tfrac{1}{2} \ln\left(\frac{z+1}{z-1}\right).$$

Application of this result to our example above gives

$$I = \frac{-1}{a} \left(\tfrac{1}{2}\right) \ln\left[\frac{\dfrac{x}{a} + 1}{\dfrac{x}{a} - 1} \right]$$

$$= \frac{1}{2a} \ln\left(\frac{x-a}{x+a}\right) + c.$$

Integral 2 in Table 3.1 can be handled in a similar manner.

When evaluating definite integrals by the substitution method, it is important to realize that the limits on the integral must also change.

Example 21. Perform the integration

$$\int_{\frac{1}{7}}^{\frac{1}{5}} \frac{dx}{x\sqrt{5x^2-6x+1}}.$$

Answer. Let $x = u^{-1}$; then $dx = -u^{-2}du$, and

$$I = \int_{7}^{5} \frac{-u^{-2}du}{u^{-1}\sqrt{5u^{-2}-6u^{-1}+1}}$$

$$= -\int_{7}^{5} \frac{du}{\sqrt{u^2-6u+5}}.$$

Table 3.2   Some Common Integrals

$f(x)$	$\int f(x)dx$
1. $\dfrac{1}{\sqrt{a^2-x^2}}$	$\sin^{-1}\left(\dfrac{x}{a}\right)$
2. $\dfrac{1}{\sqrt{x^2-a^2}}$	$\cosh^{-1}\left(\dfrac{x}{a}\right)$
3. $\dfrac{1}{\sqrt{a^2+x^2}}$	$\sinh^{-1}\left(\dfrac{x}{a}\right)$

This integral can be seen to fit one of the standard forms listed in Table 3.2. If we make use of integral 2, we can cast our problem into the form

$$I = \int_{5}^{7} \frac{d(u-3)}{\sqrt{(u-3)^2-2^2}}$$

$$= \cosh^{-1}\tfrac{1}{2}(u-3)\big|_{5}^{7}$$

$$= \cosh^{-1}2 - \cosh^{-1}1$$

$$= \boxed{1.31} \; .$$

Parts

From the differential calculus one has the relation

$$d\left(xy\right) = x\,dy + y\,dx$$

or by rearrangement

$$y\,dx = d\left(xy\right) - x\,dy.$$

Therefore, upon integration of both sides one has the identity

$$\int y\,dx = xy - \int x\,dy.$$

This result can be made more general by supposing that x and y are both functions of some single variable t:

$$\frac{d}{dt}\left[x(t)y(t)\right] = x(t)\frac{dy}{dt} + y(t)\frac{dx}{dt} \; .$$

Then upon integration of both sides and rearrangement one obtains

$$\int y(t)x'(t)\,dt = x(t)y(t) - \int x(t)y'(t)\,dt \; .$$

This expression is particularly useful when $y(t)$ is a trigonometric, exponential, logarithmic, or binomial function, and $x'(t)$ is one of the three other types. Incidentally this expression remains valid even if there are points in the region of interest where $x'(t)$ or $y'(t)$ does not exist, provided one defines the integrals as the more general Stieltjes integrals.

Example 22. Perform the integration $\int e^{3t}\sin 4t\,dt.$

Answer. Here we let $y(t) = e^{3t}$ and $x'(t)\,dt = \sin 4t\,dt$. Then one has

$$I = \int e^{3t}\sin 4t\,dt$$

$$= -\tfrac{1}{4}e^{3t}\cos 4t - \int\left(-\tfrac{1}{4}\cos 4t\right)\left(3e^{3t}\right)dt$$

$$= -\tfrac{1}{4}e^{3t}\cos 4t + \tfrac{3}{4}\left[\tfrac{1}{4}e^{3t}\sin 4t - \tfrac{3}{4}\int e^{3t}\sin 4t\,dt\right]$$

by reapplication of the parts formula. We now recognize that the integral in the brackets is just the original integral I. Hence

$$I = -\tfrac{1}{4}e^{3t}\cos 4t + \tfrac{3}{16}e^{3t}\sin 4t - \tfrac{9}{16}I$$

and so

$$\tfrac{25}{16}I = \tfrac{1}{16}e^{3t}(3\sin 4t - 4\cos 4t),$$

$$I = \boxed{\tfrac{1}{25}e^{3t}(3\sin 4t - 4\cos 4t) + c}.$$

Here is another example of integration by parts that shows that at times some ingenuity must be shown in the selection of the parts. The following complicated integral occurs in the theory of the internal pressure in a liquid:

$$I(x) = \int_x^\infty h\,dh \int_h^\infty u'(r)\,g(r)dr.$$

The function $u'(r)$ is the force that a molecule r units away exerts on another molecule, and $g(r)$ is a function known as the radial distribution function. Simplification will be achieved if we can convert $I(x)$ into one or more single integrals. To this end we rewrite $I(x)$ as

$$I(x) = \int_x^\infty \left[\int_h^\infty u'(r)g(r)dr \right](h\,dh)$$

and now we take for our parts the *integral* (!)$\int_h^\infty u'(r)g(r)\,dr$ and the differential $(h\,dh)$. Application of the general formula yields

$$I(x) = \left[\tfrac{1}{2}h^2 \int_h^\infty u'(r)g(r)dr \right]_x^\infty - \int_x^\infty \tfrac{1}{2}h^2 d\left[\int_h^\infty u'(r)g(r)dr \right].$$

Consider the first term on the right. We could write this as

$$\left[\tfrac{1}{2}h^2\{F(\infty) - F(h)\} \right]_{h=x}^{h=\infty}$$

and although the lower limit is easy to handle and is $-\tfrac{1}{2}x^2\{F(\infty) - F(x)\}$, or just $-\tfrac{1}{2}x^2\int_x^\infty u'(r)g(r)dr$, the upper limit requires more thought. It is actually of an indeterminate $(\infty \cdot 0)$ type. However, for very large h it is known that $g(h)$ behaves like 1 and $u'(h)$ behaves like h^{-7}. Theorem 3 leads to the conclusion that this indeterminate form approaches zero.

To handle the second term on the right one has to differentiate an integral. The variable of differentiation is h and from Theorem 6 one has

$$-\int_x^\infty \tfrac{1}{2}h^2\{-u'(h)g(h)\}\,dh.$$

The final result for the original integral $I(x)$ is therefore

$$I(x) = -\tfrac{1}{2}x^2 \int_x^\infty u'(r)g(r)\,dr + \tfrac{1}{2}\int_x^\infty h^2 u'(h)g(h)\,dh.$$

The elementary tricks reviewed apply equally well to single integrals and multiple integrals. In many sorts of physical problems involving multiple integrals the use of substitution (or what amounts to the same thing, the use of another coordinate system) as a simplification is somewhat tricky. As a preliminary to this, let us review briefly some ideas concerning multiple integrals. These can be defined in a way analogous to the Riemann integral discussed before. Thus suppose $f(x,y)$ is defined at all points in a closed region R of the xy plane, and let R be subdivided into an arbitrary number of subregions of area ΔA_k. Now arbitrarily select a point (ζ_k, λ_k) in each of these subregions and form the sum

$$\sum_k f(\zeta_k, \lambda_k)\Delta A_k.$$

If the limit of this sum exists as the dimensions of the subdivisions approach zero, then this limit is said to be the *double integral* of $f(x,y)$ over R.

$$\int_R\int f(x,y)\,dA$$

Extensions to situations where dA is not an element of area in the xy plane but on a more general surface, and where the integrand is a function of three or more independent variables, are obvious.

The definition above is satisfactory from a conceptual standpoint but as a working definition it provides us with little help on how to calculate the double integral. If region R in Figure 3.2 is bounded on the top by $y = g(x)$ and on the bottom by $y = h(x)$, both of these being continuous functions, then the double integral can be written in the more workable form

$$\int_a^b\left[\int_{h(x)}^{g(x)} f(x,y)\,dy\right]dx$$

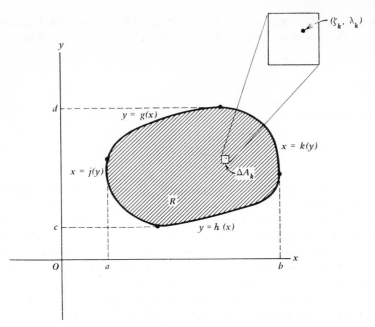

Fig. 3.2   The double integral.

where the integral in brackets is to be evaluated first (with x constant), and then integration with respect to x is carried out. We call the expression above a *twofold iterated integral*. Figure 3.2 suggests that this iterated integral could also be written as

$$\int_c^d \left[\int_{j(y)}^{k(y)} f(x,y)\,dx \right] dy$$

and since the original double integral should be unique, one should have an equality between the two iterated integrals.

$$\int_a^b \left[\int_{h(x)}^{g(x)} f(x,y)\,dy \right] dx = \int_c^d \left[\int_{j(y)}^{k(y)} f(x,y)\,dx \right] dy$$

Another way of stating the above relation is to say that the order of integration may be exchanged in a twofold iterated integral provided certain conditions are met; this is sometimes called *Fubini's theorem*. Generally, if the limits are all finite and $f(x,y)$ is continuous and well-behaved, this is true. Difficulties appear when infinities are present, and this is a complex problem to deal with. Take the case where all four limits are constants. Then in establishing the evaluation

$$\int_R \int f(x,y)\,dA = \int_c^d \left[\int_a^b f(x,y)\,dx \right] dy$$

it is important to know that the first integral

$$\int_a^b f(x,y)\,dx$$

is a continuous function of y in order that the second Riemann integral can be evaluated. For a and b finite there is no problem, but suppose the first integral is an infinite integral (this phrase, that we defined earlier, is due to Hardy) of the type shown

$$\int_a^\infty f(x,y)\,dx.$$

Now this integral need not be a continuous function of y, and so the double integral may not be equivalent to the iterated integral depending on the nature of the discontinuity.

When the integrand (first integral) in a twofold iterated integral is an improper integral, it may turn out that both possible iterated integrals exist but that they have different values. Clearly, in such a case the order of integration may not be exchanged and one is hard-pressed to make any sort of connection with the double integral. Whittaker and Watson (see Annotated Bibliography) state frankly that general conditions for the legitimacy of inverting the order of integration when the integrand is not continuous are difficult to obtain. As expected, these problems require the concept of uniform convergence and, in general, a careful analysis of the convergence properties of the integrals involved for some solution. Such a discussion is outside the scope of this book, but it is imperative that beginning students who are tackling some problem be aware of the pitfalls involved in the calculus of two variables and do not take multiple integrals for granted. The best recourse is to consult some of the classic advanced treatises on real analysis.

A word of caution is in order. Some writers do not distinguish carefully between multiple and manyfold iterated integrals, using the notation

$$\cdots \int_g^h \int_c^d \int_a^b f(x,y,z,\cdots)\,dx\,dy\,dz \cdots$$

to stand for the latter. The understanding here is that the separate integrations are to be done from the inside outward.

With this very incomplete background in mind, let us now return to our original problem of using a change in coordinate system as a means of simplifying the evaluation of a multiple integral. We henceforth assume that such integrals can be expressed as iterated integrals.

Theorem 7. *Let* T *be a transformation from* UVW *space into* XYZ *space, and let* f(x,y,z) *be a continuous function defined in* XYZ. *Then*

$$\int\int\int f(x,y,z)\,dx\,dy\,dz = \int\int\int f(T)\left|\frac{\partial(x,y,z)}{\partial(u,v,w)}\right|du\,dv\,dw$$

where the integrand on the right contains the absolute value of the Jacobian J(T) *of the transformation.*

The function of the Jacobian here is to give the correct differential or volume element in the new coordinate system. Its appearance may be made plausible by considering a two-variable situation. Suppose u and v are a pair of variables that are to be used to locate a point in the xy plane. We assume that since functions can be defined to transform x and y into u and v, inverse functions can be found to transform u and v into x and y:

$$x = x(u,v) \qquad y = y(u,v).$$

Then corresponding to an incremental change du, there will be changes along the x and y directions of $(\partial x/\partial u)du$ and $(\partial y/\partial u)du$, respectively. Similar expressions apply for an incremental change in v. The differential unit of area in the xy plane that corresponds to the incremental changes du and dv is thus the area of the parallelogram constructed as shown in Figure 3.3. The area of the rectangle shown in Figure 3.3 is easily seen to be

$$\left[\frac{\partial y}{\partial u}du + \frac{\partial y}{\partial v}dv\right]\left[\frac{\partial x}{\partial u}du + \frac{\partial x}{\partial v}dv\right]$$

and by means of simple geometry you should be able to show that if the

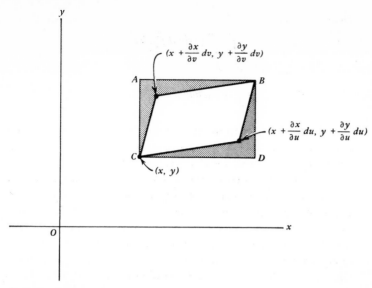

Fig. 3.3 A differential unit of area.

areas of the shaded portions are subtracted from this, then the area of the parallelogram is

$$\left[\frac{\partial x}{\partial u} \frac{\partial y}{\partial v} - \frac{\partial x}{\partial v} \frac{\partial y}{\partial u} \right] du\, dv$$

which is just $[\partial (x,y)/\partial (u,v)]du\, dv$. In a similar way, the Jacobian appears as a "conversion factor" in triple and higher multiple integrals.

To illustrate the use of Theorem 7 let us consider a two-dimensional situation involving cylindrical polar coordinates, $x = r\cos\theta$, $y = r\sin\theta$.

Example 23. Evaluate the double integral $I = \int_R \int y^2 (x^2 + y^2)^{-\frac{3}{2}} dx\, dy$, where the region R is the rectangular region shown in Figure 3.4a.

Answer. The double integral is not a trivial one to work out. We first proceed to find $J(T)$ (see Section 2.3):

$$J(T) = \begin{vmatrix} \dfrac{\partial x}{\partial r} & \dfrac{\partial x}{\partial \theta} \\[2mm] \dfrac{\partial y}{\partial r} & \dfrac{\partial y}{\partial \theta} \end{vmatrix} = r.$$

Hence

$$I = \int \int \frac{(r\sin\theta)^2 r d\theta dr}{r^3}$$

$$= \int \int \sin^2\theta d\theta dr.$$

We now have to determine the shape of the integrating region in $r\theta$ space. In a rectangular coordinate system of r and θ axes the boundary lines $x=0$, $x=1$, $y=1$, and $y=3$ become, respectively, $\theta = \frac{1}{2}\pi$, $r = \sec\theta$, $r = \csc\theta$, and $r = 3\csc\theta$. The result is to give an irregularly shaped region of integration (see Figure 3.4b) The shape of this region suggests that we carry out the integration in two steps: first over region $ABCE$ and then over region AED. If we now write the double integral as a twofold iterated integral, and integrate over r first, expressing its variation as a function of θ, then we need know only the θ coordinates of points $A-E$. From the diagram, these are easily seen to be $A = \tan^{-1}3$, $B = C = \frac{1}{2}\pi$, $D = \frac{1}{4}\pi$, and $E = \tan^{-1}3$. Study the following setup carefully:

$$I = \underbrace{\int_{\frac{1}{4}\pi}^{\tan^{-1}3} \sin^2\theta d\theta \int_{\csc\theta}^{\sec\theta} dr}_{\text{region } AED} + \underbrace{\int_{\tan^{-1}3}^{\frac{1}{2}\pi} \sin^2\theta d\theta \int_{\csc\theta}^{3\csc\theta} dr}_{\text{region } ABCE}$$

$$= \int_{\frac{1}{4}\pi}^{\tan^{-1}3} \sin^2\theta \left(\sec\theta - \csc\theta\right) d\theta + 2\int_{\tan^{-1}3}^{\frac{1}{2}\pi} \sin\theta \, d\theta$$

$$= \int_{\frac{1}{4}\pi}^{\tan^{-1}3} \sec\theta \, d\theta - \int_{\frac{1}{4}\pi}^{\tan^{-1}3} \cos\theta \, d\theta - \int_{\frac{1}{4}\pi}^{\tan^{-1}3} \sin\theta \, d\theta + 2\int_{\tan^{-1}3}^{\frac{1}{2}\pi} \sin\theta \, d\theta$$

$$= \ln\left(\frac{3+\sqrt{10}}{1+\sqrt{2}}\right)$$

$$= \boxed{0.94}.$$

You may verify that exactly the same answer is obtained if the original integral is evaluated in Cartesian coordinates. It might be remarked that if the limits in Cartesian coordinates cover all space ($-\infty$ to $+\infty$ for each of x, y, and z), then there is no special problem in deciding what the limits must be in an alternative coordinate system. For cylindrical polar

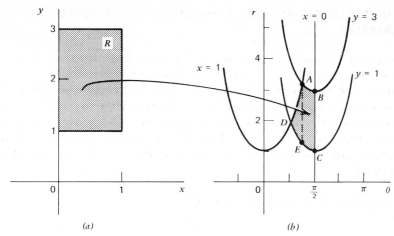

Fig. 3.4 Evaluation of a multiple integral.

coordinates this would be $0 \leqslant r < \infty$, $0 \leqslant \theta \leqslant 2\pi$, and $-\infty < z < +\infty$ (if the problem is a three-dimensional one). Other commonly employed coordinate systems are the spherical polar and confocal elliptical coordinate systems.

Spherical polar coordinates

$$x = r \sin\theta \cos\phi \qquad 0 \leqslant r < \infty$$
$$y = r \sin\theta \sin\phi \qquad 0 \leqslant \theta \leqslant \pi$$
$$z = r \cos\theta \qquad 0 \leqslant \phi \leqslant 2\pi$$

Confocal elliptical coordinates

$$x = R\sqrt{\zeta^2 - 1} \sqrt{1 - \eta^2} \cos\phi \qquad 1 \leqslant \zeta < \infty$$
$$y = R\sqrt{\zeta^2 - 1} \sqrt{1 - \eta^2} \sin\phi \qquad -1 \leqslant \eta \leqslant 1$$
$$z = R\zeta\eta \qquad 0 \leqslant \phi \leqslant 2\pi$$

More discussion on coordinate systems is presented in Chapter 6. A knowledge of several such coordinate systems is useful because the mathematical or physical symmetry present in a particular problem may suggest that the use of a certain coordinate system will simplify its mathematical formulation. However, as Example 23 shows, even for problems of a purely mathematical nature with no relevance to a physical problem at hand, the use of alternative coordinate systems as a mathematical device is useful.

2   REDUCTION FORMULAS; INTRODUCTION OF COMPLEX VARIABLES

It sometimes happens that an integral that is not immediately integrable or reducible by substitution to a standard form can be connected in a linear manner with the integral of another closely related function or with two or more integrals of other functions that are easier to integrate. A relation that connects in this way some desired integral to others is called a *reduction formula*. Integrals that quite often can be evaluated by means of reduction formulas are those involving powers, trigonometric functions, and exponentials.

Example 24.   Perform the integration

$$I = \int_0^{\pi/2} x^4 \sin x \cos x \, dx.$$

Answer.   We first recognize that $\frac{1}{2}\sin 2x = \sin x \cos x$; then set

$$I_m = \int x^m \sin 2x \, dx.$$

Integration by parts gives

$$I_m = -\frac{1}{2}x^m \cos 2x + \frac{1}{2}m \int x^{m-1} \cos 2x \, dx$$

and integration by parts again gives

$$I_m = -\frac{1}{2}x^m \cos 2x + \frac{1}{2}m \left(\frac{1}{2}x^{m-1}\sin 2x\right) - \frac{1}{2}m\left(\frac{m-1}{2}\right)\int x^{m-2}\sin 2x \, dx.$$

The integral on the right is recognized to be I_{m-2}. Hence we have the reduction formula

$$I_m = -\frac{1}{2}x^m \cos 2x + \frac{1}{4}mx^{m-1}\sin 2x - \frac{1}{4}m(m-1)I_{m-2}.$$

For even m we need only know I_0:

$$I_0 = \int \sin 2x \, dx = -\frac{1}{2}\cos 2x.$$

Finally $I = \frac{1}{2}I_4\big|_0^{\pi/2}$

$$= \left[-\tfrac{1}{4}x^4\cos 2x + \tfrac{1}{2}x^3\sin 2x + \tfrac{3}{4}x^2\cos 2x \right.$$

$$\left. -\tfrac{3}{4}x\sin 2x - \tfrac{3}{8}\cos 2x \right]_0^{\pi/2}$$

$$= \boxed{\frac{\pi^4 - 12\pi^2 + 48}{64}}.$$

Other reduction formulas that can be arrived at in the same way as the example above are listed in Table 3.3 for convenience.

Table 3.3   Some Reduction Formulas

Definition	*Result*
1. $S_m = \int x^m \sin nx\,dx$	1. $S_m = \dfrac{-x^m\cos nx}{n} + \dfrac{mx^{m-1}\sin nx}{n^2} - \dfrac{m(m-1)}{n^2}S_{m-2}$
. $C_m = \int x^m \cos nx\,dx$	. $C_m = \dfrac{x^m\sin nx}{n} + \dfrac{mx^{m-1}\cos nx}{n^2} - \dfrac{m(m-1)}{n^2}C_{m-2}$
2. $S_n = \int e^{ax}\sin^n bx\,dx$	2. $S_n = e^{ax}\sin^{n-1}bx\left\{ \dfrac{a\sin bx - nb\cos bx}{a^2 + n^2b^2} \right\}$
	$\quad + \dfrac{n(n-1)b^2}{a^2 + n^2b^2}S_{n-2}$
. $C_n = \int e^{ax}\cos^n bx\,dx$	$C_n = e^{ax}\cos^{n-1}bx\left\{ \dfrac{a\cos bx + nb\sin bx}{a^2 + n^2b^2} \right\}$
	$\quad + \dfrac{n(n-1)b^2}{a^2 + n^2b^2}C_{n-2}$
3. $I_n = \int x^m(\ln x)^n dx$	3. $I_n = \dfrac{x^{m+1}(\ln x)^n}{m+1} - \left(\dfrac{n}{m+1}\right)I_{n-1}$
$\quad (m \neq -1)$	
$\quad (n \neq -1)$	
4. $I_m = \displaystyle\int \dfrac{\sin^n x\,dx}{(a + b\cos x)^m}$	4. $I_m = \dfrac{b\sin^{n+1}x}{(m-1)(b^2 - a^2)(a + b\cos x)^{m-1}}$
$\quad (m \geqslant 2)$	$\quad + \left(\dfrac{2m - n - 3}{m - 1}\right)\left(\dfrac{a}{a^2 - b^2}\right)I_{m-1}$
$\quad (a \neq b)$	$\quad + \left(\dfrac{n - m + 2}{m - 1}\right)\left(\dfrac{1}{a^2 - b^2}\right)I_{m-2}$

Another technique that is sometimes useful, particularly in the case of definite integrals, is the introduction of complex variables. This method is conveniently employed when the integrand contains sines or cosines. Let us illustrate the technique by choosing an example that can be checked independently by means of one of the previous reduction formulas. This is not redundancy; it is convenient to have more than one technique at one's fingertips in case a given technique does not come to mind or does not work.

Example 25. Perform the integration

$$I = \int_0^\infty e^{-ax} \cos^2 bx \, dx.$$

Answer.   We choose to express the integrand in terms of a cosine to the first power so as to make it conform to the cosine term in the definition of e^{-ix} as $\text{Cis} - x$ (see Section 1.4). If we use the well-known half-angle formula for $\cos \frac{1}{2} x$ (see Section 1.3), then we can write

$$I = \frac{1}{2} \int_0^\infty e^{-ax} dx + \frac{1}{2} \int_0^\infty e^{-ax} \cos 2bx \, dx$$

$$= \frac{1}{2a} + \frac{1}{2} \text{Re} \int_0^\infty e^{-(2ib+a)x} dx$$

where Re means "the real part of." The integral on the right can be treated as a special case of

$$\int e^{-cx} dx = \frac{-e^{-cx}}{c}$$

so that we can write

$$I = \frac{1}{2a} + \frac{1}{2} \text{Re} \left[\frac{-e^{-(2ib+a)x}}{2ib + a} \right]_0^\infty$$

$$= \frac{1}{2a} + \frac{1}{2} \text{Re} \left(\frac{1}{2ib + a} \right).$$

To determine the real part of the complex fraction we make the denominator real by multiplying numerator and denominator by the complex conjugate of the denominator.

$$I = \frac{1}{2a} + \tfrac{1}{2}\mathrm{Re}\left(\frac{-2ib+a}{4b^2+a^2}\right)$$

$$= \frac{1}{2a} + \tfrac{1}{2}\left(\frac{a}{4b^2+a^2}\right)$$

$$\boxed{= \frac{a^2+2b^2}{a(a^2+4b^2)}}.$$

The same answer is obtained from reduction formula 2 with $n=2$ and $a = -a$ there.

Another interesting case is provided by the integral $\int \sec^3 x\,dx$. Here, if we let $\sec x = \cos\theta$, then from the identity $1+\tan^2 x = \sec^2 x$ it follows that $\tan x = i\sin\theta$ and $dx = i\,d\theta/\cos\theta$. The integral therefore is $i\int\cos^2\theta\,d\theta$ or $\tfrac{1}{2}[i\theta + (i\sin\theta)(\cos\theta)]$. From the definition $e^{i\theta} = \cos\theta + i\sin\theta$, it follows that $i\theta = \ln(\cos\theta + i\sin\theta)$, and hence $\int\sec^3 x\,dx = \tfrac{1}{2}[\ln(\sec x + \tan x) + \sec x \tan x]$.

DIGRESSION INTO HYPERBOLIC FUNCTIONS*

Tables 3.1 and 3.2 and other preceding material attest to the fact that hyperbolic functions arise rather naturally in mathematics. The student of physical science, therefore, must have some knowledge of their origin and behavior. This is apt to be an area of mathematics that you have not previously studied at any great length. Historically these functions were defined with reference to a hyperbola in much the same way as ordinary trigonometric functions can be defined with reference to a circle.

In Figure 3.5, point P' may be supposed to move counterclockwise around the circle $x^2 + y^2 = a^2$, and at the same time point P moves outward on the hyperbola $x^2 - y^2 = a^2$. When the x coordinate of P' is negative, the other half of the hyperbola must be drawn (recall Figure 1.2d, which is also that of a hyperbola). By analogy with the circular (trigonometric) functions, we

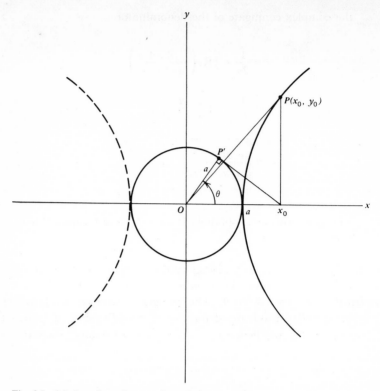

Fig. 3.5 Motion of a point on a hyperbola.

would like to describe the position of P in terms of two coordinates:

$$x_0 = \text{some distance} \times \text{cosine of some angle}$$

$$y_0 = \text{same distance} \times \text{sine of same angle}.$$

However, in our problem the only distance we know a priori is a, and the only angle we know is θ. Therefore, we shall try to describe the advance of P in terms of the motion of P'.

From the diagram we have

$$x_0 = a \sec \theta$$

$$y_0 = a \tan \theta,$$

and if we set the right-hand sides equal to expressions of the desired form, then we have

$$x_0 = a \cosh u$$

$$y_0 = a \sinh u$$

where u is a parameter in our diagram that must be related in some way to θ. The hyperbola obeys the equation $y^2 = x^2 - a^2$; hence we have

$$\sec\theta + \tan\theta = \frac{x_0 + \sqrt{x_0^2 - a^2}}{a}.$$

Now let

$$u = \ln\frac{x_0 + \sqrt{x_0^2 - a^2}}{a},$$

so it follows that

$$e^u = \frac{x_0 + \sqrt{x_0^2 - a^2}}{a}$$

$$e^{-u} = \frac{a}{x_0 + \sqrt{x_0^2 - a^2}}.$$

Addition of e^u and e^{-u} gives, after some algebra, $2x_0/a$. In other words, $x_0 = \frac{1}{2}a(e^u + e^{-u})$, and therefore we have to identify $\frac{1}{2}(e^u + e^{-u})$ with $\cosh u$. Similarly, it can be shown that $e^u - e^{-u}$ equals $2\sqrt{x_0^2 - a^2}/a$ or $2y_0/a$. In other words, $y_0 = \frac{1}{2}a(e^u - e^{-u})$, and therefore we have to identify $\frac{1}{2}(e^u - e^{-u})$ with $\sinh u$. Finally, if we define a hyperbolic tangent, $\tanh u$, to have the same relation to $\cosh u$ and $\sinh u$ as $\tan\theta$ does to $\cos\theta$ and $\sin\theta$, then

$$\tanh u = \frac{e^u - e^{-u}}{e^u + e^{-u}}$$

and other hyperbolic functions follow accordingly.

The angle θ in Figure 3.5 is called the *Gudermannian* of u, and is notated $\theta = gd\,u$. The name was used by Arthur Cayley (1821–1895) who named it after Christof Gudermann (1798–1852), a German mathematician who specially discussed this function. By symmetry one should have

$$u = gd^{-1}\theta$$

$$= \ln(\sec\theta + \tan\theta).$$

This function, however, is just the integral $\int \sec\theta\,d\theta$ and has the following consequence:

$$gd^{-1}\theta = \int \sec\theta\,d\theta$$

$$= \begin{array}{l} \text{a specific case of the more general} \\ \textit{elliptic integral} \text{ of the first kind} \end{array}$$

$$= \int \frac{d\theta}{\sqrt{1-k^2\sin^2\theta}}$$

where k (the modulus)$=1$. Elliptic integrals must usually be evaluated numerically; the modulus $k=1$ is an exceptional case.

There are some interesting connections between the circular and the hyperbolic functions that could conceivably be useful as substitutions in certain integrals. For example, in Section 1.4 we defined the cosine of a complex argument to be

$$\cos z = \frac{e^{iz}+e^{-iz}}{2}.$$

If we take z to be pure imaginary, then this relation becomes

$$\cos iy = \frac{e^{-y}+e^{y}}{2}$$

$$= \cosh y.$$

Similarly, from the definition of the sine of a complex argument, we have

$$\sin iy = \frac{e^{-y}-e^{y}}{2i}$$

$$= i\sinh y.$$

Another interesting relation can be obtained if we apply to $\cos z$ the formula for the cosine of a sum of two angles (see Section 1.3).

$$\cos z = \cos(x+iy)$$

$$= \cos x \cos iy - \sin x \sin iy$$

$$= \cos x \cosh y - i\sin x \sinh y$$

The absolute square of this is then given by

$$|\cos z|^2 = \cos^2 x \cosh^2 y + \sin^2 x \sinh^2 y$$
$$= (1 - \sin^2 x)(1 + \sinh^2 y) + \sin^2 x \sinh^2 y$$
$$= \cos^2 x + \sinh^2 y.$$

Since by their very definition the hyperbolic sine and cosine are functions that are unbounded, that is, they tend to infinity as the argument tends to infinity, then the simple relation above shows that $\cos z$ and, by a similar argument, $\sin z$ are not limited in absolute value; in contrast, the sine and cosine of a real variable are limited in absolute value to unity. Similar arguments show that $\sinh z$ and $\cosh z$ also are not limited in absolute value; for example, the following equation shows this for $\sinh z$:

$$|\sinh z|^2 = \sinh^2 x + \cos^2 y.$$

In Table 3.4 are collected together some trigonometric identities involving hyperbolic functions. Note, for example, that since $\sin z$ and $\cos z$ are differentiable (review Section 2.6), this fact plus identities 1 and 2 of Table 3.4 can be used to show that the derivative of $\sinh x$ is $\cosh x$, and so on.

Table 3.4   Trigonometric Identities Involving Hyperbolic Functions

1. $\sinh x = -i \sin ix$	7. $\sinh ix = i \sin x$
2. $\cosh x = \cos ix$	8. $\cosh ix = \cos x$
3. $\tanh x = -i \tan ix$	9. $\tanh ix = i \tan x$
4. $\sinh iz = i \sin z$	10. $\cosh iz = \cos z$
5. $|\sin z|^2 = \sin^2 x + \sinh^2 y$	11. $|\sinh z|^2 = \sinh^2 x + \sin^2 y$
6. $|\cos z|^2 = \cos^2 x + \sinh^2 y$	12. $|\cosh z|^2 = \sinh^2 x + \cos^2 y$

3   PARAMETER DIFFERENTIATION

The technique of differentiation of an integral with respect to a parameter is sometimes useful for the evaluation of integrals. To review, we said in Chapter 2 that if in the integral $F(y) = \int_{a(y)}^{b(y)} f(x,y)dx$ the function $f(x,y)$ and its partial derivative $\partial f(x,y)/\partial y$ are continuous and $a(y)$ and $b(y)$ are differentiable, then

$$F'(y) = \int_{a(y)}^{b(y)} \frac{\partial f(x,y)}{\partial y} dx + f(b,y) \frac{db(y)}{dy} - f(a,y) \frac{da(y)}{dy}.$$

Having established this relation, we can differentiate again and again, although the results rapidly get complicated. Conceivably, cases could arise where differentiation with respect to a parameter in a multiple integral is required. These offer no new problems and are not discussed here. The interested reader is referred to Volume I of the two-volume work by Edwards (see Annotated Bibliography) for discussion of this point.

As an illustration of the technique of parameter differentiation let us consider the following example.

Example 26. Perform the integration

$$I = \int_0^\infty \frac{\sin x}{x} dx.$$

Answer. First consider the related integral

$$I(\alpha) = \int_0^\infty \frac{e^{-\alpha x} \sin x}{x} dx.$$

Since the limits are not functions of α, we have on differentiation

$$\frac{dI(\alpha)}{d\alpha} = -\int_0^\infty e^{-\alpha x} \sin x \, dx$$

$$= \frac{-1}{\alpha^2 + 1}$$

after integrating by parts as in Example 22, or after introducing complex variables and integrating as in Example 25. It follows that

$$I(\alpha) = -\int \frac{d\alpha}{\alpha^2 + 1}$$

$$= -\tan^{-1}\alpha + c \text{ (from Table 3.1).}$$

To find the constant of integration, c, we note that $I(\infty) = 0$, so that

$$c = \tan^{-1} \infty$$
$$= \tfrac{1}{2}\pi.$$

Finally, this gives for our original integral[2]

$$I = I(0)$$
$$= \int_0^\infty \frac{\sin x}{x}\,dx$$
$$= \tfrac{1}{2}\pi - \tan^{-1} 0$$
$$= \boxed{\tfrac{1}{2}\pi}.$$

The above integral appears in applications occasionally, and it is referred to as the *sine integral*. When the upper limit is finite, the results cannot be written in terms of elementary functions but can be evaluated numerically. These are tabulated in handbooks along with three other such integrals.[3]

$$\text{Si}\,x = \int_0^x \frac{\sin t}{t}\,dt \qquad \text{Ei}\,x = \int_{-\infty}^x \frac{e^t}{t}\,dt$$

$$\text{Ci}\,x = \int_{-\infty}^x \frac{\cos t}{t}\,dt \qquad \text{Li}\,x = \int_0^x \frac{1}{\ln t}\,dt$$

Parameter differentiation is useful in still another way. Thus if we know that

$$\int_0^\infty e^{-ax^2}\,dx = \tfrac{1}{2}\sqrt{\frac{\pi}{a}}$$

[2]The pure mathematician G. H. Hardy (1877–1947) felt that the integral of Example 26 is actually quite difficult from a rigorous standpoint. In an interesting reprint published in *Math. Gaz.*, **55**, 152 (1971), he assigns grades to the various ways that have been used for working it out.

[3]The exponential integral occurs in the quantum mechanical treatment of the hydrogen molecule. The logarithmic integral is of interest to number theorists because for large N the number of prime numbers, $\pi(N)$, less than a given number N is closely approximated by li(N). Thus $\pi(1000) = 167$ and li(1000) $\cong 178$, for an error of about 6.6%. See any book on number theory, and the article by L. J. Goldstein, "A History of the Prime Number Theorem," *Am. Math. Mon.*, **80**, 599 (1973).

then we also know the value for $\int_0^\infty x^2 e^{-ax^2} dx$ because

$$\frac{d}{da} \int_0^\infty e^{-ax^2} dx = \frac{d}{da} \left(\frac{1}{2} \sqrt{\frac{\pi}{a}} \right)$$

or

$$-\int_0^\infty x^2 e^{-ax^2} dx = -\frac{1}{4} \sqrt{\pi} \, a^{-3/2}$$

and in general,

$$\int_0^\infty x^{2n} e^{-ax^2} dx = \frac{1 \cdot 3 \cdot 5 \cdot (2n-1)}{2^{n+1} a^n} \sqrt{\frac{\pi}{a}} .$$

Integrals such as these occur, for example, in the kinetic theory of gases.

4 DEFINITE INTEGRALS; NUMERICAL INTEGRATION

We have already mentioned some integrals that for finite limits or in their indefinite form cannot be expressed in terms of elementary functions: the sine integral, the cosine integral, elliptic integrals, etc. Let us add two more to this list, reserving for the future (Chapter 7) a more detailed discussion of their mathematical properties.

The first is the error function integral. The curve known as the *Gaussian normal curve* has the form

$$y = \frac{1}{\sqrt{2\pi}} \exp\left(-\frac{1}{2} x^2 \right)$$

where the independent variable x measures the deviation from the mean; the graph of the Gaussian normal curve is the familiar bell-shaped curve (see Figure 3.6) known to examination graders all over the world! Here the abscissa is generally measured in σ units (units of standard deviation from the mean). The total area under the curve is the probability that an object selected from the normally distributed population will possess some desired characteristic with a standard deviation lying anywhere in the range $-\infty$ to $+\infty$. Obviously this has to be unity. Now it can be shown by various means that the integral $\int_0^\infty \exp(-a^2 x^2) dx$ has the value $\sqrt{\pi}/2a$; this is really the same integral as one given near the end of the last section. Hence the total

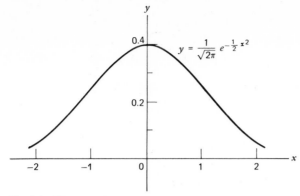

Fig. 3.6 The normal curve.

area under the Gaussian normal curve is

$$A = \int_{-\infty}^{\infty} y \, dx$$

$$= \frac{2}{\sqrt{2\pi}} \int_0^{\infty} \exp\left(-\tfrac{1}{2}x^2\right) dx$$

$$= \frac{2}{\sqrt{2\pi}} \times \frac{1}{2\sqrt{\tfrac{1}{2}}} \times \sqrt{\pi}$$

$$= 1.$$

In tables normal curve data are frequently reported as the *error function integral* (or just error function) defined as

$$\text{erf}\, t = \frac{2}{\sqrt{\pi}} \int_0^t \exp\left(-z^2\right) dz.$$

The integral represents the area of the shaded portion of the curve shown in Figure 3.7. The connection between this and a corresponding Gaussian normal curve is seen by letting $z^2 = \tfrac{1}{2}x^2$ in the above equation; this gives

$$\text{erf}\, t = \frac{2}{\sqrt{\pi}} \int_0^{t\sqrt{2}} \exp\left(-\tfrac{1}{2}x^2\right) \sqrt{\tfrac{1}{2}} \, dx$$

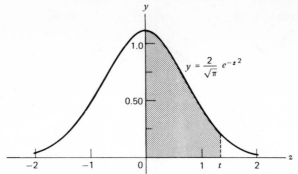

Fig. 3.7 The error function.

or

$$\mathrm{erf}\!\left(\frac{t'}{\sqrt{2}}\right)=\sqrt{\frac{2}{\pi}}\ \int_{0}^{t'}\exp\!\left(-\tfrac{1}{2}x^{2}\right)dx \qquad (t'=t\sqrt{2}\ )$$

$$=2\int_{0}^{t'}y\,dx$$

$$=\int_{-t'}^{t'}y\,dx.$$

From an error function table (such as Table 7.1 in the work by Abramowitz and Stegun listed in the Annotated Bibliography) we can estimate the following value: $\mathrm{erf}(1/\sqrt{2}\,)\cong0.682$. Hence it follows that the Gaussian normal curve integral $\int_{-1}^{1}y\,dx$ has the value 0.682; *this means that an object selected from a normally distributed population will possess the desired characteristic to within ± 1 unit of standard deviation from the mean 68.2% of the time.* On the other hand, if we consult a normal curve of error table (such as is found in the mathematical section of the *Handbook of Chemistry and Physics*), we find a value of 0.3413 for the area for the positive limit 1.00, that is, the integral $\int_{0}^{1}y\,dx$ has a value of 0.3413. Hence from the relation above we can also say that 2×0.3413 is the value of $\mathrm{erf}(1/\sqrt{2}\,)$ or erf (0.707). Similarly, we have

$$\mathrm{erf}(\sqrt{2}\ )=\int_{-2}^{2}y\,dx=0.955 \qquad (\pm2\ \sigma\ \text{units})$$

$$\mathrm{erf}\!\left(3\sqrt{2}\ /2\right)=\int_{-3}^{3}y\,dx=0.987 \qquad (\pm3\ \sigma\ \text{units}).$$

A related integral that is also tabulated is the *complementary error function*. It is related in a simple way to the error function:

$$\text{erfc}\,t = \frac{2}{\sqrt{\pi}} \int_t^\infty \exp(-z^2)\,dz$$

$$= 1 - \text{erf}\,t.$$

The second standard definite integral that occurs frequently in physical problems is the *gamma function*. It is defined to be

$$\Gamma(t) = \int_0^\infty x^{t-1} e^{-x}\,dx \qquad (t > 0).$$

Here the tabulations are commonly not for changes in the limits but for changes in the exponent variable t. In a slightly more general formulation one has

$$\int_0^\infty x^{t-1} e^{-(a+1)x}\,dx = \frac{\Gamma(t)}{(a+1)^t}.$$

$$(t > 0)$$

$$(a > -1).$$

Some special cases of the gamma function to watch for are given in the box; note that the first entry has validity only for positive integral t.

$$\boxed{\begin{aligned} \Gamma(t) &= (t-1)! \\ \Gamma(\tfrac{1}{2}) &= \sqrt{\pi} \\ \Gamma(\tfrac{3}{2}) &= \tfrac{1}{2}\sqrt{\pi} \end{aligned}}$$

Let us think back to the beginning of Section 3.1 where we saw the interpretation of an integral as an area under a curve. Suppose that we have a curve that is defined by a discrete set of points and that we are ignorant of the functional form of the curve; in a case like this how shall we find the area under some selected portion of the curve? Or equivalently, how can we evaluate the integral $\int_a^b y\,dx$ if we cannot write a formula or expression for y? This is a problem that is very common in experimental work. We must know therefore how to evaluate integrals numerically. Problems such as this make up the discipline of *numerical analysis*, a whole field in itself, so we will be content here with just learning one particular technique, namely, *Simpson's rule* for finding areas.[4]

The following is not a rigorous derivation of Simpson's rule but it should help to make the origin of the rule clear. Suppose the interval $a \leqslant x \leqslant b$ is divided into an even number of subintervals, each of width h. If we wished, we could approximate two adjacent subintervals as trapezoids (see Figure 3.8). The combined area of the two trapezoids is given by elementary geometry as

$$A = \tfrac{1}{2}h(y_2 + y_3) + \tfrac{1}{2}h(y_1 + y_2)$$

$$= h(\tfrac{1}{2}y_1 + y_2 + \tfrac{1}{2}y_3).$$

Now we suppose that this can be improved by replacing the oblique sides of the two adjacent trapezoids by a parabola whose area is *taken to be* of the form

$$A = h(ay_1 + by_2 + cy_3).$$

By analogy with the above expression we arbitrarily set $a = c$. We must now

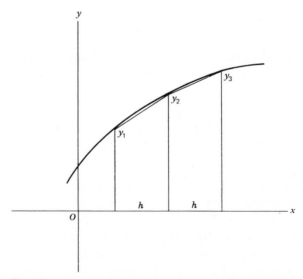

Fig. 3.8   Approximating an area under a curve by trapezoids.

[4]Thomas Simpson (1710–1761) was a British silk weaver. In his leisure he taught mathematics; in 1737 he wrote *New Treatise on Fluxions*, and 6 years later he was appointed professor of mathematics at Woolwich. See J. R. Newman (ed.), *The World of Mathematics*, Simon & Schuster, New York, 1956, p. 2372.

find values for a and b, and we do this by calibrating our area formula with two standard parabolas.

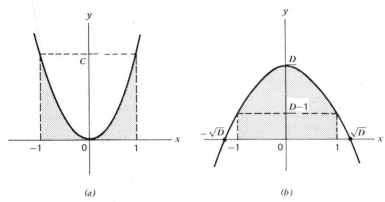

(a)   (b)

Fig. 3.9 Two standard parabolas.

Consider first the simple case of $y = Cx^2$ (see Figure 3.9a), for which the area A between $x = -1$ and $x = +1$ is $2C$. It follows that since $y_2 = 0$, then $a = c = \frac{1}{3}$. To get b consider the case of $y = D - x^2$ (see Figure 3.9b); here $y_1 = y_3 = D - 1$ and $y_2 = D$. The area in this case is easily found from integration to be $2(D - \frac{1}{3})$. Hence this implies that

$$2(D - \tfrac{1}{3}) = 1\left[\frac{D-1}{3} + bD + \frac{D-1}{3}\right]$$

$$b = \frac{4}{3}.$$

If we continue in this way for other sets of subintervals and allow for overlap, we arrive at the following approximate formula:

$$A = \int_a^b f(x)\,dx \cong \frac{h}{3}(y_1 + 4y_2 + 2y_3 + 4y_4 + 2y_5 + \cdots + y_n).$$

To illustrate Simpson's rule let us do an example that can be checked exactly.

Example 27. Evaluate by Simpson's rule

$$\int_{\frac{1}{2}}^1 \frac{dx}{x^2 + 1}.$$

Answer. From entry 1 in Table 3.1 we ascertain that the exact answer is $\frac{1}{4}\pi - \tan^{-1}\frac{1}{2}$ or 0.3222. Now we split the interval up into six subintervals each of $h = 1/12$ (see Figure 3.10), and then proceed to calculate y at each of the points of subdivision (Table 3.5). By Simpson's rule we get for the area

$$A = \tfrac{1}{36}\left[0.800 + 4(0.746) + 2(0.692) + 4(0.640) + 2(0.590)\right.$$

$$\left. + 4(0.543) + 0.500\right]$$

$$= \boxed{0.322}\,.$$

Table 3.5   Data for a Simpson's Rule Problem

x	y	x	y
1/2	0.800	5/6	0.590
7/12	0.746	11/12	0.543
2/3	0.692	1	0.500
3/4	0.640		

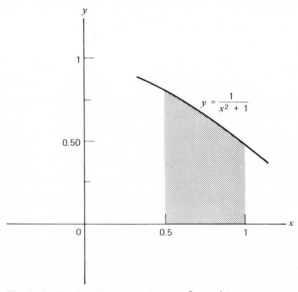

Fig. 3.10   Finding the area under $y = (x^2 + 1)^{-1}$ by Simpson's rule.

Here is another example in which this time the functional form of the integrand is not known, that is, the function is defined by a discrete set of points.

Example 28.   A certain mixture of chemical substances is separated by gas chromatography; two, cleanly separated peaks appear on the gas chromatogram. A measurement of their profiles as a function of time of elution yields the data in Table 3.6. From these data estimate the relative amounts of the two substances present in the mixture.

Table 3.6 Data for a Simpson's Rule Problem

Substance A		Substance B	
Intensity (arbitrary units)	Time (sec)	Intensity (arbitrary units)	Time (sec)
3	42	0.5	250
17	53	6	258
40	64	14	266
69	75	21	274
90	86	13	282
68	97	5	290
43	108	0	298
19	119		
4	130		

Answer.   The relative amounts of A and B stand in the same ratio as the ratio of the areas under their chromatogram peaks. By Simpson's rule we get for the area under peak A

$$A = \tfrac{11}{3}[3 + 4(17) + 2(40) + 4(69) + 2(90)$$
$$+ 4(68) + 2(43) + 4(19) + 4]$$
$$= 3832 \text{ units.}$$

A similar calculation yields an area of 487 units under peak B. Hence the relative amounts of the two substances present are

$$\boxed{\frac{\text{amount of } A}{\text{amount of } B} = \frac{3832}{487} = \frac{7.87}{1}}.$$

The mixture is $11.3\% B$ and $88.7\% A$.

5 LINE INTEGRALS

It is an experimental fact of thermodynamics that if a system is changed from state 1 to state 2 in each of two ways the amount of work done in each case need not be the same. For example, if the system is a gas and we convert this gas from one set of pressure, volume, and temperature conditions to another set by two different physical processes, then the pressure–volume work for the two processes will in general be unequal. We can think of this pictorially as in Figure 3.11. Reference to Table 2.3 shows that the

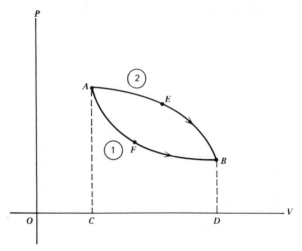

Fig. 3.11 Dependence of PV work on path.

amount of PV work done as the pressure of the gas changes continuously along path 1 is given by the negative of the area of $AFBDC$. Similarly for path 2 the work is given by the negative of the area of $AEBDC$. Clearly these two areas cannot be identical. What this means mathematically is that we cannot express the work Δw by the integral

$$\int_{\text{point}A}^{\text{point}B} dw = w(B) - w(A)$$

where the form of the function w is independent of the choice of curve connecting points A and B. This is a consequence of the way we define work in the first place. Thus we define work as a function of a force and a distance, or for the expansion or contraction of a substance, as a function of the two variables pressure and volume. If this function had the simple form

$dw = -(PdV + VdP) = -d(PV)$, for example, then we could write

$$\Delta w = \int_A^B dw = -\int_A^B d(PV)$$

$$= (-PV)_B - (-PV)_A$$

and the work would thus depend only on the end points A and B. However, work is not defined in this way but rather through the expression $dw = -PdV$, and an integration similar to the one just done is not possible. Of course, we know that if P is written as a function of V, then the work can be evaluated by the Riemann integral

$$\Delta w = -\int_C^D P(V)dV,$$

but this is not the point made above.

The considerations above prompt a slight extension of the definite integral. Let C be a smooth curve in the xy plane defined on the interval $[a,b]$ and let $f(x,y)$ be a function defined for all points (x,y) on C. We now partition C into a number of curved segments of arbitrary length; a typical segment connects points p_{i-1} and p_i and has arc length Δs_i (see Figure 3.12). Now select a point arbitrarily from each curved segment; the coordinates of the point in arc $p_{i-1}p_i$ will be denoted (ζ_i,λ_i). By analogy with the definition

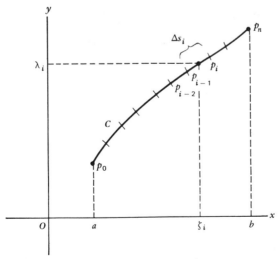

Fig. 3.12 Defining a path of integration.

of the Riemann integral, we form the sum

$$\sum_{i=1}^{n} f(\zeta_i,\lambda_i)\,\Delta s_i$$

and if the limit of this sum exists as $\Delta s_i \to 0 (n \to \infty)$ and is identical for all possible partitions of a given curve C, then we say that this limit is the *line integral* of $f(x,y)$ along C.

$$\int_C f(x,y)\,ds$$

The limit exists if $f(x,y)$ is continuous along C. Note that C and $f(x,y)$ are two entirely different entities. The curve C is *not* the graph of $f(x,y)$; the graph of $f(x,y)$ is a surface and would require a three-dimensional coordinate system for its presentation.

In the line integral suppose that $f(V,P)$ has the form $-P(dV/ds)$. This expression is also dw/ds and thus it is the rate of change of work with respect to arc length of the curve C. Substitution then gives

$$\int_C \left(-P\frac{dV}{ds}\right)ds = \int_C dw$$

and thus we see that work is describable mathematically as a line integral. Why do we choose the form we did for $f(V,P)$? If we do an integration of some function along the x axis, for example, points on this axis represent distance from the origin, but they also represent position. In order to represent position of a point on a general curve that is being used as a path of integration, two coordinates are needed, but these two coordinates can be amalgamated into a single variable by computing the distance or arc length at that point. In this way the function being integrated can be expressed in terms of the variation of a single quantity.

We have not yet answered how one evaluates a line integral. If P and Q are two points very close to one another on some curve C (see Figure 3.13), then the arc length PQ is closely approximated by ds, which is given by

$$ds = \sqrt{(dx)^2 + (dy)^2}$$

$$= \sqrt{1 + \left(\frac{dy}{dx}\right)^2}\,dx.$$

If we are given y as a function of x, then the line integral is completely

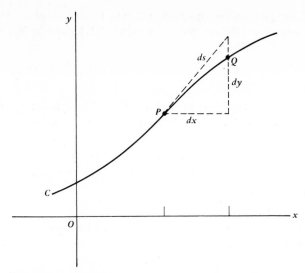

Fig. 3.13 Arc length.

expressible in terms of x:

$$\int_C f(x,y)\,ds = \int f(x,y(x))\sqrt{1+\left(\frac{dy}{dx}\right)^2}\ dx.$$

Alternatively, for C we could be given x as a function of y, and then the line integral could be expressed completely as a Riemann integral in y.

The line integral given earlier for work has a rather specialized form. If we think of the line integral as any integral where the path of integration is some specified curve, then a more general line integral in the plane can be written as

$$\int_C [M(x,y)\,dx + N(x,y)\,dy].$$

The study of integrals such as this belongs to the field of differential geometry or the study of the calculus of what are called n-forms. We define the general continuous differential *1-form* in the plane to be

$$F = M(x,y)\,dx + N(x,y)\,dy$$

where M and N are continuous functions defined in some region R. To illustrate still another way of evaluating line integrals, suppose C is described by means of the parametric equations $x = g(t)$, $y = h(t)$, and $a \leqslant t \leqslant b$. Then this curve C assigns to the line integral a value $F(C)$ given by the expression

$$F(C) = \int_a^b [M\{g(t), h(t)\} g'(t) + N\{g(t), h(t)\} h'(t)] dt.$$

In other words, the rule is that to evaluate F on C simply substitute $g(t)$ for x, $h(t)$ for y, $g'(t)$ and $h'(t)$ for dx/dt and dy/dt, and then integrate over t.[5]

Example 29. Evaluate the line integral $\int_C (xy\,dx - y^2\,dy)$ for (a) the path $C = \{(x,y): x = \sin t, y = \cos t; 0 \leqslant t \leqslant \frac{1}{2}\pi\}$, and for (b) the path $C' = \{(x,y): x = 2t, y = \sqrt{1-4t^2}; 0 \leqslant t \leqslant \frac{1}{2}\}$.

Answer. The two parameterizations are seen to be equivalent because in both cases $x^2 + y^2 = 1$.

$$(a) \qquad I = \int_0^{\pi/2} \left(\sin t \cos t \cos t\, dt - \cos^2 t (-\sin t)\, dt \right)$$

$$= 2 \int_0^{\pi/2} \cos^2 t \sin t\, dt$$

$$= -\tfrac{2}{3} \cos^3 t \Big|_0^{\pi/2} = \boxed{\tfrac{2}{3}}.$$

$$(b) \qquad I' = \int_0^{1/2} \left[2t\sqrt{1-4t^2}\,(2dt) - (1-4t^2)\left(\frac{-4t\,dt}{\sqrt{1-4t^2}} \right) \right]$$

$$= \int_0^{1/2} 8t\sqrt{1-4t^2}\, dt$$

$$= -\tfrac{2}{3}(1-4t^2)^{3/2} \Big|_0^{1/2} = \boxed{\tfrac{2}{3}}.$$

This example illustrates a general result, namely, that the particular parameterization of a given curve C does not affect the value of the line

---

[5]In this context we may point out that the line integral is an example of a more general class of functions whose domains of definition are not sets of points, but sets of functions. Thus $F(C)$ above is a number determined by the pair (C, F), and we say that $F(C)$ is a *curve functional* because its domain is a class of smooth curves; thermodynamic work is a curve functional. Roughly speaking, we may say that a functional is a function of a function. Similarly, there are quantities known as *surface functionals*, functions whose domains of definition are smooth surfaces.

integral. Now we ask another question: if we pick two different curves that connect the same pair of end points, will this affect the value of the line integral? In view of the discussion earlier on thermodynamic work, our anticipated answer is yes. For example, in the situation above the path C connected point $(0,1)$ to $(1,0)$ in that order. Another path that does this is $x = t, y = 1 - t$, or $x + y = 1$, a parameterization that is clearly not equivalent to either of the two previous ones. The line integral now has the value

$$I = \int_0^1 \left[t(1 - t)\, dt + (1 - t)^2 dt \right]$$

$$= \int_0^1 dt - \int_0^1 t\, dt$$

$$= \left(t - \tfrac{1}{2} t^2 \right)\big|_0^1 = \tfrac{1}{2}.$$

The interesting thing that emerges is that if certain conditions are placed on the 1-form F, then the line integral $\int_C F$ turns out to be *independent of the path*, that is, integrations along two different paths (not parameterizations of a single path) yield the same value of the integral. We require only that the 1-form be exact, which as you recall from Section 2.3 means that F can be expressed as the total differential of some function f:

$$df = F.$$

If this is the case, then $\int_C F = \int_a^b df = f(b) - f(a)$ by the first fundamental theorem of the integral calculus, and thus only the end points a, b matter and not the topography of the path connecting them.

An obvious corollary of this path independence is that if C is a *closed* curve lying in the region in which the 1-form F is exact, then the line integral around this contour will be zero. You will sometimes see this notated by means of the symbol $\oint$, an integral sign with a closed loop drawn through it:

$$\oint F = 0.$$

This follows because the contour C can always be thought of as being comprised of two open curves oriented in opposite directions (see Figure 3.14). Then, if the line integral has value I for the path $A \rightarrow B$, it will have value $-I$ for the path $B \rightarrow A$, and the sum will be zero.

We could use this idea to test the exactness of certain expressions, but to do so we must always be able to get values for the line integrals; in some cases this may be difficult. However, the material in the preceding chapter suggests that if $F = M(x,y)\, dx + N(x,y)\, dy$ is exact in some region R, then throughout R one must have $\partial M / \partial y = \partial N / \partial x$, and vice versa. This can be

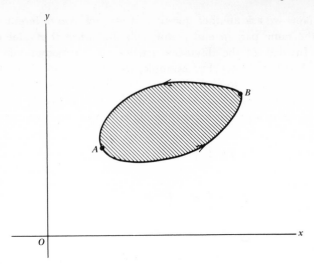

Fig. 3.14   A closed contour for a line integral.

shown rigorously with the aid of certain rules and conventions for the multiplication and differentiation of n-forms, but we simply accept the truth of this statement. To see the importance of this to thermodynamics, we must state carefully exactly what is desired. In thermodynamics we start with the empirical observation that a change in internal energy, defined to be $\Delta E = q + w$, and a change in entropy, defined to be $\Delta S = \int dq_{\text{rev}}/T$, are found without exception so far to be independent of path. It is then postulated that this is true in general of these two functions. The following theorem is then of relevance.

Theorem 8.   *If the integral of the 1-form* $F = M(x, y) dx + N(x, y) dy$ *is independent of path in an open, connected region* R, *then* F *is exact in* R, *and therefore obeys* $\partial M / \partial y = \partial N / \partial x$.

The important point here is that the region be connected, that is, not disjoint, so that it will always be possible to connect any two points in R by a smooth, continuous curve lying completely in R. This theorem allows us to say that if in a particular thermodynamic problem the differential dE, for example, is expressible in the form

$$F = dE = M(V, T) dV + N(V, T) dT$$

then it follows that $(\partial M / \partial T)_V = (\partial N / \partial V)_T$. This is the basis of the reciprocity relations (or as they are sometimes called, the *Maxwell relations*) that are much used in thermodynamic derivations.

The ideas presented in this section can be extended to curves in three-dimensional space, and conditions for the exactness of 1-forms in this space, that have the general form

$$M(x,y,z)\,dx + N(x,y,z)\,dy + P(x,y,z)\,dz$$

and that are sometimes called *Pfaffians*, can be found but are more involved than those for 1-forms in the plane. The integration of 2-forms over surfaces to give surface integerals (surface functionals) and the conditions for the exactness of 2-forms are also of interest, but are not presented here. The interested reader is referred to Chapter 7 in Buck and Chapter 18 in Olmsted.[6]

6* FOURIER TRANSFORMS

This section is concerned with a special type of integral that has found applications in a very wide number of fields. We define the *Fourier transform* of a function $f(t)$ to be the integral

$$F(\omega) = \frac{1}{\sqrt{2\pi}} \int_{-\infty}^{\infty} f(t) e^{i\omega t}\,dt$$

provided $f(t)$ is defined for $-\infty < t < \infty$ and the integral exists. Notations differ; some authors omit the factor of $1/\sqrt{2\pi}$, others write it as $1/2\pi$, and others include a factor of 2π in the exponent. Some authors write the exponent with a negative sign; to distinguish our convention from this, we say that $F(\omega)$ above is the $+i$ Fourier transform of $f(t)$.

We next inquire when the integral above will exist. To answer this we employ a test that is useful both for examining infinite series and infinite integrals. Suppose $f(t)$ and $g(t)$ are piecewise continuous for $a \le t < \infty$, that is, they are continuous except for a finite number of finite discontinuities. Then if $\int_a^\infty |g(t)|\,dt$ exists, and if $|f(t)| \le |g(t)|$, then the integral $\int_a^\infty |f(t)|\,dt$ exists also. This comparison of two integrals by comparing the absolute values of their integrands is intuitively plausible if we visualize the integral as an area under a curve (see Figure 3.15). A similar argument holds for integrals such as $\int_{-\infty}^b |f(t)|\,dt$. Next, we note that if $\int_a^\infty |f(t)|\,dt$ exists, then so does the integral $\int_a^\infty f(t)\,dt$; this is not hard to prove rigorously. Finally, we

---

[6]Readers with a nodding acquaintance of elementary topology might enjoy scanning the articles G. T. Whyburn, "What is a Curve?, *Am. Math. Mon.* **49**, 493 (1942), and J. W. T. Youngs, "Curves and Surfaces," *ibid.*, **51**, 1 (1944). These articles suggest that it is not a simple matter to give precise, unambiguous definitions for curve and surface.

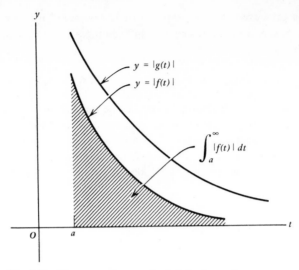

Fig. 3.15   The comparison test for infinite integrals.

recall from complex variables that the absolute value of a function of a complex variable, $h(z)$, is defined to be

$$|h(z)| = \left[h(z) \cdot \overline{h(z)} \right]^{\frac{1}{2}}$$

so that if the function $h(z)$ is $f(t)e^{i\omega t}$, then we have

$$|h(z)| = \left[f(t)e^{i\omega t} \cdot f(t)e^{-i\omega t} \right]^{\frac{1}{2}}$$

$$= f(t).$$

Theorem 9.   *Suppose* f(t) *is piecewise continuous for* $-\infty < t < \infty$, *and suppose* $\int_{-\infty}^{\infty} |f(t)|\, dt$ *exists. Then the Fourier transform of* f(t),

$$F(\omega) = \frac{1}{\sqrt{2\pi}} \int_{-\infty}^{\infty} f(t)e^{i\omega t}\, dt,$$

is defined for $-\infty < \omega < \infty$.

Some common functions do not have Fourier transforms (Figure 3.16); examples are a constant (but see Chapter 7), the sine function $\sin t$, and the exponential function e^t. Two unusual functions that technically do not have

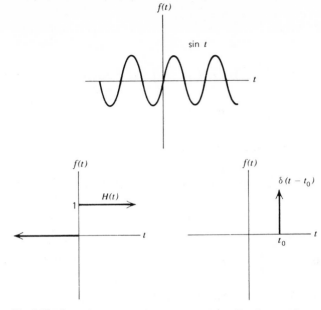

Fig. 3.16   Some functions which do not possess a Fourier transform.

a Fourier transform are the Heaviside step function $H(t)$ (related to the signum; see Exercise 30* in Chapter 2), and the Dirac delta function $\delta(t - t_0)$.

By appeal to the properties of Fourier series (see Chapter 4), it can be demonstrated that the relation between $F(\omega)$ and $f(t)$ is reversible. The *inverse Fourier transform* of $F(\omega)$ is defined to be

$$\frac{1}{\sqrt{2\pi}} \int_{-\infty}^{\infty} F(\omega) e^{-i\omega t} d\omega$$

and it is, in fact, $f(t)$ when $f(t)$ is piecewise continuous. At places where $f(t)$ is finitely discontinuous, the value of the inverse Fourier transform is equal to the average of the left and right limits, that is, the midpoint of the discontinuity.

There is an equivalent way of expressing the Fourier transform of a function that is useful when $f(t)$ has certain symmetry properties. A function $f(t)$ is an *even function* if $f(t) = f(-t)$, and it is an *odd function* if $f(t) = -f(-t)$. From this it follows that if we integrate $f(t)$ times either $\sin t$ or

$\cos t$ over an interval $[-L, +L]$, then the following results emerge.

$$\underline{f(t) \text{ even}} \qquad\qquad\qquad\qquad \underline{f(t) \text{ odd}}$$

$$\int_{-L}^{L} f(t) \sin t \, dt = \int_{0}^{L} f(t) \sin t \, dt \qquad \int_{-L}^{L} f(t) \sin t \, dt = \int_{0}^{L} f(t) \sin t \, dt$$

$$+ \int_{0}^{L} f(t) \sin(-t) \, dt \qquad\qquad + \int_{0}^{L} f(-t) \sin(-t) \, dt$$

$$= 0 \text{ by cancellation} \qquad\qquad\qquad = 2 \int_{0}^{L} f(t) \sin t \, dt$$

$$\int_{-L}^{L} f(t) \cos t \, dt = \int_{0}^{L} f(t) \cos t \, dt \qquad \int_{-L}^{L} f(t) \cos t \, dt = \int_{0}^{L} f(t) \cos t \, dt$$

$$+ \int_{0}^{L} f(t) \cos(-t) \, dt \qquad\qquad + \int_{0}^{L} f(-t) \cos(-t) \, dt$$

$$= 2 \int_{0}^{L} f(t) \cos t \, dt \qquad\qquad\qquad = 0 \text{ by cancellation}$$

Since $e^{i\omega t}$ is identical to $\cos \omega t + i \sin \omega t$, then it follows that for $f(t)$ an even function, one has

$$\int_{-\infty}^{\infty} f(t) e^{i\omega t} \, dt = 2 \int_{0}^{\infty} f(t) \cos \omega t \, dt.$$

The integral on the right is sometimes referred to as a *Fourier cosine transform*; often Fourier cosine transforms are tabulated for cases where the range is finite, usually 0 to π.

Similarly, a *Fourier sine transform* is the integral

$$\int_{0}^{\infty} f(t) \sin \omega t \, dt$$

and tables such as those in the *Handbook of Chemistry and Physics* often list only the finite version. More complete listings, however, can be found in monographs on Fourier transforms and integrals (see Annotated Bibliography) and in certain handbooks such as G. A. Korn and T. M. Korn, *Mathematical Handbook for Scientists and Engineers*, 2nd ed., McGraw-Hill, New York, 1968, Appendix D.

For functions that are neither odd nor even, the exponential form of the Fourier transform must be used. However any function can be split into an odd and an even part. To illustrate, the function $f(t) = [\sin(1-t)]/t$ is neither odd nor even. If we expand the sine function in terms of sines and cosines of 1 and t, then $f(t)$ can be written as

$$f(t) = \sin 1 \underbrace{\frac{\cos t}{t}}_{\text{odd part}} - \cos 1 \underbrace{\frac{\sin t}{t}}_{\text{even part}}$$

and in view of the previous discussion regarding transforms of odd and even functions we have

$$F(\omega) = \frac{1}{\sqrt{2\pi}} \int_{-\infty}^{\infty} \frac{\sin(1-t)}{t} e^{i\omega t} dt$$

$$= i\sqrt{\frac{2}{\pi}} \, \sin 1 \int_{0}^{\infty} \frac{\cos t \sin \omega t}{t} \, dt$$

$$- \sqrt{\frac{2}{\pi}} \, \cos 1 \int_{0}^{\infty} \frac{\sin t \cos \omega t}{t} \, dt.$$

Example 30. Work out the following Fourier transforms:
 (a) the Fourier transform of $(\sin at)/t$;
 (b) the inverse Fourier transform of $a \cos a\omega$, where $-\pi/2a \leqslant \omega \leqslant +\pi/2a$ and $\omega = 0$ elsewhere;
 (c) the cosine transform of $\exp(-\frac{1}{2}t^2)$.

Answer.

(a) $(2\pi)^{-\frac{1}{2}} \int_{-\infty}^{\infty} \frac{\sin at}{t} e^{i\omega t} dt$

$$= \sqrt{\frac{2}{\pi}} \int_{0}^{\infty} \frac{\sin at \cos \omega t}{t} \, dt$$

$$= \frac{1}{2}\sqrt{\frac{2}{\pi}} \int_{0}^{\infty} \frac{\sin(a+\omega)t + \sin(a-\omega)t}{t} \, dt$$

$$= (2\pi)^{-\frac{1}{2}} \int_{0}^{\infty} \frac{\sin(a+\omega)t}{t} \, dt + (2\pi)^{-\frac{1}{2}} \int_{0}^{\infty} \frac{\sin(a-\omega)t}{t} \, dt$$

Each integral is the sine integral; the first has value $\frac{1}{2}\pi$ if $a+\omega>0$, and $-\frac{1}{2}\pi$ if $a+\omega<0$. Similarly, the second has value $\frac{1}{2}\pi$ if $a-\omega>0$, and $-\frac{1}{2}\pi$ if $a-\omega<0$. Hence

$$(2\pi)^{-\frac{1}{2}}\int_{-\infty}^{\infty}\frac{\sin at}{t}e^{i\omega t}\,dt=\begin{cases}\sqrt{\frac{1}{2}\pi} & \text{if } |\omega|<a\\ 0 & \text{if } |\omega|>a.\end{cases}$$

$(b)\quad (2\pi)^{-\frac{1}{2}}\int_{-\infty}^{\infty}a\cos a\omega\, e^{-i\omega t}\,d\omega$

$$=\frac{a}{\sqrt{2\pi}}\int_{-\pi/2a}^{\pi/2a}\cos a\omega\, e^{-i\omega t}\,d\omega$$

$$=\frac{a}{\sqrt{2\pi}}\left[e^{-i\omega t}\left\{\frac{-it\cos a\omega+a\sin a\omega}{a^2-t^2}\right\}\right]_{-\pi/2a}^{\pi/2a}$$

from reduction formula 2 in Section 3.2

$$=\frac{a}{\sqrt{2\pi}}\left\{\frac{ae^{-i\pi t/2a}}{a^2-t^2}+\frac{ae^{i\pi t/2a}}{a^2-t^2}\right\}$$

$$=\frac{2a^2\cos\frac{1}{2}\frac{\pi t}{a}}{\sqrt{2\pi}\,(a^2-t^2)}$$

(c) This transform is best approached by integration by parts.

$$\int_0^{\infty}\exp\left(-\tfrac{1}{2}t^2\right)\cos\omega t\,dt=\frac{\sin\omega t\exp\left(-\tfrac{1}{2}t^2\right)}{\omega}\bigg|_0^{\infty}$$

$$-\frac{1}{\omega}\int_0^{\infty}t\exp\left(-\tfrac{1}{2}t^2\right)(-\sin\omega t)\,dt$$

The first term on the right vanishes; the integral on the right is the derivative of the transform $F(\omega)$ with respect to ω. This leads to the differential equation

$$\frac{dF(\omega)}{F(\omega)}=-\omega\,d\omega$$

and integration gives $F(\omega)=Ce^{-\frac{1}{2}\omega^2}$. To evaluate the constant of integration C, we note that $F(0)$ is essentially an area under a normal curve, and has the value $\sqrt{\pi/2}$.

$$\int_0^\infty \exp\left(-\tfrac{1}{2}t^2\right)\cos\omega t\,dt = \sqrt{\frac{\pi}{2}}\ \exp\left(-\tfrac{1}{2}\omega^2\right)$$

The results of parts (a) and (b) are shown in Figure 3.17. From the figure for part (a), for example, we see that the Fourier transform of a damped sine wave of arbitrary height a and corresponding arbitrary narrowness is a single square pulse of height $\sqrt{\pi/2}$ and arbitrary width $2a$. Part (c) in Example 30 shows that the transform of a Gaussian function is another Gaussian function.

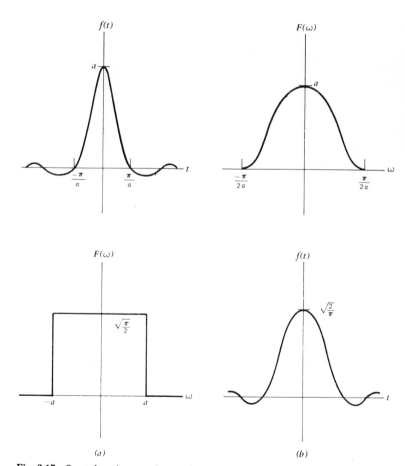

(a) (b)

Fig. 3.17 Some function-transform pairs.

Fourier transforms appear in many places in chemistry. For instance, Fourier methods have been employed in X-ray crystallography for a long time. The following discussion is based on material contained in the book by G. N. Ramachandran and R. Srinivasan, *Fourier Methods in Crystallography*, Wiley-Interscience, New York, 1970. When X rays are beamed on a substance, they are scattered by the electrons present. Let us calculate the resultant scattered radiation in a given direction making an angle 2θ with the incident radiation (the 2 here is only a convenience to eliminate a $\frac{1}{2}$ elsewhere in the theory). In Figure 3.18 let P be a discrete scattering center (an atom) and let O be an arbitrary origin at which there is also a scattering center. The vector s_i is a unit vector of the incident radiation of wavelength λ; we take up vectors later in the book, but for now just look upon s_i as a dimensionless entity with magnitude 1 and pointing in the direction shown. Analogously, s_r is a unit vector in the direction of the reflected radiation. From the figure it can be seen that there will be a difference in phase angle between the radiation scattered from point O and that from point P because the former has to travel a distance $OB - AP$ farther than the latter in order to reach a distant observer. Making use of the properties of the vector dot product one can write this phase difference (in radians) as $2\pi \mathbf{r} \cdot \mathbf{r}^*/\lambda$, where the vector $\mathbf{r}^*$ is defined as $(\mathbf{s}_r - \mathbf{s}_i)$. If A is the amplitude of the wave scattered by P when the amplitude of the incident wave is arbitrarily designated as unity, then the wave from P has amplitude and phase given by $A \exp[2\pi i \times (\mathbf{r} \cdot \mathbf{r}^*)/\lambda]$. The A can be looked on as a scattering factor of P and it is a function of $\mathbf{r}^*$, $A = A(\mathbf{r}^*)$. When several discrete scattering centers are present the total radiation scattered in the direction of s_r has amplitude and phase given by the expression

$$f(\mathbf{r}^*) = \sum_j A_j \exp\left[\frac{2\pi i (\mathbf{r}_j \cdot \mathbf{r}^*)}{\lambda} \right]$$

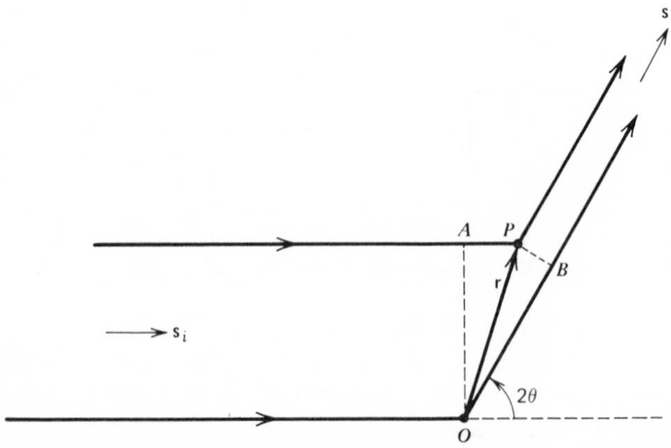

Fig. 3.18 X-ray scattering.

and in this the $\mathbf{r}^*$ is the same for all terms because we are interested in the total scattering in a fixed direction 2θ from all the centers.

Now suppose that instead of having a discrete collection of scattering centers one has a continuous distribution of scattering medium. According to quantum mechanics this is the case with the electrons in an atom. We must then replace the summation above by an integration, using the electron density distribution $\rho(\mathbf{r})$ in place of the A_j's. The amplitude of the scattered wave in a volume element $d\tau$ at $\mathbf{r}$ is now $\rho(\mathbf{r})d\tau$ and the total scattering is thus

$$f(\mathbf{r}^*) = \int_0^\infty \rho(\mathbf{r}) \exp\left[\frac{2\pi i(\mathbf{r} \cdot \mathbf{r}^*)}{\lambda}\right] d\tau.$$

The integration, as indicated, should be done over the volume of the atom (i.e., up to ∞), but in practice it may be done only over a finite region at the boundary of which the electron density is negligibly small (this might be a few angstroms beyond the extent of the internuclear distances). The $f(\mathbf{r}^*)$ is called the *atomic scattering factor* for the atom, and is tabulated for various atoms and for various values of $\mathbf{r}^*$. Such factors are used in interpreting the scattering from crystalline polyatomic substances.

The atomic scattering factor is basically a Fourier transform of the electron density function for the atom. The factor 2π seems to be out of place and the limits on the integral aren't quite right as far as our definition is concerned, but neither of these alterations will affect the basic properties of the integral. For example, $\rho(\mathbf{r})$ can be expressed as the inverse Fourier transform of $f(\mathbf{r}^*)$. The use of Fourier methods in crystallography does not end here. The electron density in the *crystal* is a Fourier series of structure factors, that in turn are obtained from the atomic scattering factors. We take up Fourier series in the next chapter.

The scattering of X rays by liquids has also been extensively investigated. As early as 1927 F. Zernike and J. A. Prins in Groningen pointed out that the structure factor of a liquid can be obtained from a Fourier transform of the radial distribution function. If a monatomic liquid of N atoms, each having atomic scattering factor f, is bombarded with X rays, then the intensity of radiation scattered at an angle 2θ is given by

$$I(2\theta) = Nf^2 + Nf^2 \int_0^\infty 4\pi r^2 [\rho(r) - \rho_0] \frac{\sin kr}{kr} dr.$$

The first term on the right is the scattering if all the atoms scattered independently of each other; the second term takes into account the interference between atoms situated r units apart. In it the parameter k is defined as $(4\pi \sin\theta)/\lambda$ and $\rho(r)$ is the local density of atoms in a thin spherical shell of thickness dr and lying at a radius r from an arbitrary atom selected as the origin. This density is not in general the same as the bulk density, ρ_0, of the liquid. The ratio $g(r) = \rho(r)/\rho_0$ is referred to as the *radial distribution function* for the liquid and it is important because the thermodynamic properties of the liquid can be computed once the radial distribution function is known.

The *structure factor*, $S(k)$, of the liquid is the ratio $I(2\theta)/Nf^2$, and in terms of it the above equation may be written

$$S(k) - 1 = \frac{4\pi\rho_0}{k} \int_0^\infty r[g(r) - 1]\sin kr\, dr.$$

Thus the experimental quantity the structure factor is derivable from a sine Fourier transform of r times the theoretical quantity the radial distribution function. From values of $S(k)$ the function $g(r)$ may be obtained by Fourier inversion. Figure 3.19 shows an experimental structure factor for a mon-

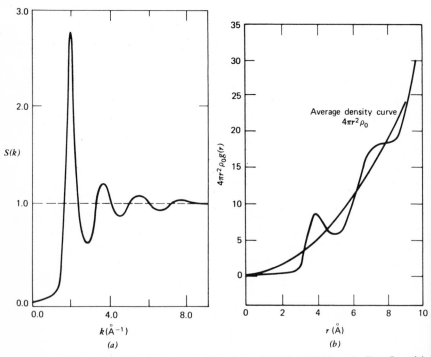

Fig. 3.19 (*a*) The structure factor $S(k)$ [redrawn from A. J. Greenfield et al., *Phys. Rev.*, **A4**, 1607 (1971), with permission by Professor Arthur J. Greenfield and the American Institute of Physics]; (*b*) the radial distribution function $g(r)$ [redrawn from N. S. Gingrich and L. Heaton, *J. Chem. Phys.*, **34**, 873 (1961), with permission by Professor Newell S. Gingrich and the American Institute of Physics] for liquid sodium at 100°C.

atomic liquid and a calculated radial distribution function (the two curves
are from different sources). The first peak in $g(r)$ comes at about 3.82 Å,
which indicates the distance of the first shell of neighbors from a given atom.
The area under the first peak indicates that the number of nearest neighbors
is roughly 9. Recent theoretical calculations also indicate that the $S(k)$ curve
is very well reproduced if it is assumed that the repulsive part of the
potential energy function for liquid sodium is an r^{-4} term [J.-P. Hansen and
D. Schiff, *Mol. Phys.*, **25**, 1281 (1973)].

A recent development in nuclear magnetic resonance (nmr) spectroscopy
has been the introduction of Fourier transform nmr spectroscopy. In the
conventional nmr experiment a sample immersed in a magnetic field is
subjected to radio-frequency radiation of continuously varying frequency.
The spectrum is a plot of the intensity of absorbed radiation $I(\omega)$ versus the
frequency ω. Each frequency in the range scanned is experienced by the
sample only once, and consequently the spectrum always contains a certain
amount of noise in addition to the signals of interest (see Figure 3.20).

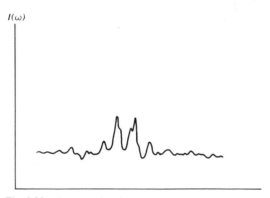

Fig. 3.20   A conventional nmr spectrum.

In the Fourier transform experiment a strong pulse of radio-frequency
radiation of about 10 μsec duration and at a frequency not necessarily equal
to any of the resonance frequencies in the spectrum is applied to the sample,
and then repeated about once a second several times. A plot of the decay
$G(t)$ of the nmr signal following the radio-frequency pulse versus time is
called the *spectral response pattern* (see Figure 3.21a); the function $G(t)$ is
known to be the Fourier transform of the frequency intensity $I(\omega)$. The
results of the several pulses are accumulated in a digital computer and the
inverse Fourier transform of the spectral response pattern is taken (see
Figure 3.21b).

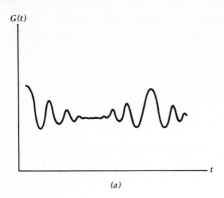

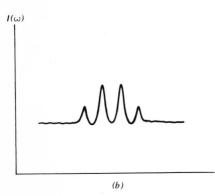

Fig. 3.21 (a) Spectral response pattern; (b) its inverse Fourier transform.

Now in Section 4.5 you will learn that any sufficiently well-behaved function, even one as ill-behaved as a rectangular pulse, can be approximated by a sum of sines and/or cosines. What this means in the nmr experiment is that a short radio-frequency pulse is actually equivalent to the simultaneous application of a large range of frequencies to the sample. Consequently the final spectrum is obtained in less time than is required in the conventional nmr experiment. In addition, because the sample experiences the frequency range several times (that is, once each pulse), most of the noise is time averaged to close to zero, thus improving the sensitivity or signal-to-noise ratio in the experiment.[7]

To conclude this section let us ask what happens if we multiply one Fourier transform by another. It happens that we can actually say something rather simple. Suppose that $f(t)$ is a function with Fourier transform

---

[7]A recent monograph is that by T. C. Farrar and E. D. Becker, *Pulse and Fourier Transform NMR*, Academic Press, New York, 1971.

$F(\omega)$, and $g(t)$ is another function with transform $G(\omega)$. Then we can perform the following operations on the product.

$$C(\omega) = \frac{1}{\sqrt{2\pi}} \int_{-\infty}^{\infty} f(t) e^{i\omega t} dt \int_{-\infty}^{\infty} \frac{1}{\sqrt{2\pi}} g(t) e^{i\omega t} dt$$

$$= \frac{1}{(\sqrt{2\pi})^2} \int_{-\infty}^{\infty}\int_{-\infty}^{\infty} f(t) g(x) e^{i\omega(t+x)} dt\, dx$$

$$= \frac{1}{2\pi} \int_{-\infty}^{\infty}\int_{-\infty}^{\infty} f(t) g(t'-t) e^{i\omega t'} dt\, dt' \quad \text{if } x = t' - t$$

$$= \frac{1}{\sqrt{2\pi}} \int_{-\infty}^{\infty} \left[\frac{1}{\sqrt{2\pi}} \int_{-\infty}^{\infty} f(t) g(t'-t) dt \right] e^{i\omega t'} dt'$$

Thus we see that the product of the Fourier transforms of $f(t)$ and $g(t)$ is the Fourier transform of the integral $(2\pi)^{-1/2} \int_{-\infty}^{\infty} f(t) g(t'-t) dt$. This integral is called the *convolution* or *convolution integral*. Note that the change of variables above allows one to write the integrand in the convolution either as $f(t) g(t'-t)$ or as $f(t'-t) g(t)$. The convolution theorem has some limited use in the evaluation of Fourier transforms. It might also be pointed out that convolutions also arise independently of Fourier transforms in certain applications in engineering and astronomy. Thus if a system is affected at the present time t' by some event or stimulus, $W(t) dt$, that occurred in the past during the time interval dt, and if we assume that the magnitude of the system's response to this stimulus is dependent on the time difference between past and present, then beginning from time $t = 0$ up to time $t = t'$, the total response $R(t')$ of the system may be obtained by a summation over all of the intervals dt and one is therefore led to the integral

$$R(t') = \int_{0}^{t'} W(t) f(t'-t) dt.$$

The function $W(t)$ thus has the physical interpretation of a weighting function for times past.

EXERCISES

1. Integrate using new methods as much as possible:

   (a) $\displaystyle \int \frac{x^3\,dx}{\left(x^2+1\right)^3}$ (e) $\displaystyle \int \tan^5\theta\,d\theta$

   (b) $\displaystyle \int \frac{x\,dx}{1+x^3}$ (f) $\displaystyle \int_0^\infty \frac{e^{-bx}}{\csc rx}\,dx$

   (c) $\displaystyle \int \frac{d\theta}{a\cos^2\theta + 2b\cos\theta\sin\theta + c\sin^2\theta}$ (g) $\displaystyle \int_0^\infty x^5 e^{-2x}\,dx$

   (d) $\displaystyle \int_0^1 z\tan^{-1}z\,dz$ (h) $\displaystyle \int_0^\infty e^{-t^4}\,dt$

2. Consider the integral $\int_0^1 (dx/\sqrt{1-x^2}\,)$; make a rough plot of the integrand. What problem arises in the evaluation of this integral according to the Riemann definition, and how do you resolve it? Does it automatically follow that if an integrand becomes infinite at some point in the range of integration, then the integral itself is infinite? Give an example of an integral which "blows up" and whose integrand also "blows up."

3. Show that the substitution $e^x = \tan u$ converts the infinite integral $\int_{-\infty}^\infty [e^x/(1+e^{2x})]\,dx$ into an integral which is neither improper nor infinite.

4. Demonstrate the equivalence of the two forms for integral 2 in Table 3.1. Also show that if $y = \operatorname{csch}^{-1} z$, then it follows that

$$y = \ln\left[\frac{1}{z}\left(1 \pm \sqrt{z^2+1}\,\right)\right].$$

5. Starting from the definition of dG (see Table 2.3) and from the Eyring formulation for the rate constant of a chemical reaction (see Example 1 in Chapter 1), derive the differential expression

$$\left(\frac{\partial \ln k}{\partial P}\right)_T = \frac{-\Delta V^*}{RT}$$

where ΔV^* is the *volume of activation* of the reaction, that is, the difference in molar volume between the transition state and the reactants.

   (a) Now write the above relation in integrated form by integrating between the limits $P = 0$ and $P = P$. Assume that ΔV^* is independent of pressure.

(b) Laidler and Chen [Trans. Faraday Soc., 54, 1026 (1958)] obtained the data shown in Table 3.7 for the base-catalyzed saponification of methyl acetate. The chemical equation for this reaction is

$$CH_3 - \overset{\overset{\displaystyle O}{\displaystyle \|}}{C}\text{-}OCH_3 + OH^- \underset{25^\circ C}{\overset{k}{\rightarrow}} CH_3\text{-}CO_2^- + CH_3OH \ .$$

Calculate the volume of activation and comment on the significance of the sign of ΔV^*.

Table 3.7 Rate Data for the Hydrolysis of Methyl Acetate

P (atm)	0.988	272.0	545.0	817.0
k (liter mole^{-1} sec^{-1})	0.146	0.163	0.181	0.203

6. A mechanical dumbbell which can rotate but not vibrate is called a *rigid rotor*, and it represents a convenient model for discussing the rotations of molecules. Now, in general, rotation is quantized so that there exist rotational energy levels (with rotational quantum numbers J) just as there are electronic energy levels. A good approximation to the rotational partition function (recall Example 14) for a rigid rotor is obtained by replacing the summation by an integration

$$Z_{rot} = \int_0^\infty (2J+1) \exp\left\{ \frac{-J(J+1)h^2}{8\pi^2 IkT} \right\} dJ$$

where I is a constant called the moment of inertia (see Exercise 42* in Chapter 1). Work out Z_{rot}.

7. According to the *Handbook of Chemistry and Physics*, the indefinite integral $\int dx / x\sqrt{a + bx}$ can be expressed ($a > 0$) as either

$$\frac{1}{\sqrt{a}} \ln\left(\frac{\sqrt{a+bx} - \sqrt{a}}{\sqrt{a+bx} + \sqrt{a}} \right) \qquad \text{or} \qquad \frac{-2}{\sqrt{a}} \tanh^{-1}\left(\frac{a+bx}{a} \right).$$

Demonstrate the equivalence of these two expressions and verify that either one is indeed the integral of the quantity given in the preceding integrand.

8. In kinetics one is interested in determining the rates of chemical reactions; a rate may be defined as the time rate of change in the concentration of a product.

$$\text{rate} = \frac{d[C]}{dt}$$

Now consider the case $A + 2B \xrightarrow{k} C$. Suppose the rate of this reaction *is found experimentally* to be equal to the product of a constant, k, called the *rate constant*, and the instantaneous concentrations of A and B. At time $t = 0$ suppose the concentration of A is A_0 and that if B is B_0 (C, of course, is zero). At some future time t the concentration of C will be x and that of A will necessarily be $A_0 - x$. By integration show that the time variation of the concentration of C is given by

$$x = \frac{A_0 B_0 \left[1 - \exp\left\{kt(2A_0 - B_0)\right\}\right]}{B_0 - 2A_0 \exp\left\{kt(2A_0 - B_0)\right\}}.$$

Next, show by taking the limit that this expression goes to the correct answer in the limit of infinite time; consider both the case where $2A_0 > B_0$ and the case where $2A_0 < B_0$.

9. A reaction whose rate depends only on the concentration of a single substance is said to obey kinetics of order n if the rate of disappearance (negative of the time rate of change of concentration) of the substance is proportional to the nth power of its concentration. The *half-life*, $t_{1/2}$, of the reaction is the time required for the concentration (C) of the substance to drop to half its initial value, (C_0). By integration show that $t_{1/2}$ is proportional to C_0^{1-n}.

10. When ammonia is decomposed on a hot tungsten wire, it is observed that the half-life varies with the pressure (pressure is a suitable variable to use to express the concentration of a gas at constant temperature and volume) (Table 3.8). On the basis of your solution to Exercise 9, determine graphically the order of the decomposition reaction. These results are interesting and can be accounted for if the metal surface is essentially saturated by reacting ammonia molecules. Does this explanation make sense to you? Similar kinetic results are also obtained in the cases of the decomposition of hydrogen iodide on a gold surface and of phosphine on a molybdenum surface at high pressures.

Table 3.8   Rate Data for the Decomposition of Ammonia

P_{NH_3} (atm)	0.079	0.165	0.263	0.369	0.408
$t_{1/2}$ (sec)	103.	215.	337.	467.	546.

11. Hardy has shown that rational functions of $\cos x$ and $\sin x$ may often be integrated more easily by making the substitution $\tan \frac{1}{2}x = t$, whence

$$\cos x = \frac{1-t^2}{1+t^2} \qquad \sin x = \frac{2t}{1+t^2} \qquad dx = \frac{2dt}{1+t^2}.$$

Use this device to work out the indefinite integral

$$\int \frac{(1+\sin x)}{(1-\cos x)}\, dx.$$

12. In the pressure example which was discussed after Example 22, show with the aid of Theorem 3 that

$$\lim_{h \to \infty} \tfrac{1}{2}h^2 \int_h^\infty u'(r)\, g(r)\, dr$$

is zero.

13. Finally, to complete the discussion of the internal pressure in a liquid, we have that the desired pressure is given by the integral

$$-2\pi\rho_0^{\,2} \int_0^\infty I(x)\, dx,$$

where ρ_0 is the density of the liquid. From this show that

$$P_{\text{int}} = -\tfrac{2}{3}\pi\rho_0^{\,2} \int_0^\infty r^3 u'(r)\, g(r)\, dr.$$

14. Verify that the area of the parallelogram in Figure 3.3 is $J(T)\, du\, dv$.

15. Carry out the integration of Example 23 in Cartesian coordinates without resorting to a table of integrals, and thus demonstrate that the value of the integral is 0.94.

16. Suppose that T is the transformation from $r\theta$ space (two-dimensional cylindrical polar coordinates) to xy space. You have just set up and transformed an integral from xy coordinates into $r\theta$ coordinates, when you decide to change coordinate systems again and employ parabolic coordinates. For two dimensions these are defined as follows:

$$T'': \quad x = \alpha^2 - \beta^2 \qquad y = 2\alpha\beta.$$

A similar definition was stated in Exercise 43[**] of Chapter 2. Rather than start anew you decide to transform $f(r,\theta)$ into $f(\alpha,\beta)$ and $J(T)$ into $J(T')$, where T' would be the transformation from $\alpha\beta$ space into

$r\theta$ space. Verify the validity of the expression

$$J(T) \times J(T') = J(T'').$$

To gain some experience with parabolic coordinates, transform the twofold iterated integral

$$\int_1^2 dy \int_0^y \frac{dx}{\sqrt{x^2 + y^2}}$$

into a new one, showing clearly the limits. Work out the value of this integral if you feel so inclined.

17. Here is an elaboration of a problem you worked earlier (Exercise 35* of Chapter 2). Suppose a sample of molecules with permanent dipole moment μ_0 is placed in an electric field of strength E and oriented along the z axis. Then, if a molecule is oriented away from the z axis by an angle θ, the potential energy of interaction is given by

$$\varepsilon = -\mu_0 E \cos\theta$$

and the usual Boltzmann factor becomes $e^{-\varepsilon/kT}$. We now remove the restriction of allowing only two orientations and we permit the molecules to pick any orientation. Consequently, the observed dipole moment will be a weighted average.

$$\langle \mu \rangle = \frac{\displaystyle\int_0^{2\pi} \int_0^\pi \mu_0 \cos\theta \, e^{-\varepsilon/kT} \sin\theta \, d\theta \, d\phi}{\displaystyle\int_0^{2\pi} \int_0^\pi e^{-\varepsilon/kT} \sin\theta \, d\theta \, d\phi}$$

What is $\langle \mu \rangle$?

18. Consider the following twofold iterated integral:

$$\int_0^1 dx \int_0^1 \frac{x - y}{(x + y)^3} \, dy.$$

Evaluate this first by integrating with respect to y followed by integration with respect to x. Then reverse the order of integration and show that a different result obtains.

19. Evaluate the integral $\int_0^1 dx \int_x^{2-x} (x/y) \, dy$ by reversing the order of integration and carrying out the necessary operations. Be careful here! In

this case you have to make some alterations in the limits and you may want to split the integral up into two or more twofold iterated integrals. A sketch of the region of integration will be helpful.

20. Quantum mechanical integrals for H_2^+ are best done in confocal elliptical coordinates. In using this coordinate system the two hydrogen nuclei A and B are positioned at points $+R$ and $-R$ along the z axis. The variables ζ and η are then defined as

$$\zeta = \frac{r_A + r_B}{2R} \qquad \eta = \frac{r_A - r_B}{2R}$$

where r_A and r_B are the distances of the electron from nuclei A and B. Finally, the angle ϕ is an angle of rotation about the z axis. From a sketch of the system thus described, work out the maximum and minimum values of ζ and η. Then work out the volume element in this coordinate system.

21. Using basic properties of hyperbolic functions, derive relations 5, 9, and 12 in Table 3.4.

22. Answer the following questions regarding hyperbolic functions:

    (a) What is the value of $\sin i$?

    (b) If $e^{2ix} = \cos 2x + i \sin 2x$, what must e^{-2ix} be?

    (c) Does $\cos^2 ix + \sin^2 ix$ equal 1, or is it $\cos^2 ix - \sin^2 ix$ which equals 1?

    (d) Does $\cosh^2 y + \sinh^2 y$ equal 1, or is it $\cosh^2 y - \sinh^2 y$ which equals 1?

    (e) Does $\sinh 2x$ equal $2 \sinh x \cosh x$?

23. Show trivially that the following statements regarding the gudermannian function are true:

    (a) $\sin(\mathrm{gd}\, u) = \tanh u$ \qquad (b) $d\,(\mathrm{gd}\, u)/du = \mathrm{sech}\, u$.

24. In Exercise 26 of Chapter 2, you showed that the heat capacity of a Debye crystal is given by

$$C_v = \frac{9R}{\tau^3} \int_0^{\tau} \frac{x^4 e^x}{\left(e^x - 1\right)^2}\, dx$$

where $x = h\nu/kT$ and $\tau = h\nu_{max}/kT$.

(a) Show that

$$C_v = \frac{9R}{\tau^3} \left[4 \int_0^{\tau} \frac{x^3}{e^x - 1}\, dx - \frac{\tau^4}{e^\tau - 1} \right].$$

(b) The integral in part (a) is still intractable, although it could be estimated numerically. Another possibility is to convert the integral into some sort of series which could then be summed by taking as many terms as we please. After first dividing the denominator into the numerator in the integral of part (a), show that C_v can also be written in the form below. You will need to know that $\sum_{n=1}^{\infty} n^{-4} = \pi^4/90$.

$$C_v = \frac{9R}{5\tau^3} \left[\frac{3\pi^4}{2} - \frac{5\tau^4}{e^\tau - 1} - 20 \sum_{n=1}^{\infty} \frac{n^3\tau^3 + 3n^2\tau^2 + 6n\tau + 6}{n^4 e^{n\tau}} \right]$$

25. Use the technique of parameter differentiation to work out the integral

$$\int_0^1 \frac{x^a - 1}{\ln x} \, dx \qquad a \geqslant 0.$$

26. Show that $\text{Ei}(x) = \text{Li}(e^x)$.

27. In the theory of electromagnetic radiation it is found upon studying the problem of absorption by a molecule that the probability of a transition occurring from state n (with energy E_n) to state m in a time t when light consisting of a whole range of frequencies is beamed on the sample is given by the integral

$$P(t) = 4\mu^2 |\mathbf{E}|^2 \int_{-\infty}^{\infty} \frac{\sin^2[\pi(E_m - E_n - h\nu)t/h]}{(E_m - E_n - h\nu)^2} \, d\nu$$

The quantity $|\mathbf{E}|$ is the strength of the electric field component of the radiation and is a constant here; μ is related to the electric dipole moment (also a constant), and ν is the frequency. Work out the expression for $P(t)$.

28. It is well-known that the equation of state of a real gas at densities below the critical density can be expressed as a series in powers of the reciprocal volume:

$$\frac{PV}{RT} = A + B(T)V^{-1} + C(T)V^{-2} + \cdots + .$$

The coefficients A, B, C,... are called the *virial coefficients*. Statistical mechanics shows that $B(T)$ depends only upon the interactions between isolated pairs of molecules, and that if the molecules have spherical symmetry, then

$$B(T) = 2\pi N_0 \int_0^{\infty} (1 - e^{-U(r)/kT}) r^2 \, dr.$$

One of the simplest forms for the potential energy function $U(r)$ is that representing the interaction of two rigid spheres of diameter σ in a square well.

$$U(r) = \begin{cases} \infty & \text{if } r < \sigma \\ -\varepsilon & \text{if } \sigma < r < \alpha\sigma \\ 0 & \text{if } r > \alpha\sigma \end{cases}$$

From this find the form for $B(T)$. Make a plot of $U(r)$ versus r; what does the parameter α represent?

29. Use numerical integration to evaluate Si (2), and compare your result with the handbook value of 1.605.

30. Show by a trivial substitution that an error function problem is also a gamma function problem.

31. In solid-state nmr spectroscopy line shapes are sometimes analyzed by the method ‚of second moments. The *second moment* of a signal centered at angular frequency ω_0 is defined to be the integral

$$\int_{\omega_0}^{\infty} (\omega - \omega_0)^2 g(\omega)\, d\omega = \overline{(\Delta\omega)^2}$$

where $g(\omega)$ is a shape function for the signal. Commonly, in solids, the shape function is approximately a Gaussian curve; the factor T

$$g(\omega) = \sqrt{\frac{2}{\pi}}\; T \exp\left[-\tfrac{1}{2} T^2 (\omega - \omega_0)^2\right]$$

is a constant known as the *transverse relaxation time*. Find $\overline{(\Delta\omega)^2}$.

32. Why does Simpson's rule method of integration require division of the interval into an even number of subintervals?

33. Nuclear magnetic resonance (nmr) signals are often assumed to possess the shape of a Lorentz curve (recall Exercise 8 of Chapter 2):

$$g(\omega) = \frac{T}{\pi} \frac{1}{1 + T^2(\omega - \omega_0)^2}.$$

(a) Show that the width of the signal at half-height is $2T^{-1}$.

(b) Shown in Figure 3.22 is the resonance signal for a hypothetical substance. Find the area under this curve in two ways:

1. Integration of the $g(\omega)$ function:

2. Tracing of the curve onto finely ruled graph paper, followed by counting of squares.

Compare the agreement between the two methods.

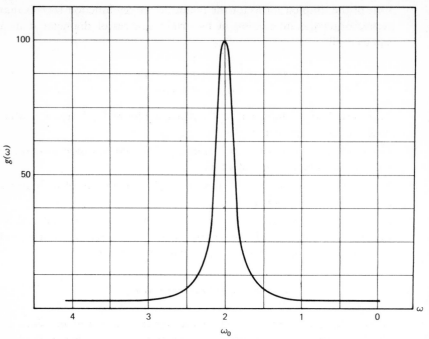

Fig. 3.22   A nuclear magnetic resonance signal.

34. Example 28 illustrated a case where two peaks of interest were widely separated. How might you apply Simpson's rule to the case of a gas chromatogram where the two peaks of interest displayed significant overlapping?

35. Define clearly what is meant by a line integral, and then illustrate this by making up and evaluating an example of your own.

36. Work out the line integral $\int_C [V^2 T\, dV + (V^2+1)^{-1} dT]$, where the path C is the boundary of the unit square $\{(V, T): 0 \leqslant V \leqslant 1, 0 \leqslant T \leqslant 1\}$.

37. According to classical mechanics a wave at time zero moving in the x direction can be represented by the function $\psi = A e^{ikx}$. In quantum mechanics we know that particle and wave properties appear simultaneously; in order to represent a free particle (at time zero) traveling in the x direction, we must superimpose several waves in such a way that their amplitudes constructively interfere in a small, localized region of space:

$$\psi(x) = (2\pi)^{-\frac{1}{2}} \int_{-\infty}^{\infty} A(k) e^{ikx} dk.$$

A function of this type is called, according to Schrödinger, a *wave packet*; it is nothing more than a Fourier transform of the function $A(k)$, the so-called *spectral distribution*, which represents the distribution of amplitudes of the component waves with different frequencies. As a special case, suppose that $A(k) = (2\pi)^{\frac{1}{2}}$ for $|k - \bar{k}| \leqslant \varepsilon$, and $A(k) = 0$ everywhere else. Find the function $|\psi(x)|^2$, which corresponds to the intensity of the wave packet at point x.

38. State the contrapositive of Theorem 8, and then in light of this go back and rethink Exercise 41* of Chapter 2. The contrapositive of the proposition "if A, then B" is the equivalent proposition "if not B, then not A."

39. In the scattering of X rays by liquids, the quantity measured is $I(2\theta)$. Write an equation that shows how you could deduce the radial distribution function, $g(r)$, from this.

40.* A general problem in quantum mechanics is the following: what is the probability, P, of finding an electron in a given region of space? The answer is given by integrating the absolute square of the wave function over that region of space.

$$P = \int \int \int |\psi|^2 d\tau$$

$$(d\tau = \text{volume element})$$

For a hydrogen atom in the ground state the wave function is

$$\psi_{1s} = (\pi)^{-\frac{1}{2}} (a_0)^{-\frac{3}{2}} \exp\left(-\frac{\sqrt{x^2 + y^2 + z^2}}{a_0} \right)$$

where a_0 is the radius of the first Bohr orbit and has the value 0.529 Å. Transform to spherical polar coordinates and determine the chances of finding the electron in a spherical region (about the nucleus) of radius a_0.

41.* Solution of the Schrödinger equation for Li^{2+} gives for the $2p_x$ wave function

$$\psi_{2p_x} = \frac{1}{4}(2\pi)^{-\frac{1}{2}} \left(\frac{3}{a_0} \right)^{\frac{3}{2}} \left(\frac{3r}{a_0} \right) \exp\left(-\frac{3r}{2a_0} \right) \sin\theta \cos\phi.$$

Show that this wave function is normalized, that is, show that

$$\int \int \int_{\substack{\text{all} \\ \text{space}}} |\psi_{2p_x}|^2 d\tau = 1.$$

42.* To a good approximation, the partition function, corrected for indistinguishability of the particles, for *the system* of N_0 translating, noninteracting structureless particles of mass m in a cube of volume V is given by $Q = (N_0!)^{-1} Z^{N_0}$, where Z is the integral

$$Z = \int_0^\infty \frac{1}{2} \pi n^2 e^{-n^2 h^2 / 8m V^{2/3} kT} \, dn.$$

(a) Show that $Z = (2\pi mkT)^{3/2} V / h^3$.

(b) From thermodynamics it can be shown that the entropy of a system with partition function Q is given by

$$S = k \left[\frac{\partial (T \ln Q)}{\partial T} \right]_V.$$

Evaluate the *standard* entropy for mercury vapor, assuming that the only contribution to Q is translational. Compare with experiment.

43.* If a hydrogen atom is placed in an external magnetic field of strength H_{ext}, the strength of the field felt at the surface of the nucleus will be less than that external because of a shielding effect of the electron. The *shielding parameter*, σ, is a measure of this.

$$H_{nucleus} = H_{ext}(1 - \sigma)$$

A theory due to W. Lamb gives the shielding parameter as

$$\sigma = \frac{4\pi e^2}{3mc^2} \int_0^\infty r \rho(r) \, dr$$

where the electron density function $\rho(r)$ is just the square of the radial part of the wave function, $[\psi(r)]^2$, for hydrogen. After referring back to Exercise 40*, evaluate numerically the shielding parameter. What are its units?

44.* For a system of reacting species at thermal equilibrium, collision theory gives for the rate constant

$$k(T) = \left(\frac{2}{k'T} \right)^{\frac{3}{2}} \left(\frac{1}{m\pi} \right)^{\frac{1}{2}} \int_0^\infty E \sigma(E) e^{-E/RT} \, dE$$

, where k' is Boltzmann's constant, E is the relative kinetic energy of the two reacting particles, and $\sigma(E)$ is the *reaction cross section*. Now, by definition, the experimental activation energy, E_a, is calculated from the slope of a plot of $\ln k$ versus $1/T$, and is given by

$$E_a = RT^2 \frac{d[\ln k(T)]}{dT}.$$

From this derive Tolman's equation:

$$E_a = \frac{\int_0^\infty E^2 \sigma(E) e^{-E/RT} dE}{\int_0^\infty E \sigma(E) e^{-E/RT} dE} - \frac{3}{2} RT.$$

The first term on the right is the average molar energy of those collisions that are chemically effective; the $3RT/2$ term is the average energy of all collisions. Why is Tolman's equation not simply $E_a = E - 3RT/2$?

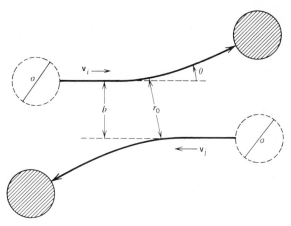

Fig. 3.23   Collision of two molecules.

45.* Figure 3.23 shows a collision between two like molecules of diameter σ interacting according to classical mechanics. The potential energy function is $U(r)$; the quantity b is the *impact parameter*, the distance between the straight-line paths of the two molecules in the absence of $U(r)$. The *scattering angle*, θ, depends upon the initial relative kinetic energy $E = \frac{1}{2} m (v_i - v_j)^2$ and upon b according to the equation

$$\theta(E, b) = \pi - 2b \int_{r_0}^\infty \left[1 - \frac{b^2}{r^2} - \frac{U(r)}{E} \right]^{-\frac{1}{2}} r^{-2} dr.$$

Here r_0 is the distance of closest approach of the two molecules.
(a) Work out what the scattering angle, $\theta(E,b)$, is for two like
molecules interacting according to the hard sphere potential:

$$U(r) = \begin{cases} \infty & \text{if } r < \sigma \\ 0 & \text{if } r > \sigma \end{cases}.$$

(b) Now show that for this simple case the same result obtains from
purely trigonometric considerations. Use Figure 3.24 as a guide.

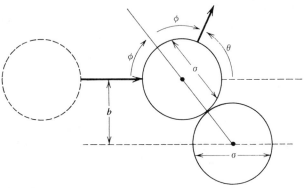

Fig. 3.24   The scattering angle.

46.* A pulse of exactly two wavelength's duration of a pure cosine ra-
diofrequency wave is applied to a sample (Figure 3.25). After referring
back to Exercise 37, work out the spectral distribution $A(k)$ that would
result, and then make a rough sketch to see what $A(k)$ looks like.

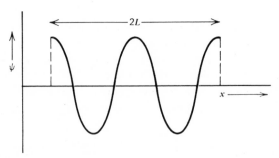

Fig. 3.25   A cosine pulse.

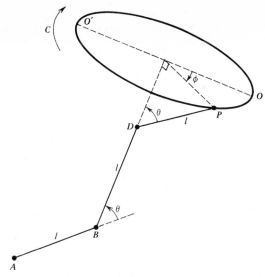

Fig. 3.26 The *n*-butane chain.

47.** Consider the molecule *n*-butane, which we may take to be a model for a polymethylene chain. In Figure 3.26 points A, P represent methyl groups, and points B, D represent methylene groups. If we assume completely free rotation about the B–D bond, then P can be found anywhere on circle C with equal likelihood. We now inquire about the end-to-end distance AP of the molecule; clearly, it is a maximum when P is at O, and a minimum when P is at O'. Find by integration the mean value of the square of the distance from A to P (this is easier to find than the mean of the distance); your answer will be a function of the angle θ. Now assume that all carbon–carbon–carbon bond angles are tetrahedral and show that the above expression reduces to

$$\overline{AP^2} = \frac{41}{9} l^2 = 4.56 \, l^2$$

where l is the length of a carbon–carbon link. When this sort of problem is carried through for polymethylene chains containing N carbon–carbon links (N very large), the general result is

$$\overline{AP^2} = 2Nl^2$$

which, *if it were accurate for short chains* such as in *n*-butane, would clearly give $\overline{AP^2} = 6l^2$.

48.** In the application of the Wilson–Sommerfeld rules of the old quantum theory to a description of the elliptical electron orbits of atomic hydrogen, there arises the equation

$$\frac{kh}{2\pi}\varepsilon^2 \int_0^{2\pi} \frac{\cos^2(\theta-\theta_0)}{[1+\varepsilon\sin(\theta-\theta_0)]^2}\, d\theta = (n-k)h$$

where k is the azimuthal quantum number, n is a total quantum number, and ε is the eccentricity of the elliptical orbit, defined here as $b = a\sqrt{1-\varepsilon^2}$ with a being the length of the semimajor axis and b the length of the semiminor axis. Show that the above equation reduces to the following condition for an allowed orbit.

$$\frac{a}{b} = \frac{n}{k}$$

49.** This problem is strictly for readers with a knowledge of vectors. We start with the equation given in the text for the scattering of X rays from a continuous medium.

$$f(\mathbf{r}^*) = \int_0^\infty \rho(\mathbf{r})\exp\left[\frac{2\pi i \mathbf{r}\cdot\mathbf{r}^*}{\lambda}\right] d\tau$$

As written, this is a vector equation. Now suppose that the electron density of the free atom is taken to be spherically symmetric so that $\rho(\mathbf{r})$ becomes $\rho(r)$. Then put $\mathbf{r}$ into general spherical polar coordinates r, θ, and ϕ, and likewise put $\mathbf{r}^*$ into spherical polar coordinates r^*, θ^* and ϕ^*. Perform the necessary integrations to show that the above vector equation reduces to the simpler form

$$f(r^*) = \int_0^\infty 4\pi r^2 \rho(r)\frac{\sin(2\pi r r^*\lambda^{-1})}{2\pi r r^*\lambda^{-1}}\, dr.$$

FOUR

Expansions in Series

"Where shall I begin, please your Majesty?" he asked.
"Begin at the beginning," the King said gravely,
"and go on till you come to the end: then stop."

CHAS. LUTWIDGE DODGSON

1 SERIES IN GENERAL

The first three chapters of this book constitute what might be called "core" material, namely, basic algebra and geometry, differential calculus, and integral calculus. In this and the following chapters we take up somewhat more specialized subjects, which are nevertheless of great practical importance in chemistry.

A series is a collection of terms, either finite in number or not, that are to be added. The notation used to indicate the summation was first introduced in Section 1.6:

$$\sum_{n=i}^{k} a_n.$$

In this notation each term a_n is a function of an index n, called a *dummy index*, that can assume integral values from $n = i$ to $n = k$. We call n a dummy index because it can be replaced willy-nilly by any other symbol having the same range of summation. Purists make a point of the fact that one should not say "The series $\sum_n a_n$ has the property that... ," because one is here using the notation for the operation summation to stand for the concept series. In other words, one should not confuse the series itself with the operation of summing the terms in the series. Actually, when analyzed more closely, a series is seen to be a concept with several aspects, and to adequately produce a notation for the series separate from its summation would, for present purposes, probably lead to confusion.

Although series are among the most useful tools in physical science, one cannot take their use for granted. Questions that must be asked are the following:

1. Does the series have a finite sum?
2. How fast does the series approach this sum?
3. Assuming a sum exists, how can it be evaluated?

The answer to the third question is much like that to the question of integration: no general technique exists. An answer to the second question can often be obtained in a qualitative way by writing down the first few terms of the series. The first question has long been a big problem in mathematical analysis (only for infinite series, of course).

Let us first of all sharpen up what we mean by the sum of an infinite series. Consider the infinite series

$$\sum_{n=0}^{\infty} a_n ;$$

for finite k each of the partial sums $S_k = \sum_{n=0}^{k} a_n$ has some finite value. We then say that the infinite series has a sum, or better, *converges* if there exists an S such that

$$\lim_{k \to \infty} S_k = S.$$

Once again as in the cases of the derivative and the definite integral we see that the salient feature of a definition is that of a limiting process. This definition tells us what to do, but the problem of writing a general expression for S_k may be difficult. Mathematicians have therefore investigated other ways to test for convergence thus saving the chemists a lot of grief. We can do no more than examine a few of the commonest tests; for most physical applications more elaborate tests are not necessary.

There is one obvious result that follows from the definition of convergence. If a series is convergent, then

$$\lim_{k \to \infty} S_k = S$$

and also

$$\lim_{k \to \infty} S_{k-1} = S,$$

so that one has

$$\lim_{k\to\infty} (S_k - S_{k-1}) = 0.$$

But, $S_k - S_{k-1}$ is nothing more than a_k.

If the series $\sum_{n=0}^{\infty} a_n$ is convergent, then a_n must approach 0 as $n\to\infty$, or contrapositively, if a_n does not approach 0 as $n\to\infty$, then the series must diverge (does not converge).

Note that the theorem makes no statement about the converse question, namely, if a_n approaches 0 as $n\to\infty$, does the series converge?

We state without proof three common tests for convergence.

Theorem 10. *Let $\sum_{n=i}^{\infty} a_n$ be a series of positive terms. Then,*

(a) (d'Alembert's ratio test)[1] *if $\lim_{n\to\infty}(a_{n+1}/a_n) = L < 1$, the series converges, and if $L > 1$ the series diverges; otherwise, the test fails;*

(b) (Maclaurin's integral test) *if a_n steadily decreases as n increases, the series converges or not according as the integral $\int_i^c a_n \, dn$ does or does not tend to some finite limit L as $c\to\infty$, and in the first case the sum of the series is less than $L + a_i$;*

(c) (Cauchy's root test)[2] *if $\lim_{n\to\infty}(\sqrt[n]{a_n}) = L < 1$, the series converges, and if $L > 1$ the series diverges; otherwise, the test fails.*

Some examples will help to make this multi-part theorem clearer.

Example 31. Examine the harmonic series $\sum_{n=1}^{\infty} 1/n$ for convergence.

Answer. The nth term approaches 0 as $n\to\infty$, but this does not guarantee convergence. We try first d'Alembert's ratio test:

$$\lim_{n\to\infty} \left(\frac{a_{n+1}}{a_n}\right) = \lim_{n\to\infty} \frac{1/(n+1)}{1/n} = 1.$$

The test fails, so we now go to the integral test:

$$\int_1^{\infty} \frac{1}{x} \, dx = \ln x \big|_1^{\infty} = \infty$$

$$\therefore \boxed{\text{Series diverges}}.$$

---

[1] The French mathematician and *philosophe* Jean Lerond d'Alembert (1717–1783) was one of the most colorful figures of the eighteenth-century Enlightenment. He was one of the editors, along with Denis Diderot (1713–1759), of the famous *Encyclopédie*. See T. L. Hankins, *Jean d'Alembert: Science and the Enlightenment*, Clarendon Press, Oxford, 1970.

[2] After the French mathematician Augustin Cauchy (1789–1857).

It is perhaps worth pointing out that in part (b) of Theorem 10, the lower limit on the integral *need not* be the initial value of the dummy index in the summation in order for the test to work. It may be anything larger as well; indeed, some workers omit it entirely since the crux of the problem is the nature of those terms coming at the *end* of the series and not the beginning. Purists, however, who object to the idea of writing a definite integral with only one limit will prefer to supply any convenient value for the lower limit.

Example 32. In Exercise 24 of Chapter 3 you needed to know the *Riemann zeta function*,[3] $\zeta(s)$, evaluated for the argument $s = 4$. Is $\zeta(4)$ convergent?

Answer. This series (also called the *hyperharmonic series*) is, formally,

$$\zeta(s) = 1^{-s} + 2^{-s} + 3^{-s} + \cdots + .$$

The ratio test again fails and the integral test gives the following result:

$$\int_1^\infty \frac{1}{x^s}\, dx = \left.\frac{x^{1-s}}{1-s}\right|_{x=\infty} - \frac{1}{1-s}.$$

The result depends on the magnitude of s. If $s = 1$, the second term on the right becomes infinite; if $s > 1$, then $1 - s$ is negative and the first term on the right can be written as

$$\left.\frac{1}{(1-s)x^{s-1}}\right|_{x=\infty} = 0$$

so that the definite integral then simply has the value $1/(s-1)$. We say, therefore, that the *region of convergence* for $\zeta(s)$ is $s > 1$, and thus $\zeta(4)$ should converge. Later we see that its value is, in fact, $\pi^4/90$. What can you say about the series for $s < 1$?

To summarize what has been learned up to this point one can say that for a series to converge, the point of the matter is not only whether the terms become small, but also whether they become small fast enough. This is really what convergence tests are all about. Now the results of the Riemann zeta series above sometimes lead to a misunderstanding. It is often thought that the harmonic series is the series that diverges "most slowly." Let us define "most slowly" as follows: any positive a_n that becomes small faster than $1/n$, that is, the limit $\lim_{n \to \infty} [a_n/(1/n)]$ equals zero, must give a convergent series

[3] A brief history of this interesting function and a discussion of work done on it by Euler 100 years before Riemann is given in R. Ayoub, "Euler and the Zeta Function," *Am. Math. Mon.*, **81**, 1067 (1974).

$\Sigma_n a_n$. As a counterexample to this intuitive notion of slowest divergence, consider the case $a_n = 1/(n \ln n)$. A series of terms of this form becomes small faster than $1/n$ (use Theorem 3 to show this), but $\Sigma_{n=2}^{\infty} 1/(n \ln n)$ still diverges. Therefore there is no such thing as a series that diverges "most slowly" in this sense.[4]

2 MACLAURIN'S AND TAYLOR'S SERIES

Among the most useful series are power series, that is, series of the form

$$\sum_{n=0}^{\infty} a_n x^n$$

for which there are numerous simple and useful theorems and that, from a practical standpoint, are particularly easy to manipulate. Often one finds a need of approximating a given function $f(x)$ by such a series. It is easy to see how one should set this up. Suppose $f(x)$ has continuous derivatives up to order n at some point $x = a$, and let us try to find a polynomial $P(x)$ that agrees with $f(x)$ and its n derivatives at this point. The following equations have to be satisfied:

$$\left. \begin{array}{l} P(a) = f(a) \\ P'(a) = f'(a) \\ P''(a) = f''(a) \\ P'''(a) = f'''(a) \\ \vdots \end{array} \right\} \quad n+1 \text{ equations.}$$

Take $P(x)$ to be of the form

$$P(x) = c_0 + c_1(x-a) + c_2(x-a)^2 + \cdots +$$

so that from the four equations above we have

$$\begin{array}{l} c_0 = f(a) \\ c_1 = f'(a) \\ c_2 = \frac{1}{2} f''(a) \\ c_3 = \frac{1}{6} f'''(a) \\ \vdots \end{array}$$

[4]The interested reader is referred to the article by P. Shiu, "How Slowly Can a Series Converge?," *Math. Gaz.*, **56**, 285 (1972).

The general form of c_n is not difficult to see. After a finite number of terms in $P(x)$ there will still be some remainder that one can often estimate and that is hopefully small. The following statement is due to the English mathematician Brook Taylor (1685–1731).

Theorem 11. *If* f(x) *has a continuous derivative up to order* n *in some interval containing* a, *then for every* x *in this interval*

$$f(x) = \sum_{k=0}^{n-1} \frac{f^{(k)}(a)}{k!}(x-a)^k + R_n(x)$$

where $R_n(x)$ *is the remainder after* n *terms.*

The series so obtained is referred to as the *Taylor series expansion* of $f(x)$ at the point $x = a$.

$$f(x) = f(a) + f'(a)(x-a) + \frac{f''(a)(x-a)^2}{2} + \frac{f'''(a)(x-a)^3}{6} + \cdots + .$$

As is well-known, the remainder can be expressed in a number of different ways. One way is as an integral; in another way, the so-called *Lagrange form of the remainder*, we have the expression

$$R_n(x) = \frac{f^{(n)}(x_n)}{n!}(x-a)^n$$

where x_n is some point between a and x.

The Taylor series would seem to rest on very practical grounds. However there is another and more rigorous way of looking at Theorem 11. Because of the enormous importance of the theorem in applications, let us examine Taylor's theorem more closely. Suppose that we have a function $f(x)$ that is continuous in the interval $[a,b]$, and differentiable there also except possibly at the end points. With a mathematician's insight we now concoct the new function

$$F(x) = f(b) - f(x) - \left(\frac{b-x}{b-a}\right)[f(b) - f(a)].$$

This function has the property that it is zero when $x = a$ and when $x = b$ (see Figure 4.1). Therefore, there must be some point x_1 lying between a and b at which the derivative of $F(x)$ is zero. If we differentiate $F(x)$ above, then we

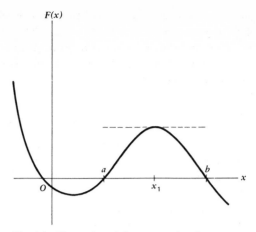

Fig. 4.1 Illustration of the mean value theorem.

arrive at

$$F'(x_1) = -f'(x_1) + \left(\frac{1}{b-a}\right)[f(b)-f(a)]$$

$$= 0,$$

from which it follows that $f(b)=f(a)+f'(x_1)(b-a)$. If the right-hand end point is now left unspecified by simply replacing b by x, this equation becomes

$$\boxed{f(x)=f(a)+f'(x_1)(x-a)}\,.$$

Already this begins to look like the Taylor's series expansion of $f(x)$, where $f'(x_1)(x-a)$ is the error made when $f(x)$ is approximated by $f(a)$. In fact, the result above is the very famous statement you first learned in beginning calculus under the name of the *mean value theorem*. Now we can carry the analysis above further. Let the same function $f(x)$ have n derivatives in the interval (a,b); our brilliant mathematician now constructs the new function $G(x)$:

$$G(x)=f(b)-f(x)-\sum_{k=1}^{n-1}\frac{(b-x)^k}{k!}f^{(k)}(x)$$

$$-\left(\frac{b-x}{b-a}\right)^n\left[f(b)-f(a)-\sum_{k=1}^{n-1}\frac{(b-a)^k}{k!}f^{(k)}(a)\right].$$

This looks complicated, but notice two things. First, our previous $F(x)$ is just a special case of $G(x)$ with $n=1$. Second, $G(x)$ like $F(x)$ vanishes at $x=a$ and at $x=b$. Therefore there must be some point x_n in between a and b at which $G'(x_n)$ is zero. If $G(x)$ is differentiated and then b is replaced by x as before, one arrives at the equation

$$f(x)=f(a)+(x-a)f'(a)+\tfrac{1}{2}(x-a)^2 f''(a)+\cdots+\frac{(x-a)^n}{n!}f^{(n)}(x_n)$$

which is seen to be Taylor's series. Thus we see that the famous Taylor expansion of the function $f(x)$ about the point $x=a$ is just the generalization of the equally famous mean value theorem. One technical point is that according to this treatment the nth derivative of $f(x)$ need not be continuous anywhere in the interval $[a,b]$, nor even exist at the end points.

Let us now illustrate Taylor's theorem by approximating e^x with simple polynomials.

Example 33. Approximate e^x in the interval $[1,2]$ by Taylor polynomials of the first and second degree.

Answer. If x_1 is some point lying between 1 and 2, then the mean value theorem allows us to write

$$e^x = e^1 + \exp(x_1)(x-1).$$

This expression is automatically an identity at $x=1$. Agreement at $x=2$ requires that $\exp(x_1)=e^2-e^1=4.67$. Insertion of this into the above equation gives

$$e^x \cong 4.67x - 1.95.$$

This is shown graphically in Figure 4.2a.

Now let x_2 be some other point lying between 1 and 2. The extension of the mean value theorem to give what might be called a higher mean value theorem leads to the general relation

$$f(x)=f(a)+(x-a)f'(a)+\tfrac{1}{2}(x-a)^2 f''(x_2)$$

and if the function $f(x)$ is e^x, then this relation becomes

$$e^x = e^1 + (x-1)e^1 + \tfrac{1}{2}(x-1)^2 \exp(x_2).$$

Again, this is an identity at $x=1$; for agreement at $x=2$ we must have $\exp(x_2)=2(e^2-2e)=3.90$. Insertion of this into the above

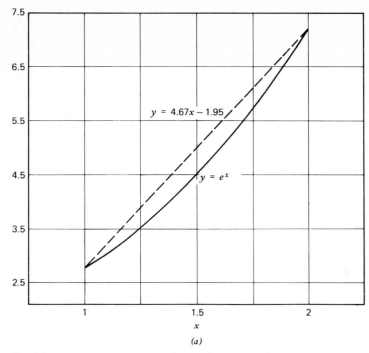

Fig. 4.2   Agreement between e^x and (a) a linear expression,

gives the result

$$e^x \cong 1.95x^2 - 1.18x + 1.95.$$

This is shown graphically in Figure 4.2b; even for the quadratic expression the polynomial is already approaching the true function e^x quite closely. It is clear that even better approximations would be obtained if cubic, quartic, and still higher terms were retained in the Taylor expansion.

To return to Theorem 11 we note that one must choose a sensible point a for the theorem to work. Thus the function must be defined and differentiable at $x = a$, so that $\tan x$, for example, cannot be expanded about $x = \frac{1}{2}\pi$, and $\ln x$ cannot be expanded about $x = 0$. For many functions the point $x = 0$ can be used. Taylor's series then reduces to Maclaurin's series (after the Scottish mathematician Colin Maclaurin, 1698–1746):

$$f(x) = f(0) + xf'(0) + \tfrac{1}{2}x^2 f''(0) + \frac{x^3 f'''(0)}{6} + \cdots .$$

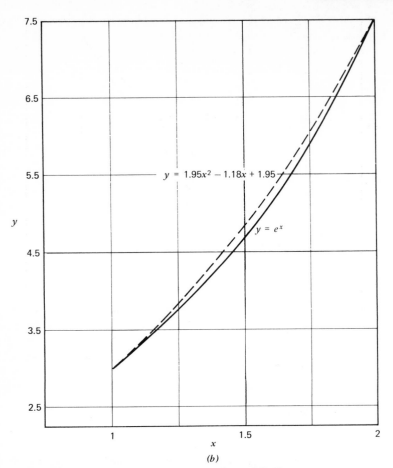

Fig. 4.2 (*b*) a quadratic expression in the interval $[1, 2]$.

There are two common misconceptions about the use of Taylor's theorem. The first is that it can be used only when x is small; no such restriction exists, and within the range of x for which $f(x)$ is defined and differentiable and the Taylor series converges to $f(x)$, the expansion is valid for any x. What can be said is that for certain narrow ranges of x the first few terms of the series, when evaluated at some $x = x_0$, will give a result close to $f(x_0)$.

Another misconception is that the Taylor series expansion of any function automatically produces a series that converges to the value of the function for all $x = x_0$. Some tricky examples can be constructed to show that this is not so. An exercise at the end of this chapter contains one of the standard examples of this type. For nearly all applied situations, however, this difficulty does not arise.

The utility of Theorem 11 in physical problems is that it allows us to replace a given function that may be difficult to deal with by an approximate function that is easier to handle.

Example 34. Find an approximate value of Si (1).

Answer. The required integral is (see Section 3.3)

$$Si\,(1) = \int_0^1 \frac{\sin x}{x}\, dx.$$

Since this cannot be done exactly, we obtain a polynomial expansion for $\sin x$. If we expand about $x = 0$, we obtain

$$\sin x \cong x - \frac{x^3}{6} + \frac{x^5}{5!} - \cdots +.$$

Taking the first two terms only is seen to be suitable since

$$\sin 0 = 0 - 0 + \cdots$$

$$\sin 1 \cong \tfrac{5}{6}$$

$$= 0.833 \text{ (exact value 0.841..).}$$

Then, for the desired integral we get

$$Si\,(1) \cong \int_0^1 dx - \frac{1}{6}\int_0^1 x^2\, dx$$

$$= 1 - \tfrac{1}{6}\left(\tfrac{1}{3}\right)$$

$$= \boxed{0.944}\,.$$

The tabulated value is 0.946; the approximation is in error by 0.2%.

Example 35. In the region of high temperatures, what is the limiting value of the heat capacity of an Einstein crystal?

Answer. From Example 7 we have

$$C_v = \frac{3N_0\varepsilon^2 k}{(kT)^2}\,\frac{e^{\varepsilon/kT}}{\left(e^{\varepsilon/kT}-1\right)^2}\,.$$

From material presented in Chapter 3 we also saw that

$$\sinh u = \tfrac{1}{2}(e^u - e^{-u})$$

$$= \frac{e^{2u} - 1}{2e^u}.$$

Thus we can express the heat capacity as

$$C_v = \frac{3R}{4} \frac{(\varepsilon/kT)^2}{\sinh^2(\varepsilon/2kT)}$$

and we seek a Taylor series expansion of the denominator when $\varepsilon/2kT$ is very small:

$$\sinh u = \sinh a + (u-a)\cosh a + \tfrac{1}{2}(u-a)^2 \sinh a + \cdots +.$$

If we take $a = 0$, then we have

$$\sinh u \cong u + \frac{u^3}{6}$$

and for very small u this is almost u. Hence

$$C_v = \frac{3R}{4} \frac{(\varepsilon/kT)^2}{(\varepsilon/2kT)^2}$$

$$= \boxed{3R}.$$

Although the need for it in applications is not great there is a corresponding Taylor's theorem for functions of two variables. It has the same form as the Taylor theorem for one variable:

$$f(x,y) = f(a,b) + (x-a)\left(\frac{\partial f}{\partial x}\right)_y + (y-b)\left(\frac{\partial f}{\partial y}\right)_x$$

$$+ \frac{1}{2}\left[(x-a)^2\left(\frac{\partial^2 f}{\partial x^2}\right)_y + 2(x-a)(y-b)\left(\frac{\partial^2 f}{\partial x\,\partial y}\right) + (y-b)^2\left(\frac{\partial^2 f}{\partial y^2}\right)_x\right] + \cdots$$

$$= \sum_{k=0}^{\infty} \sum_{n=0}^{k} \frac{\binom{k}{n}}{k!}(x-a)^n (y-b)^{k-n}\left[\frac{\partial^k f}{\partial x^n \partial y^{k-n}}\right].$$

It is understood that each of the derivatives is to be evaluated at the point (a,b).

Example 36. Expand $z = e^{-x}\sin y$ in a Taylor series about the point $(0, \frac{1}{2}\pi)$.

Answer. From the double summation above with $a = 0$ and $b = \frac{1}{2}\pi$, we can write

$$z \cong 1 + x\left(-e^{-x}\sin y\right)_{0,\frac{1}{2}\pi} + \left(y - \frac{1}{2}\pi\right)\left(e^{-x}\cos y\right)_{0,\frac{1}{2}\pi}$$

$$+ \frac{1}{2}\left[x^2\left(e^{-x}\sin y\right)_{0,\frac{1}{2}\pi} + 2x\left(y - \frac{1}{2}\pi\right)\left(-e^{-x}\cos y\right)_{0,\frac{1}{2}\pi}\right.$$

$$\left. + \left(y - \frac{1}{2}\pi\right)^2 \cdot \left(-e^{-x}\sin y\right)_{0,\frac{1}{2}\pi}\right]$$

$$= 1 - x + \frac{1}{2}x^2 - \frac{1}{2}\left(y - \frac{1}{2}\pi\right)^2.$$

To see how well this works we compute $z(x,y)$ for the point $x = 1/10$, $y = 95°$. The exact value from tables is $e^{-0.1}\sin 95° = 0.9013$. From the series above the approximate value is $1 - 0.1 + \frac{1}{2}(0.01) - \frac{1}{2} \cdot \frac{1}{4}\pi(5/90)^2 = 0.9002$, for an error of 0.12%.

To return to power series in general we want to inquire about four operations on such series: multiplication, division, differentiation, and integration. In order to do this properly we have to introduce two new types of convergence not implied by the contents of Theorem 10. This will cover the cases of series that do not consist exclusively of positive terms. A series in which the signs alternate is called an *alternating series*: $a_1 - a_2 + a_3 - a_4 + \cdots -$. A series such as this, or indeed any series containing some negative terms, is said to be *absolutely convergent* if the series of absolute terms $\sum_n |a_n|$ converges. A series is said to be *conditionally convergent* if the series as written converges but the series of absolute terms does not converge. The ratio test, for example, can be used to ascertain absolute convergence or not of a series, but never conditional convergence. The following theorem is useful regarding alternating series.

Theorem 12. *Let $\sum_n a_n$ be an alternating series. Then if $\sum_n |a_n|$ is convergent, so is $\sum_n a_n$. If the test for absolute convergence fails, then $\sum_n a_n$ is conditionally convergent if* (a) $|a_{n+1}| < |a_n|$ *for all* n, *and* (b) $\lim_{n\to\infty} a_n = 0$.

Example 37. Examine the alternating hyperharmonic series for convergence.

Answer.   The series in question is

$$1^{-s} - 2^{-s} + 3^{-s} - 4^{-s} + \cdots - .$$

The ratio test fails to give a conclusive result for the series of absolute terms, but in Example 32 it was shown by the integral test that the hyperharmonic series converges for $s > 1$. Hence the alternating series is absolutely convergent for $s > 1$. For $0 < s \leqslant 1$, we apply Theorem 12:

$$\frac{1}{(n+1)^{s}} < \frac{1}{n^{s}} \quad \text{and} \quad \lim_{n \to \infty} \frac{1}{n^{s}} = 0.$$

Hence the alternating hyperharmonic series is conditionally convergent for $0 < s \leqslant 1$. Finally, for $s = 0$ the series diverges because the limit $\lim_{n \to \infty} a_{n}$ does not exist, and for $s < 0$ the series diverges because $|a_{n+1}| > |a_{n}|$.

The plausibility of Theorem 12 becomes more obvious when a sketch of the partial sums of an alternating series is made. Let us consider the alternating harmonic series and let S_n be the nth partial sum. A graph of S_n versus n is shown in Figure 4.3. One sees several things from this graph. First, as n increases, the difference between successive partial sums decreases, or in other words, the nth term of the series tends to zero. Second the partial

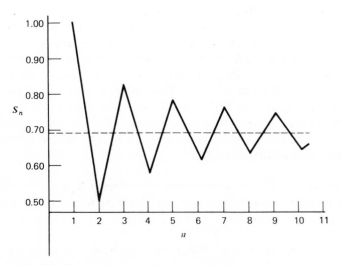

Fig. 4.3   The partial sums of the alternating harmonic series.

sums oscillate with the magnitude of each oscillation smaller than the one before. This shows that the absolute value of the $(n+1)$st term in the series is less than the absolute value of the nth term. Finally, as the partial sums seem to oscillate about a fixed line that we are to identify with the value of the sum of the infinite series, it is seen that the error in the sum by taking only the first n terms is less than the magnitude of the $(n+1)$st term. Thus after 10 terms we predict the error to be less than $1/11$, or about 0.091.

With this additional background in mind we are now ready to look at some manipulations with series. In the discussion we restrict ourselves to *power series*, that is, series with the general term $a_n x^n$.

Multiplication

Let $S_1(x)$ and $S_2(x)$ be two infinite power series:

$$S_1(x) = \sum_n a_n x^n = \sum_n u_n$$

$$S_2(x) = \sum_n b_n x^n = \sum_n v_n.$$

By analogy with the way one multiplies ordinary finite polynomials, we define the *Cauchy product* of the two series above to be $\sum_{n=0}^{\infty}\sum_{k=0}^{n} a_k b_{n-k} x^n$. The question that we want to ask is, does the convergence of $\sum_n u_n$ and of $\sum_n v_n$ (both of which may, in general, consist of negative and positive terms) guarantee convergence of their product? It does not unless the two series are absolutely convergent. In this case the product series is also absolutely convergent. The final question is, if for some specified x the sum of the $S_1(x)$ series is A and the sum of the $S_2(x)$ series is B, will the sum of the product series be AB? Fortunately the answer is affirmative; this result is a consequence of a theorem regarding the rearrangements of series.

Let us take the $S_1(x)$ and $S_2(x)$ series and arrange in tabular form the various possible products of the u's and v's.

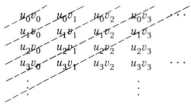

An important theorem permits us to select values from this table in any order we like without altering the value of their total, whenever $S_1(x)$ and $S_2(x)$ are absolutely convergent.

Theorem 13 (Dirichlet's[5] Theorem). *The sum of an absolutely convergent series is the same in whatever order the terms are grouped.*

Is this a trivial statement? After all, what about the commutativity of addition for real numbers that we mentioned in Section 1.1? Theorem 13 is not a trivial statement because what we are talking about is rearrangements of infinite numbers of terms in a series. Rearrangement of a finite number of terms can never alter a sum; whenever the infinite is involved we have to always suppose that the results may be different. Actually this is rather interesting. A conditionally convergent series may be made to converge to anything or even to diverge by a suitable infinite rearrangement of terms. Take as an example again the alternating harmonic series.

$$1 - \tfrac{1}{2} + \tfrac{1}{3} - \tfrac{1}{4} + \tfrac{1}{5} - \tfrac{1}{6} + \cdots - .$$

It converges as written to $\ln 2$ or 0.693, roughly. Suppose we rewrite the series as shown below by taking enough positive terms to just give a positive partial sum, then enough negative terms to just give a negative partial sum, then again enough positive terms to give a positive partial sum, and so on:

$$1 \ \Big| -\tfrac{1}{2} - \tfrac{1}{4} - \tfrac{1}{6} - \tfrac{1}{8} \ \Big| \ +\tfrac{1}{3} \ \Big| \ -\tfrac{1}{10} - \tfrac{1}{12} - \tfrac{1}{14} - \tfrac{1}{16} \ \Big|$$
$$S_k \qquad\qquad -.042 \qquad .292 \qquad\qquad\qquad -.024$$

$$+\tfrac{1}{5} \ \Big| \ -\tfrac{1}{18} - \tfrac{1}{20} - \tfrac{1}{22} - \tfrac{1}{24} \ \Big| \ +\tfrac{1}{7} \ \Big| \ -\cdots .$$
$$.176 \qquad\qquad -.016 \qquad\qquad .127$$

It is clear that according to this approach one will be able to make the sum of the infinite series tend to zero as closely as one desires!

Returning to the table just before Theorem 13, if we now select terms in the order indicated by the cross lines, then an easily remembered formula for the product is obtained. Our purpose here is to get a power series for the product, and this arrangement gathers all terms containing the same power of the parameter x:

$$\boxed{\;\begin{aligned} S_1(x)\,S_2(x) &= a_0 b_0 + (a_0 b_1 + a_1 b_0)x + (a_0 b_2 + a_1 b_1 + a_2 b_0)x^2 + \cdots + \\ &= \sum_{n=0}^{\infty} \sum_{k=0}^{n} a_k b_{n-k} x^n \end{aligned}\;}.$$

If each of the original two series is absolutely convergent for $|x| < R$, then the

[5]After the German mathematician Peter Gustav Lejeune Dirichlet (1805–1859).

product will be also. The formula may or may not work for conditionally convergent series.

Example 38. Find a series expansion for the product $\sin x \cos x$.

Answer. From Maclaurin's series expansions we have

$$\sin x = x - \frac{x^3}{3!} + \frac{x^5}{5!} - \frac{x^7}{7!} + \cdots -$$

and

$$\cos x = 1 - \frac{x^2}{2!} + \frac{x^4}{4!} - \frac{x^6}{6!} + \cdots -.$$

Both these series are absolutely convergent for all finite x (show this!). Hence the product is

$$\sin x \cos x = 0 + (0+1)x + (0+0+0)x^2 + (0 - \tfrac{1}{2} + 0 - \tfrac{1}{6})x^3 + 0x^4$$

$$+ (0 + \tfrac{1}{24} + 0 + \tfrac{1}{12} + 0 + \tfrac{1}{120})x^5 + \cdots +$$

$$= x - \tfrac{2}{3}x^3 + \tfrac{2}{15}x^5 - \cdots +$$

$$= \tfrac{1}{2}\Big[(2x)^1 - \tfrac{1}{6}(2x)^3 + \tfrac{1}{120}(2x)^5 - \cdots + \Big]$$

$$= \boxed{\tfrac{1}{2}\sin 2x}\,.$$

Division

Again, let $S_1(x)$ and $S_2(x)$ be two power series that are absolutely convergent for $|x| < R$:

$$S_1(x) = \sum_n a_n x^n \qquad S_2(x) = \sum_n b_n x^n.$$

The following formula can be used to express the quotient if $b_0 \neq 0$:

$$\boxed{\frac{S_1(x)}{S_2(x)} = \frac{a_0}{b_0} + \frac{a_1 b_0 - a_0 b_1}{b_0^2}x + \frac{a_2 b_0^2 - a_1 b_0 b_1 + a_0 b_1^2 - a_0 b_0 b_2}{b_0^3}x^2 + \cdots +\,.}$$

Generally, the region of convergence is smaller than that for either $S_1(x)$ or $S_2(x)$.

Integration

The situation here is more complicated. The general case of a series that is not a power series necessitates consideration of uniform convergence. We do not do this here but simply state that the uniform convergence of a series over some interval is sufficient to make the sum a continuous function of the parameter so that term-by-term integration is legitimate. Convergent power series are nice because one can always find an interval where there is uniform convergence. The result that emerges is that if the power series $\mathcal{S}(x) = \sum_n a_n x^n$ converges for $|x| < R$, then the series of integrals obtained by term-by-term integration will converge to the integral of the sum for $|x| < R$:

$$\int \mathcal{S}(x)\, dx = \sum_n \frac{a_n x^{n+1}}{n+1}.$$

It will be noticed that since integration always supplies a factor of n to the denominator of each term, the rate of convergence is, in general, speeded up.

Differentiation

In the case of differentiation of general series that are convergent, we require that the individual terms be continuous functions and that the sum of the derivatives be uniformly convergent over some interval. This is true for power series so that if the series $\mathcal{S}(x) = \sum_n a_n x^n$ converges for $|x| < R$, then the series of derivatives obtained by term-by-term differentiation will converge to the derivative of the sum for $|x| < R$:

$$\mathcal{S}'(x) = \sum_n n a_n x^{n-1}.$$

Here the rate of convergence is slowed down because of the presence in the numerator of each term of the factor of n.

Differentiation or integration can often be employed as tricks to help evaluate sums of series. Here is a clever example of the use of both integration and differentiation.

Example 39.   Find the sum of the series $\mathcal{S} = \dfrac{1}{2!} + \dfrac{2}{3!} + \dfrac{3}{4!} + \dfrac{4}{5!} + \cdots +$.

Answer.   There is no variable here so let us temporarily make this a power series in x:

$$\mathcal{S}(x) = \frac{x^2}{2!} + \frac{2x^3}{3!} + \frac{3x^4}{4!} + \frac{4x^5}{5!} + \cdots +$$

$$= \sum_{n=2}^{\infty} \frac{(n-1)x^n}{n!}.$$

The ratio test shows that this series is convergent for all x. Term-by-term differentiation gives

$$\mathcal{S}'(x) = \sum_{n=2}^{\infty} \frac{n(n-1)x^{n-1}}{n!}$$

$$= x \sum_{n=2}^{\infty} \frac{x^{n-2}}{(n-2)!}$$

$$= x \sum_{k=0}^{\infty} \frac{x^k}{k!}.$$

Now the series of terms $x^k/k!$ is nothing more than the Maclaurin series for the well-known function e^x. Hence $\mathcal{S}'(x) = xe^x$, and therefore

$$\mathcal{S}(x) = \int_0^x xe^x \, dx$$

$$= xe^x - e^x + 1.$$

We write the upper limit as x so as to leave the answer as a function of x, and we write the lower limit as 0 because for this choice of x, $\mathcal{S}(0) = 0$. That is, the lower limit supplies our constant of integration. Finally, for the original series we have

$$\mathcal{S} = \mathcal{S}(1)$$

$$= e^1 - e^1 + 1$$

$$= \boxed{1}.$$

3   FAMILIAR SERIES

In this section we gather some common series that you will frequently need.

The first is the well-known binomial series, that was presented briefly in Section 1.5.

At the age of twenty-one he wrote
a treatise upon the binomial theorem,
which has had a European vogue.

A. CONAN DOYLE

(1) $$(x+y)^n = x^n + nx^{n-1}y + \frac{n(n-1)x^{n-2}y^2}{2!} + \cdots + y^n$$

$$= \sum_{k=0}^{n} \frac{n!x^{n-k}y^k}{(n-k)!k!} \qquad \text{if } n \text{ is a positive integer.}$$

If n is negative or fractional, a series with the same form as that above can still be written, but now such a series will be an infinite series:

$$(x+y)^n = x^n + nx^{n-1}y + \frac{n(n-1)x^{n-2}y^2}{2!} + \cdots + \qquad (y^2 < x^2).$$

Situations involving the latter case occur frequently in physical science.

Example 40. A particle of charge q_1 is placed at a point with spherical polar coordinates $(a,0,0)$; another particle of charge q_2 is placed at (r,θ,ϕ), located R units from the first particle. The potential energy of interaction is given by the expression

$$U = -\frac{q_1 q_2}{4\pi\varepsilon_0 R}.$$

Express U as a function of r (see Figure 4.4).

Answer. The separation of the two charges is given by the usual distance formula:

$$R = \sqrt{(x_2 - x_1)^2 + (y_2 - y_1)^2 + (z_2 - z_1)^2}$$

$$= \sqrt{r^2 \sin^2\theta \cos^2\phi + r^2 \sin^2\theta \sin^2\phi + (r\cos\theta - a)^2}$$

$$= \sqrt{r^2 - 2ar\cos\theta + a^2}.$$

We now wish to expand $(r^2 - 2ar\cos\theta + a^2)^{-\frac{1}{2}}$ in a series by the binomial theorem. After some algebraic manipulation this becomes

$$\frac{1}{r}\left[1-\frac{1}{2}\left(\frac{a}{r}\right)^2+\left(\frac{a}{r}\right)\cos\theta+\frac{3}{8}\left\{\left(\frac{a}{r}\right)^2-2\left(\frac{a}{r}\right)\cos\theta\right\}^2\right.$$

$$\left.-\frac{5}{16}\left\{\left(\frac{a}{r}\right)^2-2\left(\frac{a}{r}\right)\cos\theta\right\}^3+\cdots-\right]$$

and thus after collecting terms the potential energy is

$$U=-\frac{q_1q_2}{4\pi\varepsilon_0}\frac{1}{r}\left[1+\frac{a}{r}\cos\theta+\left(\frac{a}{r}\right)^2\left(\frac{3\cos^2\theta-1}{2}\right)\right.$$

$$\left.+\left(\frac{a}{r}\right)^3\left(\frac{5\cos^3\theta-3\cos\theta}{2}\right)+\cdots+\right]$$

The trigonometric terms in parentheses are quantities referred to as Legendre polynomials; we meet them again in Chapter 7.

(2)
$$e^x=1+x+\frac{x^2}{2!}+\frac{x^3}{3!}+\frac{x^4}{4!}+\frac{x^5}{5!}+\cdots+$$

$$=\sum_{n=0}^{\infty}\frac{x^n}{n!} \qquad\qquad (|x|<\infty)$$

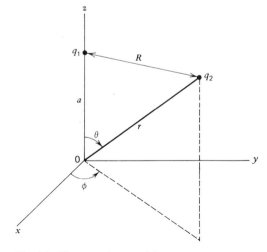

Fig. 4.4 Electrostatic potential energy.

(3) $$\ln x = (x-1) - \tfrac{1}{2}(x-1)^2 + \tfrac{1}{3}(x-1)^3 - \cdots +$$

$$= \sum_{n=1}^{\infty} \frac{(-1)^{n+1}(x-1)^n}{n} \qquad (0 < x \leqslant 2)$$

or

$$\ln(1+x) = x - \tfrac{1}{2}x^2 + \tfrac{1}{3}x^3 - \tfrac{1}{4}x^4 + \cdots -$$

$$= \sum_{n=1}^{\infty} \frac{(-1)^{n+1}x^n}{n} \qquad (-1 < x \leqslant 1)$$

or

$$\ln(1-x) = -x - \tfrac{1}{2}x^2 - \tfrac{1}{3}x^3 - \tfrac{1}{4}x^4 - \cdots -$$

$$= -\sum_{n=1}^{\infty} \frac{x^n}{n} \qquad (-1 \leqslant x < 1)$$

(4) $$\sin x = x - \frac{x^3}{3!} + \frac{x^5}{5!} - \frac{x^7}{7!} + \cdots -$$

$$= \sum_{n=0}^{\infty} \frac{(-1)^n x^{2n+1}}{(2n+1)!} \qquad (|x| < \infty)$$

$$\cos x = 1 - \frac{x^2}{2!} + \frac{x^4}{4!} - \frac{x^6}{6!} + \cdots -$$

$$= \sum_{n=0}^{\infty} \frac{(-1)^n x^{2n}}{(2n)!} \qquad (|x| < \infty)$$

$$\tan x = x + \frac{x^3}{3} + \frac{2x^5}{15} + \frac{17x^7}{315} + \cdots + \qquad (x^2 < \pi^2/4)$$

(5) $$\sin^{-1} x = x + \frac{x^3}{2 \cdot 3} + \frac{1 \cdot 3 x^5}{2 \cdot 4 \cdot 5} + \frac{1 \cdot 3 \cdot 5 x^7}{2 \cdot 4 \cdot 6 \cdot 7} + \cdots + \qquad (x^2 < 1)$$

$$\cos^{-1} x = \tfrac{1}{2}\pi - \left(x + \frac{x^3}{2 \cdot 3} + \frac{1 \cdot 3 x^5}{2 \cdot 4 \cdot 5} + \cdots + \right) \qquad (x^2 < 1)$$

$$\tan^{-1} x = x - \frac{x^3}{3} + \frac{x^5}{5} - \frac{x^7}{7} + \frac{x^9}{9} - \cdots +$$

$$= \sum_{n=0}^{\infty} \frac{(-1)^n x^{2n+1}}{2n+1} \qquad (x^2 \leqslant 1)$$

(6)
$$\sinh x = x + \frac{x^3}{3!} + \frac{x^5}{5!} + \frac{x^7}{7!} + \frac{x^9}{9!} + \cdots +$$

$$= \sum_{n=0}^{\infty} \frac{x^{2n+1}}{(2n+1)!} \qquad (|x| < \infty)$$

$$\cosh x = 1 + \frac{x^2}{2!} + \frac{x^4}{4!} + \frac{x^6}{6!} + \frac{x^8}{8!} + \cdots +$$

$$= \sum_{n=0}^{\infty} \frac{x^{2n}}{(2n)!} \qquad (|x| < \infty)$$

$$\tanh^{-1} x = x + \frac{x^3}{3} + \frac{x^5}{5} + \frac{x^7}{7} + \frac{x^9}{9} + \cdots +$$

$$= \sum_{n=0}^{\infty} \frac{x^{2n+1}}{2n+1} \qquad (x^2 < 1)$$

It will be noted that not all of the series above are Taylor or Maclaurin expansions. Some series are difficult to express in the summation notation, that is, it is difficult to see what is the form of the general term. In this regard there are special numbers that are useful for this purpose. We mention just two types.

Bernoulli Numbers[6]

These numbers are defined as follows:

$$\frac{x}{e^x - 1} = \sum_{n=0}^{\infty} \frac{B_n x^n}{n!} \qquad (|x| < 2\pi).$$

[6]Those marvelous Bernoullis! The Bernoullis were a Protestant family driven from Antwerp in the last quarter of the sixteenth century. They settled in Basel and for over a century produced an extraordinary line of scientists and mathematicians (many other fields were well-represented, also), much like the Bachs in music. A partial family line is shown below.

Jakob (James)—— Nicolaus —— Johann (John)
1654–1705   1662–1716   1667–1748

Nicolaus   Nicolaus   Daniel   Johann
1687–1759   1695–1726   1700–1782   1710–1790

The Bernoulli numbers are named after Jakob, but in fact it is difficult to establish who did what because the Bernoullis were quarrelsome and unamiable, often claiming prizes or credit for what others in the family had actually done. A definitive biography in English of this remarkable family is sorely needed.

Multiplication of both sides by $e^x - 1$ and introduction of a double summation gives

$$x = \sum_{n=0}^{\infty} \sum_{k=0}^{n} \frac{B_k x^n}{k!(n-k)!} - \sum_{n=0}^{\infty} \frac{B_n x^n}{n!}.$$

The double summation arises because we have replaced e^x by its Maclaurin expansion and then multiplied the two series according to the formula given earlier for the product of two series. Let us now equate the various powers of x on the two sides of the equation above:

for x^0 $(n=0)$: $0 = \dfrac{B_0}{0!0!} - \dfrac{B_0}{0!}$

for x^1 $(n=1)$: $1 = \dfrac{B_0}{0!1!} + \dfrac{B_1}{1!0!} - \dfrac{B_1}{1!}$

for x^n $(n>1)$: $0 = \displaystyle\sum_{k=0}^{n} \frac{B_k}{k!(n-k)!} - \frac{B_n}{n!}.$

The first equation is an identity. From the second equation one gets $B_0 = 1$. If we solve the third equation for B_n, we get

$$B_n = \sum_{k=0}^{n} \frac{n! B_k}{k!(n-k)!}$$

$$= \sum_{k=0}^{n} \binom{n}{k} B_k \qquad (n \geqslant 2).$$

Thus we have for B_2 the following expression

$$B_2 = \binom{2}{0} B_0 + \binom{2}{1} B_1 + \binom{2}{2} B_2$$

$$= \frac{2!}{0!2!} + \frac{2!}{1!1!} B_1 + \frac{2!}{2!0!} B_2$$

which simplifies to

$$B_2 = 1 + 2B_1 + B_2$$

$$B_1 = -\tfrac{1}{2}.$$

From a similar expression for B_3 one can get $B_2 = +\tfrac{1}{6}$, and so on. Table 4.1

lists the first few Bernoulli numbers; you are cautioned, however, that notations differ in various sources, so that the *Handbook of Chemistry and Physics* mathematical section, for example, gives different values for these numbers.

Table 4.1   Bernoulli Numbers

$B_0 = 1$	$B_4 = -\frac{1}{30}$
$B_1 = -\frac{1}{2}$	$B_5 = 0$
$B_2 = \frac{1}{6}$	$B_6 = \frac{1}{42}$
$B_3 = 0$	$B_{2n+1} = 0$

Here is a derivation of a useful series. By definition,

$$\frac{x}{e^x - 1} = B_0 - \tfrac{1}{2}x + \sum_{k=2}^{\infty} \frac{B_k x^k}{k!}$$

and after transposing $-\tfrac{1}{2}x$ to the left side there results

$$\tfrac{1}{2}x \left[\frac{e^{\frac{1}{2}x} + e^{-\frac{1}{2}x}}{e^{\frac{1}{2}x} - e^{-\frac{1}{2}x}} \right] = B_0 + \sum_{k=2}^{\infty} \frac{B_k x^k}{k!} .$$

But from material in Chapter 3 we see that the quantity in brackets is just $\coth \tfrac{1}{2}x$. Since the odd Bernoulli numbers after B_1 are zero (see Table 4.1), we can write this equation as

$$\coth \tfrac{1}{2}x = \sum_{n=0}^{\infty} \frac{B_{2n} x^{2n}}{(2n)!} \frac{2}{x}$$

and if we now let $x = 2u$, we have finally

$$\boxed{ \coth u = \sum_{n=0}^{\infty} \frac{2^{2n} B_{2n} u^{2n-1}}{(2n)!} .}$$

Note that this series could not have been obtained from a Maclaurin expansion because $\coth 0 = \infty$. From the above series it is now possible to obtain series for certain other trigonometric functions, for example $\cot x$, since $\coth ix = -i \cot x$ as inferred from Table 3.4.

An interesting and useful relation involving the Bernoulli numbers that we shall not prove is the following:

$$\sum_{k=1}^{\infty} \frac{1}{k^{2n}} = \frac{(-1)^{n+1}(2\pi)^{2n}B_{2n}}{2(2n)!}$$

This leads to the following results:

$$\sum_{k=1}^{\infty} \frac{1}{k^2} = \frac{\pi^2}{6}$$

$$\sum_{k=1}^{\infty} \frac{1}{k^4} = \frac{\pi^4}{90}$$

$$\sum_{k=1}^{\infty} \frac{1}{k^6} = \frac{\pi^6}{945}.$$

The second series was mentioned in Example 32 and in Exercise 24 of Chapter 3. Interestingly enough, even though we know they must converge, it is not known whether sums of reciprocal odd powers, $\sum_{k=1}^{\infty} 1/(k^{2n+1})$ ($n \geqslant 1$), can be expressed in as simple a form as that for the even powers above.[7]

Euler Numbers

These are defined as follows:

$$\frac{2e^x}{e^{2x}+1} = \sum_{n=0}^{\infty} \frac{E_n x^n}{n!} \qquad (|x| < \tfrac{1}{2}\pi)$$

and the first few may be worked out using the methods similar to those in the discussion of the Bernoulli numbers. These are given in Table 4.2.

Table 4.2   Euler Numbers

$E_0 = 1$	$E_4 = 5$
$E_1 = 0$	$E_5 = 0$
$E_2 = -1$	$E_6 = -61$
$E_3 = 0$	$E_{2n+1} = 0$

[7]The reader mathematically interested in these formulas is referred to two short articles: I. Papadimitriou, *Am. Math. Monthly*, **80**, 424 (1973); T. M. Apostol, *ibid.*, **80**, 425 (1973).

Here is a derivation of another useful series. We have, by definition

$$\frac{2e^x}{e^{2x}+1} = \frac{2}{e^x + e^{-x}} = \frac{1}{\cosh x}.$$

Since the odd Euler numbers are zero, this can also be written as

$$\operatorname{sech} x = \sum_{n=0}^{\infty} \frac{E_{2n} x^{2n}}{(2n)!}$$

and from Table 3.4 we can infer that $\operatorname{sech} ix = \sec x$. Therefore,

$$\sec x = \sum_{n=0}^{\infty} \frac{E_{2n} (ix)^{2n}}{(2n)!}$$

$$\boxed{= \sum_{n=0}^{\infty} \frac{(-1)^n E_{2n} x^{2n}}{(2n)!}}.$$

4* EULER–MACLAURIN SUMMATION FORMULA; STIRLING'S APPROXIMATION

The Bernoulli numbers have some interesting applications and our object in this section will be to get to that famour relation that we all learn practically from the cradle, Stirling's approximation for $\ln(n!)$, via the Bernoulli numbers. Along the way we shall encounter one or two interesting results.

First let us define the *Bernoulli function* of degree n, $f_n(t)$, as the coefficient of $x^n/n!$ in the series expansion of

$$\frac{x(e^{tx}-1)}{e^x - 1}.$$

From the Maclaurin expansion of e^{tx} and the definition of the Bernoulli numbers, this leads immediately to

$$\sum_{n=1}^{\infty} f_n(t) \frac{x^n}{n!} = \left(\frac{B_0 x^0}{0!} + \frac{B_1 x^1}{1!} + \frac{B_2 x^2}{2!} + \cdots + \right)\left(tx + \frac{t^2 x^2}{2!} + \frac{t^3 x^3}{3!} + \cdots + \right).$$

The first few Bernoulli functions can be found easily by equating like powers of x on the two sides of the equation. These are given in Table 4.3.

Table 4.3   Bernoulli Functions

$f_1(t) = t$	$f_4(t) = t^4 - 2t^3 + t^2$
$f_2(t) = t^2 - t$	$f_5(t) = t^5 - \frac{5}{2}t^4 + \frac{5}{3}t^3 - \frac{1}{6}t$
$f_3(t) = t^3 - \frac{3}{2}t^2 + \frac{1}{2}t$	$f_6(t) = t^6 - 3t^5 + \frac{5}{2}t^4 - \frac{1}{2}t^2$

Now let us find $f_n(t+1) - f_n(t)$. This is just the coefficient of $x^n/n!$ in the expansion of

$$\frac{x(e^{tx+x} - 1) - x(e^{tx} - 1)}{e^x - 1}$$

or, in other words, the coefficient of xe^{tx}. But from the series expansion of e^{tx} we have

$$xe^{tx} = \sum_{n=0}^{\infty} \frac{t^n x^{n+1}}{n!}$$

so that the desired coefficient is $[t^{n-1}/(n-1)!]n!$. Therefore, we have the result that $f_n(t+1) - f_n(t) = nt^{n-1}$. To see what this gets us, let t take on various integral values:

$$f_n(2) - f_n(1) = n1^{n-1}$$
$$f_n(3) - f_n(2) = n2^{n-1}$$
$$f_n(4) - f_n(3) = n3^{n-1}$$
$$\vdots$$
$$f_n(t+1) - f_n(t) = nt^{n-1}.$$

Now sum these t equations to give the result

$$f_n(t+1) - f_n(1) = n \sum_{k=1}^{t} k^{n-1}.$$

When n is greater than 1, it is easy to see that $f_n(1)$ must equal zero since otherwise one would be trying to expand $x(e^{tx} - 1)/(e^x - 1) = x$ in a power series. Hence we have

$$\sum_{k=1}^{t} k^{n-1} = \frac{1}{n}f_n(t+1)$$

and using the previous result above, this can be rewritten as

$$\boxed{\sum_{k=1}^{t} k^{n-1} = \frac{1}{n} f_n(t) + t^{n-1}}.$$

This is a useful and interesting result. It gives us a quick, algebraic way of summing the first t $(n-1)$st powers of the positive integers.

Example 41. Find the sum of the first 10 cubes.

Answer. In the formula above take $n = 4$. Then, one has

$$S = \tfrac{1}{4} f_4(t) + t^3$$

$$= \tfrac{1}{4}(t^4 - 2t^3 + t^2) + t^3$$

$$= \left[\frac{t(t+1)}{2} \right]^2.$$

This agrees with the expression given in the *Handbook of Chemistry and Physics* mathematics section and with the recursion relationship given parenthetically in Exercise 45** of Chapter 1. Substitution of $t = 10$ gives the sum of the first 10 cubes as 3025.

If we now go back to the original definition of the Bernoulli functions and look at the general term for the coefficient of $x^n / n!$, we can pick out the following contributions.

$$\frac{t^n x^n B_0}{n!}$$

$$\frac{t^{n-1} x^{n-1}}{(n-1)!} \frac{x^1 B_1}{1!}$$

$$\frac{t^{n-2} x^{n-2}}{(n-2)!} \frac{x^2 B_2}{2!} \qquad \text{or} \qquad \frac{x^n}{n!} \left\{ \begin{array}{l} B_0 \dfrac{t^n}{0!} \\[2mm] B_1 \dfrac{n t^{n-1}}{1!} \\[2mm] B_2 \dfrac{n(n-1) t^{n-2}}{2!} \\[2mm] B_3 \dfrac{n(n-1)(n-2) t^{n-3}}{3!} \end{array} \right.$$

$$\frac{t^{n-3} x^{n-3}}{(n-3)!} \frac{x^3 B_3}{3!}$$

$$\vdots$$

From the form of these contributions we can write

$$f_n(t) = \frac{B_0 t^n}{0!} + \frac{nt^{n-1}B_1}{1!} + \frac{n(n-1)t^{n-2}B_2}{2!} + \cdots +$$

$$= \sum_{r=0}^{n-1} \binom{n}{r} t^{n-r} B_r.$$

Elementary manipulations yield the derived series

$$\frac{f_n'(t)}{n!} = \sum_{r=0}^{n-1} \frac{t^{n-r-1}B_r}{r!(n-r-1)!} \qquad \frac{f_{n-1}(t)}{(n-1)!} = \sum_{r=0}^{n-2} \frac{t^{n-r-1}B_r}{r!(n-r-1)!}$$

and it is thus seen that the two series are identical except for the fact that the first series contains one additional term (that when $r = n-1$). By subtraction we get the result

$$\frac{f_n'(t)}{n!} - \frac{f_{n-1}(t)}{(n-1)!} = \frac{B_{n-1}}{(n-1)!}$$

which will be useful presently.

In order to actually obtain the Euler–Maclaurin summation formula, we begin by integrating $g(x)dx$ by parts over the range 0 to 1.

$$\int_0^1 g(x)dx = xg(x)\big|_0^1 - \int_0^1 xg'(x)dx$$

$$= (x - \tfrac{1}{2})g(x)\big|_0^1 - \int_0^1 (x - \tfrac{1}{2})g'(x)dx$$

$$= \tfrac{1}{2}g(1) + \tfrac{1}{2}g(0) - \int_0^1 (x - \tfrac{1}{2})g'(x)dx$$

You will notice that $\tfrac{1}{2}g(x)$ has been added to and subtracted from the terms, thus leaving the expression unchanged; the reason for this will be clear shortly. Now we integrate by parts again to obtain

$$\int_0^1 (x - \tfrac{1}{2})g'(x)dx = (\tfrac{1}{2}x^2 - \tfrac{1}{2}x)g'(x)\big|_0^1 - \int_0^1 (\tfrac{1}{2}x^2 - \tfrac{1}{2}x)g''(x)dx$$

and now we notice that $(\tfrac{1}{2}x^2 - \tfrac{1}{2}x)$ is just $f_2(x)/2!$. But we know from the result above that $f_2(x)/2!$ is equivalent to $f_3'(x)/3! - (B_2/2!)$. Let us therefore add and subtract $(B_2/2!)g'(x)$ to the right side of the above equation:

$$\int_0^1 \left(x - \tfrac{1}{2}\right) g'(x)\,dx = \left(\tfrac{1}{2}x^2 - \tfrac{1}{2}x + \tfrac{1}{12}\right) g'(x)\big|_0^1 - \int_0^1 \left(\tfrac{1}{2}x^2 - \tfrac{1}{2}x + \tfrac{1}{12}\right) g''(x)\,dx$$

$$= \frac{B_2}{2!}\left[g'(1) - g'(0)\right] - \frac{1}{3!}\int_0^1 f_3'(x)\, g''(x)\,dx.$$

Clearly this process can be continued so long as $g(x)$ is differentiable; of particular interest are those cases where $g(x)$ is infinitely differentiable. This leads to an infinite series

$$\int_0^1 g(x)\,dx = \tfrac{1}{2}g(1) + \tfrac{1}{2}g(0) + \sum_{r=2}^{\infty} (-1)^{r-1}\frac{B_r}{r!}\left[g^{r-1}(1) - g^{r-1}(0)\right]$$

and if we write a similar expression for intervals $[1,2]$, $[2,3], \ldots, [(n-1),n]$ and add, noting once again that the odd Bernoulli numbers are zero, we can get one final useful form of the Euler–Maclaurin summation formula:

$$\boxed{\begin{aligned}
\sum_{r=0}^{n} g(r) &= \int_0^n g(x)\,dx + \tfrac{1}{2}\left[g(n) + g(0)\right] + \frac{B_2}{2!}\left[g'(n) - g'(0)\right] \\
&\quad + \sum_{r=2}^{\infty} \frac{B_{2r}}{(2r)!}\left[g^{2r-1}(n) - g^{2r-1}(0)\right]
\end{aligned}}$$

We have gone to a lot of work to derive what is obviously a very forbidding formula, and we are certainly entitled to ask what good is it. *The Euler–Maclaurin summation formula shows us how we may replace a summation (left side) by an integration plus some additional terms (right side).*[8] If $g(x)$ is a polynomial, then the right side will consist of a finite number of terms because after a certain point all of the derivatives will be zero, and nothing more need be said. The results of Example 41 are contained in the above formula. If $g(x)$ is a common transcendental function, then the series on the right is indeed an infinite series, and in general, it need not converge. Even in cases like this, however, the Euler–Maclaurin summation formula is still very useful because it is found that the first few terms on the right provide what is called

[8]In a footnote Whittaker and Watson state that the formula was discovered by Euler in 1732. He communicated his result to Stirling who replied that it included his own theorem, and that the general theorem had also been discovered by Maclaurin. Euler, who by then was not particularly hard up for fame, later waived his claim to priority. There are many Euler formulas, but there is only one Euler–Maclaurin formula.

an "asymptotic approximation" to the sum on the left side.[9] Although asymptotic series are very interesting, we do not pursue this topic here; the interested reader is urged to consult any of the works by Hardy, Erdélyi, and Bromwich listed in the Annotated Bibliography.

There is a special application of the summation formula in statistical thermodynamics. You will recall from Example 14 that a quantity called the molecular partition function, Z, is defined as a summation over all of the energy states of a particular type for a system.

$$Z = \sum_i \exp\left(\frac{-\varepsilon_i}{kT}\right)$$

Example 42.   Find an expansion for the rotational partition function of a rigid rotor.

Answer.   The energy levels of a rigid rotor are given by

$$\varepsilon_J = \frac{J(J+1)h^2}{8\pi^2 I}$$

where J is the rotational quantum number and I is the moment of inertia. Because of the presence of degeneracy, a factor of $2J+1$ appears so that we have

$$Z_{\text{rot}} = \sum_{J=0}^{\infty} (2J+1)\exp\left(\frac{-J(J+1)h^2}{8\pi^2 IkT}\right).$$

[9] A series $\sum a_n(x-x_0)^n$ is an asymptotic expansion for $f(x)$ if for *each fixed n*, the following limit holds:

$$\lim_{x\to x_0}\left|\frac{f(x)-S_n(x)}{(x-x_0)^n}\right| = 0.$$

This says that for a given n, the difference between the function and the sum of the first $n+1$ terms vanishes to a higher order than the nth when x is very close to x_0. Note that this is not a statement about convergence; convergence tells what happens for a fixed x as $n\to\infty$. Here we specify and hold n fixed and look what happens as $x\to x_0$. An asymptotic series need not converge, and most of those encountered in applications don't. It is sometimes true of asymptotic series that the absolute error made in computing the sum function by discarding all terms after the nth is less than the magnitude of the $(n+1)$st term; this is what makes such series computationally useful, in spite of their divergence.

An interesting discussion of how obstreperous series such as $1-1+1-1+1-\cdots+$ or $1-2+3-4+5-\cdots+$, which according to criteria given in this chapter should diverge, are handled by modern theory unknown to mathematicians in Euler's time is given in F. Rhodes, "$1-1+1-1+\cdots = \frac{1}{2}$?", *Math. Gaz.*, **55**, 298 (1971).

From the Euler–Maclaurin summation formula one then has

$$Z_{rot} = \int_0^\infty (2J+1)\exp\left(\frac{-J(J+1)h^2}{8\pi^2IkT}\right)dJ + \tfrac{1}{2}(0+1)$$

$$+ \frac{1}{12}\left[\exp\left(\frac{-J(J+1)h^2}{8\pi^2IkT}\right)\left\{2-\left(\frac{h^2}{8\pi^2IkT}\right)(2J+1)^2\right\}\right]_0^\infty$$

$$- \frac{1}{720}[\text{terms of order } T^{-2}] + \cdots -$$

$$\cong \boxed{\frac{8\pi^2IkT}{h^2} + \frac{1}{3} + \frac{1}{12}\left(\frac{h^2}{8\pi^2IkT}\right)}.$$

At low temperatures, therefore, the correction should be important, but at high temperatures only the first term (that arises from the integral; recall Exercise 6 of Chapter 3) is important.

We can now get easily an important result by letting $g(x)=\ln x$ in the Euler–Maclaurin formula: there results (lower limit is now 1 instead of 0) the following:

$$\ln 1 + \ln 2 + \ln 3 + \ldots + \ln n = \int_1^n \ln x\, dx + \tfrac{1}{2}[\ln n + \ln 1]$$

$$+ \frac{1}{12}\left[\frac{1}{n}-1\right] - \frac{1}{720}\left[\frac{2}{n^3}-2\right] + \cdots -.$$

The left-hand side is just $\ln (n!)$, and for large n one has, therefore, after integration one approximate form due to the Scottish mathematician James Stirling (1692–1770):

$$\boxed{\ln(n!) \cong (n+\tfrac{1}{2})\ln n - \left(n - \frac{1}{12n} - \frac{11}{12}\right)}.$$

For very large n this is approximately $n\ln n - n$.

Example 43.   Estimate from Stirling's formula a value for 100!.

Answer. If we use the more accurate form above, we get

$$\ln(100!) \cong (100.5)\ln 100 - \left(100 - \tfrac{1}{1200} - \tfrac{11}{12}\right)$$

$$= 363.821.$$

Hence $100! = 9.3 \times 10^{157}$, a result that agrees well with the value given in the *Handbook of Chemistry and Physics* mathematics section. Use of the short form $n \ln n - n$ leads to the result $100! = 3.5 \times 10^{156}$, which is in error by a factor of about $1/30$. For n as large as Avogadro's number (as in Example 14), use of the short form causes no detectable error.

5 FOURIER SERIES

The simplest periodic processes that occur in Nature are those described by the sine or cosine function although, in fact, no real process can be exactly periodic because of the presence of gravity, friction, and other dissipative forces. Nevertheless, processes such as the oscillation of a pendulum and the vibration of a diatomic molecule over small amplitudes can be mathematically analyzed to a good degree of approximation as periodic. A periodic process is a process described by some function $f(x)$ that has the property that there exists a smallest and finite value of $2T$ such that $f(x) = f(x + 2T)$ for all allowed x. The process is then said to be periodic with a *least period* of $2T$. Thus for $f(x) = \tan x$, $2T = \pi$, and for $f(x) = \sin nx$, $2T = 2\pi/n$.

Not all periodic processes can be described by a function as simple as a sine function. Figure 4.5 shows some examples of more complex waveforms.

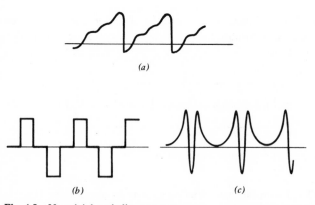

(a)

(b)   (c)

Fig. 4.5 Nontrivial periodic processes.

The idea occurred to the French mathematician Jean Baptiste Joseph Baron Fourier (1768–1830) to try to represent more complex processes such as these in terms of combinations of sines and/or cosines. The theorem to be stated allows us to do this under fairly general conditions, even for functions that have some discontinuities and cannot be represented by a single, analytic expression. The conditions stated in the theorem are generally referred to as *Dirichlet conditions*.

Theorem 14. *Suppose that*
(a) f(x) *is defined and single-valued except perhaps at a finite number of points in* $(-T, T)$;
(b) f(x) *is periodic outside* $(-T, T)$ *with period* $2T$;
(c) f(x) *and* f'(x) *are piecewise continuous in* $(-T, T)$.
Then the series

$$\tfrac{1}{2}a_0 + \sum_{n=1}^{\infty} \left(a_n \cos \frac{n\pi x}{T} + b_n \sin \frac{n\pi x}{T} \right)$$

where

$$a_n = \frac{1}{T} \int_{-T}^{T} f(x) \cos \frac{n\pi x}{T} dx$$

$$b_n = \frac{1}{T} \int_{-T}^{T} f(x) \sin \frac{n\pi x}{T} dx$$

converges to f(x) *if* x *is a point of continuity, and to* $[f(x\uparrow) + f(x\downarrow)]/2$ *if* x *is a point of discontinuity.*

The meaning of piecewise continuity is that a function in some interval consists of a finite number of continuous strips separated by finite discontinuities (see Figure 4.6). The notations $x\uparrow$ and $x\downarrow$ mean, respectively, x being approached from below and from above. The Fourier theorem says, in other words, that at a discontinuity the series converges to the midpoint.

It is important to realize that not all series of sines and cosines are Fourier series. In order to qualify as a Fourier series the coefficients must be given by the prescriptions stated in Theorem 14. To see how this comes about, recall from Section 3.6* that functions may be classed as odd, even, or neither. Since $\sin x$ is an odd function, the a_n's must be 0 if $f(x)$ is an odd function, and since $\cos x$ is an even function, the b_n's must be 0 if $f(x)$ is an even function. Otherwise, both a_n's and b_n's are needed to represent the function.

Let us take $f(x)$

$$f(x) = \tfrac{1}{2}a_0 + \sum_{n=1}^{\infty} \left(a_n \cos \frac{n\pi x}{T} + b_n \sin \frac{n\pi x}{T} \right)$$

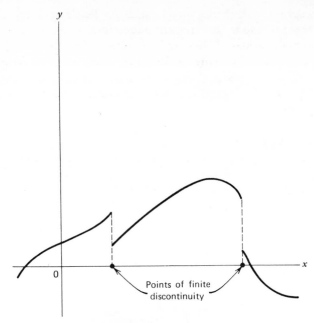

Fig. 4.6   Piecewise continuity.

and multiply both sides by $\cos(m\pi x/T)$, then integrate from $-T$ to T. The integer m must be positive.

$$\int_{-T}^{T} f(x)\cos\frac{m\pi x}{T}\,dx = \tfrac{1}{2}a_0\int_{-T}^{T}\cos\frac{m\pi x}{T}\,dx + \int_{-T}^{T}\sum_{n=1}^{\infty} a_n\cos\frac{n\pi x}{T}\cos\frac{m\pi x}{T}\,dx$$

$$+ \int_{-T}^{T}\sum_{n=1}^{\infty} b_n\sin\frac{n\pi x}{T}\cos\frac{m\pi x}{T}\,dx$$

On the right-hand side we have

1st integral

$$\tfrac{1}{2}a_0\int_{-T}^{T}\cos\frac{m\pi x}{T}\,dx = \frac{a_0 T\sin m\pi}{m\pi}$$

$$= 0 \text{ if } m\neq 0;$$

2nd integral

This is given, assuming the validity of term-by-term integration, by the expression

$$\sum_{n=1}^{\infty} a_n\left[\frac{\sin(n-m)\pi}{[(n\pi/T)-(m\pi/T)]} + \frac{\sin(n+m)\pi}{[(n\pi/T)+(m\pi/T)]}\right].$$

If $m \neq n$, the terms are zero since $\sin x$ has a zero every period of π. If $m = n$, the second term is 0, but the first term has the value $T \lim_{x \to 0}(\sin x / x)$, which by Theorem 3 is just T.

3rd integral

This is given by (again, assuming that integration and summation can be interchanged)

$$\sum_{n=1}^{\infty} b_n \left\{ \frac{\cos(m-n)\pi}{2[(n\pi/T)-(m\pi/T)]} + \frac{\cos(-m-n)\pi}{2[(n\pi/T)+(m\pi/T)]} \right.$$

$$\left. - \frac{\cos(n-m)\pi}{2[(n\pi/T)-(m\pi/T)]} - \frac{\cos(m+n)\pi}{2[(n\pi/T)+(m\pi/T)]} \right\}$$

and since $\cos x$ is an even function, this is identically 0.

It follows, then, that the required integral just has the value $a_m T$ when $n = m$. Hence the result is

$$a_n = \frac{1}{T} \int_{-T}^{T} f(x) \cos \frac{n\pi x}{T} dx$$

and similarly, it can be shown, after multiplying $f(x)$ by $\sin(m\pi x/T)$ and integrating, that

$$b_n = \frac{1}{T} \int_{-T}^{T} f(x) \sin \frac{n\pi x}{T} dx .$$

The first formula also shows that $a_0 = (1/T)\int_{-T}^{T} f(x)dx$, so that $\frac{1}{2}a_0$ is just the mean value of $f(x)$ over the period $(-T, T)$.

As an illustration of how to apply Theorem 14, consider the voltage output of a *square wave generator*. It is possible to build oscillators whose voltage output is not constant with time, but rather assumes the shape of a series of square pulses. Such oscillators enjoy wide use in electronic circuitry, and are discussed in standard texts on electronics (see, for example, W. C. Michels, *Electrical Measurements and Their Applications*, 2nd ed., Van Nostrand, Princeton, N. J., 1957, pp. 166–168).

Example 44. Voltage from a square wave generator takes the form

$$V(t) = \begin{cases} 3 & \text{if } 0 < t < 5 \\ 0 & \text{if } 5 < t < 10, \end{cases}$$

and so on, periodically. Represent this by a Fourier series.

Answer. The period is obviously 10; it can be considered to run from -5 to $+5$ since this interval has the same length as one from 0 to 10.

$$a_n = \tfrac{1}{5} \int_{-5}^{5} V(t)\cos\frac{n\pi t}{5}\, dt$$

$$= \tfrac{1}{5} \int_{-5}^{0} V(t)\cos\frac{n\pi t}{5}\, dt + \tfrac{1}{5} \int_{0}^{5} V(t)\cos\frac{n\pi t}{5}\, dt$$

$$= 0 + \tfrac{1}{5} \int_{0}^{5} 3\cos\frac{n\pi t}{5}\, dt$$

$$= \frac{3}{n\pi}\sin\frac{n\pi t}{5}\,\Big|_{0}^{5}$$

$$= 0 \ \text{if} \ n \neq 0.$$

For the case where $n = 0$, we have

$$a_0 = \tfrac{1}{5} \int_{-5}^{5} V(t)\, dt$$

$$= \tfrac{1}{5} \int_{0}^{5} 3\, dt$$

$$= 3.$$

A similar integration for the b_n's gives

$$b_n = \frac{3}{n\pi}(1 - \cos n\pi).$$

Hence the required Fourier series is

$$\boxed{\,V(t) = \frac{3}{2} + \frac{3}{\pi}\sum_{n=1}^{\infty}\frac{(1 - \cos n\pi)}{n}\sin\frac{n\pi t}{5}\,.}$$

Let us write out the first few terms of this series.

$$V(t) = \tfrac{3}{2} + \tfrac{3}{\pi}(1 - \cos\pi)\sin\frac{\pi t}{5} + \frac{3}{2\pi}(1 - \cos 2\pi)\sin\frac{2\pi t}{5}$$

$$+ \frac{3}{3\pi}(1 - \cos 3\pi)\sin\frac{3\pi t}{5} + \cdots +$$

$$= \tfrac{3}{2} + \tfrac{6}{\pi}\left(\sin\frac{\pi t}{5} + \tfrac{1}{3}\sin\frac{3\pi t}{5} + \tfrac{1}{5}\sin\pi t\right) + \cdots +.$$

To see how good an approximation this is, we plot this function for various values of the argument (see Figure 4.7). Each of the peaks and troughs actually consists of several maxima and minima, although the few data in Table 4.4 do not allow us to see this. The resemblance of the three-term series to the true voltage output (dashed sections) is striking. It is clear that addition of several more terms to the series could give a very close fit.

One can imagine the tumult created by series such as the one above when Fourier introduced them at a meeting of the French Academy in 1807 and later in 1822 in his book *Théorie Analytique de la Chaleur*. The superposition of an infinite sequence of the simplest continuous functions to give a discontinuous chain was hard to take![10]

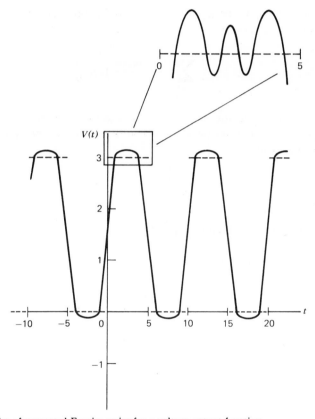

Fig. 4.7 Plot of truncated Fourier series for a voltage output function.

[10]For an interesting historical article see E. B. Van Vleck, "The Influence of Fourier's Series upon the Development of Mathematics," *Science*, **39**, 113 (1914).

Table 4.4   Data for a Fourier Series
Calculation

t	$V(t)$	t	$V(t)$
-5	1.50	5	1.50
-2.50	-0.15	6.25	-0.02
0	1.50	7.50	-0.15
1.25	3.02	8.75	-0.02
2.50	3.15	10	1.50
3.75	3.02		

We can actually get a bonus from our example above. At $t = 5/2$ the series must converge to $V(t) = 3$:

$$3 = \tfrac{3}{2} + \frac{3}{\pi} \sum_{n=1}^{\infty} \left(\frac{1 - \cos n\pi}{n} \right) \sin \frac{n\pi}{2}.$$

For even n the terms in the series are zero because of the sine function. For odd n, $\sin(n\pi/2)$ alternates between $+1$ and -1, but $\cos n\pi$ is always -1. Hence we can write

$$3 - \tfrac{3}{2} = \frac{3}{\pi} \sum_{k=0}^{\infty} \frac{2}{2k+1} (-1)^k,$$

which can be written our more explicitly as

$$\tfrac{1}{4}\pi = 1 - \tfrac{1}{3} + \tfrac{1}{5} - \tfrac{1}{7} + \tfrac{1}{9} - \tfrac{1}{11} + \cdots - .$$

This particular series is sometimes called *Gregory's series*. Thus with the aid of a Fourier series we have found the sum of a series that might otherwise be difficult to evaluate exactly.

We already know what conditions on $f(x)$ are needed to ensure that the Fourier series converge. What about operations on the series? Sums and differences of two convergent Fourier series must also give convergent series. Differentiation presents a problem, as we should expect from the discussion given in Section 4.2 on the differentiation of infinite series. The solution requires the concept of uniform convergence; however, we do know from material presented at the very beginning of this chapter that a necessary condition for convergence is that the last term go to zero. Consider the Fourier series from Example 44; if it is differentiated term-by-term with respect to t, then we get

$$g(t) = \frac{3}{5} \sum_{n=1}^{\infty} (1 - \cos n\pi) \cos \frac{n\pi t}{5}$$

and as $n \to \infty$ the nth term does not tend toward zero, but oscillates instead. Thus differentiation here is not valid. It is not hard to see that this results from our having lost the factor of n in the denominator of each term.

This should recall a statement we made earlier that differentiation generally slows down the convergence of a series. Roughly speaking, then, we could say that if the series of Fourier coefficients behaves something like a harmonic series, then differentiation is probably not possible. If the series of Fourier coefficients behaves like $1/n^2$, then this series can probably be differentiated once, but not twice, and so on.[11]

Integrations usually present less of a problem than differentiations because integration generally speeds up convergence of a series. A Fourier series can be integrated term-by-term from a to x if $f(x)$ is piecewise continuous in $(-T, T)$ and $-T < a < x < T$.

A generalization of Fourier series that is of great theoretical utility is the following. Fourier series may be considered to be compounded from the infinite set of functions

$$\frac{1}{\sqrt{2T}}, \frac{1}{\sqrt{T}} \sin \frac{n\pi x}{T}, \frac{1}{\sqrt{T}} \cos \frac{n\pi x}{T}, \frac{1}{\sqrt{T}} \sin \frac{2n\pi x}{T}, \frac{1}{\sqrt{T}} \cos \frac{2n\pi x}{T}, \ldots$$

This set is an example of what is called an *orthonormal set* on the interval $(-T, T)$. This means that if $f(x)$ and $g(x)$ are any two members from this set, then these functions are *orthogonal*

$$\int_{-T}^{T} f(x) g(x) dx = 0$$

and they are *normalized*

$$\int_{-T}^{T} [f(x)]^2 dx = \int_{-T}^{T} [g(x)]^2 dx = 1.$$

In Chapter 6 we will see that orthogonality is just a logical extension of the fact that the dot product of two perpendicular vectors is zero.

---

[11]More extensive remarks can be found in the article A. E. Taylor, "Differentiation of Fourier Series and Integrals," *Am. Math. Mon.*, **51**, 19 (1944).

Now, in general, any function that is well behaved can be expanded in an orthonormal set of functions $f_n(x)$

$$\psi(x) = \sum_{n=0}^{\infty} c_n f_n(x)$$

where the c_n coefficients are given by

$$c_n = \int_{-T}^{T} \psi(x) f_n(x) dx.$$

So you see that a Fourier series is simply a particular case of expanding some function in an orthonormal set. In Chapter 7 you will meet other functions (besides the simple trigonometric functions that make up a Fourier series) that constitute orthonormal sets and that can be used to expand functions in particular intervals. However, we mention in passing one use of orthonormal sets in chemistry, namely, that where the $f_n(x)$ may stand for atomic hydrogenic wave functions. If $\psi(x)$ is a molecular orbital, then in LCAO–MO theory (*l*inear *c*ombination of *a*tomic *o*rbitals) one expands $\psi(x)$ as a series of atomic orbital functions that are known to constitute an orthonormal set. Such a set must also be what is called *complete*; this guarantees that there will be enough members in the set to ensure expansion of any desired function defined on the interval of interest.

An alternative way of expressing a function as a Fourier series makes use of exponentials instead of sines and cosines. Recall that one can write

$$\cos \frac{n\pi t}{T} = \tfrac{1}{2}\left(e^{in\pi t/T} + e^{-in\pi t/T} \right)$$

$$\sin \frac{n\pi t}{T} = \frac{1}{2i}\left(e^{in\pi t/T} - e^{-in\pi t/T} \right).$$

The Fourier expansion of $F(t)$ can then be expressed as

$$F(t) = \tfrac{1}{2}a_0 + \sum_{n=1}^{\infty} \left[\underbrace{\tfrac{1}{2}a_n\left(e^{in\pi t/T} + e^{-in\pi t/T} \right)}_{\text{even}} + \underbrace{\frac{1}{2i}b_n\left(e^{in\pi t/T} - e^{-in\pi t/T} \right)}_{\text{odd}} \right]$$

Now the function $F(t)$ can, as mentioned in Section 3.6*, always be partitioned into an even part, $e(t)$, and an odd part, $o(t)$,

$$F(t) = e(t) + o(t)$$

having the properties

$$e(t) = e(-t)$$
$$o(t) = -o(-t).$$

Since the cosine is an even function, it follows that all the a_n terms go together to describe $e(t)$, and all the b_n terms represent $o(t)$.

Consider first the a_n terms:

$$\tfrac{1}{2}a_0 + \sum_{n=1}^{\infty} \tfrac{1}{2}a_n \left(e^{in\pi t/T} + e^{-in\pi t/T} \right).$$

These can be written in the shortened form

$$\tfrac{1}{2} \sum_{n=-\infty}^{\infty} a_n e^{in\pi t/T}$$

with $a_n = a_{-n}$; this relation among the a_n's is a reflection of the evenness of $e(t)$. The b_n terms can be written as

$$\frac{1}{2i} \sum_{n=1}^{\infty} b_n e^{in\pi t/T} - \frac{1}{2i} \sum_{n=1}^{\infty} b_n e^{-in\pi t/T}$$

and because of the oddness of $o(t)$ one can define $b_n = -b_{-n}$ (b_0 is then automatically zero), so that the above can be compressed to

$$\frac{1}{2i} \sum_{n=-\infty}^{\infty} b_n e^{in\pi t/T}.$$

The Fourier expansion of $F(t)$ as would normally be given by Theorem 14 is thus equivalent to

$$\boxed{F(t) = \sum_{n=-\infty}^{\infty} c_n e^{in\pi t/T}}$$

where the c_n coefficients are given by $c_n = \tfrac{1}{2}a_n - (1/2i)b_n$.

This is not a useful relation, however. Let us multiply $F(x)$ by $e^{-im\pi x/T}$ and integrate from $-T$ to T.

$$\int_{-T}^{T} e^{-im\pi x/T} F(x)\, dx = \sum_{n=-\infty}^{\infty} \int_{-T}^{T} c_n e^{i(n-m)\pi x/T} dx$$

$$= \sum_{n=-\infty}^{\infty} c_n \left[\frac{e^{i(n-m)\pi x/T}}{\left(\dfrac{i(n-m)\pi}{T}\right)} \right]_{-T}^{T}$$

$$= \sum_{n=-\infty}^{\infty} 2Tc_n \left[\frac{\sin(n-m)\pi}{\pi(n-m)} \right].$$

All terms in this series vanish except the one where $n = m$. For that term the expression in brackets is equal to unity. Hence we have, finally

$$\boxed{c_n = \frac{1}{2T}\int_{-T}^{T} e^{-in\pi x/T} F(x)\, dx}\,.$$

We are now in a position to respond to a point made in the last chapter regarding the relation between Fourier transforms and Fourier series. It is natural to inquire about a Fourier series when the length of the period becomes infinitely large. The following argument is not rigorous but is suggestive of what happens. From the two relations in the boxes above we write

$$F(t) = \sum_{n=-\infty}^{\infty} \frac{1}{2T}\int_{-T}^{T} F(x) e^{in\pi(t-x)/T} dx.$$

Make the substitution $\Delta\omega = \pi/T$:

$$F(t) = \frac{1}{2\pi} \sum_{n=-\infty}^{\infty} \Delta\omega \int_{-T}^{T} F(x) e^{in(t-x)\Delta\omega} dx.$$

Now we can look upon the integral as a function of $n\Delta\omega$, say, $h(n\Delta\omega)$.

$$F(t) = \frac{1}{2\pi} \sum_{n=-\infty}^{\infty} h(n\Delta\omega)\Delta\omega$$

But this summation is very much like one we would encounter in viewing an

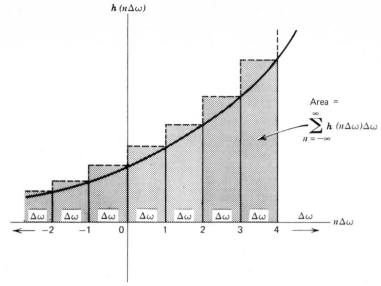

Fig. 4.8 The integral as a limit of a sum.

integral as an area under a curve (see Figure 4.8). If we let the width $\Delta\omega$ of the strips approach 0, then the shaded area should approach the area under the curve:

$$\int_{-\infty}^{\infty} h(\omega)\,d\omega = \lim_{\Delta\omega\to 0} \sum_{n=-\infty}^{\infty} h(n\Delta\omega)\Delta\omega.$$

Hence it follows that as $T\to\infty$, the expression for $F(t)$ above should pass over into

$$F(t) = \frac{1}{2\pi}\int_{-\infty}^{\infty} d\omega \int_{-\infty}^{\infty} F(x)e^{i\omega(t-x)}\,dx$$

$$= \frac{1}{2\pi}\int_{-\infty}^{\infty} e^{i\omega t}\,d\omega \int_{-\infty}^{\infty} F(x)e^{-i\omega x}\,dx.$$

If we designate the integral over x as $f(\omega)$, then we have

$$F(t) = \frac{1}{2\pi}\int_{-\infty}^{\infty} f(\omega)e^{i\omega t}\,d\omega \; .$$

Thus we see that except possibly for a definitional, multiplicative constant, a Fourier transform $F(t)$ is nothing more than a Fourier series of a function taken to the limit where the function is not periodic (that is, the period has increased without bound).

EXERCISES

1. The notations $\sum_j \sum_i$ and $\sum_{i,j}$ are identical, and you will see both in books. By writing out some of the terms, demonstrate that $\sum_{i,j} x_i y_j$ does not mean the same thing as $\sum x_i y_i$.

2. Find the general term for each of the following sets of numbers:
    (a) $0, 1, 0, 1, 0, 1, \ldots, a_n, \ldots$
    (b) $\frac{1}{2}, -\frac{1}{4}, \frac{1}{8}, -\frac{1}{16}, \frac{1}{32}, \ldots, a_n, \ldots$
    (c) $1, 3, 7, 15, 31, \ldots, a_n, \ldots$
    (d) $2, 2, \frac{8}{6}, \frac{16}{24}, \frac{32}{120}, \ldots, a_n, \ldots$

3. Consider the following series: $\sum_{n=1}^{\infty} (-1)^{n+1} \cos \frac{1}{2} n\pi x$. Is there any hope of this series converging or not?

4. Mark the following statements as always true (T) or not always true (F):
    (a) If all the partial sums of a series are less than some constant L, then the series converges;
    (b) If a series does not converge, then its nth term does not approach 0 as n tends to infinity;
    (c) If $\sum_n a_n$ and $\sum_n b_n$ are two series and $a_n < b_n$ for all n, and $\sum_n b_n$ is convergent, then so is $\sum_n a_n$.

5. It is sometimes necessary to take a given series

    $$y = a_1 x + a_2 x^2 + a_3 x^3 + \cdots +$$

    and find the coefficients of the inverted series

    $$x = A_1 y + A_2 y^2 + A_3 y^3 + \cdots +.$$

    Find expressions for A_1, A_2, and A_3 as functions of the a's.

6. In Planck's theory of the blackbody radiation the following integral had to be evaluated:

    $$\int_{\infty}^{0} \frac{dx}{x^5(e^{1/x} - 1)}.$$

    Show that this integral is $6\zeta(4)$ and hence $\pi^4/15$ (recall Example 32).

7. Do the following series converge?

(a) $\displaystyle\sum_{n=1}^{\infty} \frac{1}{\sqrt[3]{n}}$ (e) $\displaystyle\sum_{n=1}^{\infty} \frac{n}{n^2+1}$

(b) $\displaystyle\sum_{n=0}^{\infty} \frac{e^n}{n!}$ (f) $\displaystyle\sum_{n=0}^{\infty} \frac{10^n}{(n!)^{2n}}$

(c) $\displaystyle\sum_{n=1}^{\infty} \frac{n^n}{n!}$ (g) $\displaystyle\sum_{n=0}^{\infty} e^{-n^2}$

(d) $\displaystyle\sum_{n=2}^{\infty} \frac{1}{n\ln n}$ (h) $\displaystyle\sum_{n=1}^{\infty} (-1)^n \frac{n\ln n}{e^n}$

8. Take the statement of the mean value theorem given in the text, $f(x)=f(a)+f'(x_1)(x-a)$, solve it for $f'(x_1)$, and then interpret your expression geometrically.

9. Carry through the steps in the derivation of Taylor's formula from the function $G(x)$ given in the text.

10. Write the first few terms of the Taylor series expansion of
(a) $\tan\theta$ about $\theta=\frac{1}{4}\pi$ (b) e^x about $x=2$.

11. Show that the ratio test fails for the series

$$\sum_{n=1}^{\infty} \frac{1}{n(n+1)(n+2)}.$$

Although the integral test can be applied with a little labor, convince yourself that the series does converge by actually working out the sum.

12. In the Maclaurin series for e^x, let $x=i\theta$. What does the result simplify to? Now let $\theta=\pi$, and deduce a famous identity first discovered by Euler.

13. Using the identity $a^x = e^{x\ln a}$, obtain the Maclaurin series expansion for a^x. Then show how this may be used as an alternative to Theorem 3 to evaluate the following limit ($a,b,c,d>0$ and $c\neq d$).

$$\lim_{x\to 0} \frac{a^x - b^x}{c^x - d^x}$$

14. Without the use of a slide rule or a table of logarithms, work out approximate values of $e^{0.20}$ and $1/\sqrt[5]{35}$.

15. Making use of the series expansion for $\sin^{-1}x$, estimate a value for pi. For a practical calculation to a few decimal places, why is use of this series preferred to use of the series for $\tan^{-1}x$? Why would the latter be preferred for a more accurate computation to several decimal places?

16. Provide an estimate of the Fresnel integral $\int_0^1 \sin(x^2)\,dx$, and compare your value with a tabulated one.

17. John Wallis (1616–1703), a contemporary of Isaac Newton, derived a relation which bears his name:

$$\tfrac{1}{2}\pi = \tfrac{2}{1}\cdot\tfrac{2}{3}\cdot\tfrac{4}{3}\cdot\tfrac{4}{5}\cdot\tfrac{6}{5}\cdot\tfrac{6}{7}\cdot\tfrac{8}{7}\cdots$$

$$= \prod_{n=1}^{\infty} \frac{(2n)^2}{(2n-1)(2n+1)}\,.$$

Using Wallis' formula express $\ln\pi$ as an infinite series. How useful would this series be as a method of evaluating π?

18. Consult your freshman text (or other text) for a picture of the unit cell of KCl (or NaCl). The lattice is a face-centered cubic array; now focus attention on the central Cl^- ion. It is surrounded by 6 nearest-neighbor cations at a distance R; the electrostatic interaction is thus $-6e^2/R$. Then there are 12 neighbors at $R\sqrt{2}$, followed by 8 at $R\sqrt{3}$, then 6 at $2R$, and so on. The contribution to the electrostatic part of the crystal lattice energy due to this central Cl^- ion can thus be written as

$$L = \frac{-e^2}{R}\left(6 - \frac{12}{\sqrt{2}} + \frac{8}{\sqrt{3}} - 3 + \cdots - \right)$$

$$= -\alpha e^2/R.$$

The constant α is called the *Madelung constant* (after E. Madelung, 1918) and it has been tabulated for various lattice systems. Now the series above converges *very* slowly, and indeed a formula for the nth term of the series is not obvious [see H. M. Evjen, *Phys. Rev.*, **39**, 675 (1932)], so let us examine a simpler system. Suppose we have 1 mole of a one-dimensional solid of stoichiometric formula AB, which consists of alternating monopositive and mononegative ions separated by a distance R. What is the total electrostatic contribution to the molar lattice energy for this hypothetical system? Do not attempt to do this same kind of calculation for a two-dimensional solid.

19. Using the properties of convergent alternating series show that the sum of the first two terms for the Maclaurin series for $\cos x$ will provide an estimate good to three decimal places for $x < 19°$; that the first three terms will provide an estimate good to three decimal places for $x < 48°$.

(Hint: "good to three decimal places" means a computational error of less than 0.0005.)

20. Let the symbol H_n stand for the nth harmonic sum, that is, $1 + \frac{1}{2} + \frac{1}{3} + \cdots + (1/n)$. Then with the aid of the formula for the multiplication of two series, show the following:

$$(|x| < 1) \qquad \frac{\ln(1+x)}{1+x} = \sum_{n=1}^{\infty} (-1)^{n+1} H_n x^n.$$

21. Show how the alternating harmonic series can be rearranged to give an infinite series with a sum of unity. How many terms have to be rearranged in order to accomplish this?

22. Show that if n and m are positive integers, then

$$\frac{1}{n} - \frac{1}{n+m} + \frac{1}{n+2m} - \cdots + = \int_0^1 \frac{t^{n-1}dt}{1+t^m}.$$

Then use this result to sum the series

$$1 - \tfrac{1}{4} + \tfrac{1}{7} - \tfrac{1}{10} + \cdots - .$$

23. Evaluate the sums of the following series:

(a) $\displaystyle\sum_{n=0}^{\infty} \frac{1}{3^{2n}}$

(d) $\displaystyle\sum_{n=0}^{\infty} e^{-zn}$

(b) $\displaystyle\sum_{n=10}^{150} (2n+1)$

(e) $\displaystyle\sum_{n=0}^{\infty} \frac{1}{n!(n+3)}$

(c) $\displaystyle\sum_{n=1}^{\infty} \left(\tan^{-1}n - \tan^{-1}(n-1) \right)$

(f) $0.343434\ldots$

(g) $\displaystyle\sum_{n=0}^{\infty} \frac{(-1)^n x^{3n+1}}{3n+1} \qquad (0 \leqslant x < 1)$

24. A body with a rest mass m_0 and moving at a speed near that of light, as in the case of an electron close to the nucleus of a heavy atom, has a kinetic energy given by the relativistic formula

$$K = m_0 c^2 \left[\frac{1}{\sqrt{1 - (v^2/c^2)}} - 1 \right].$$

Express K as a series in v and then show that for $v \ll c$ it reduces to the usual nonrelativistic expression.

25. Here is another example of a relativistic formula which reduces to a familiar Newtonian relation when one is dealing with ordinary velocities. Suppose a force F acts on a body, initially at rest, for a time t. (a) Show that the velocity of the body is given by

$$v = c \left[1 + \left(\frac{m_0 c}{Ft} \right)^2 \right]^{-\frac{1}{2}} .$$

(Hint: use force equals time derivative of the linear momentum; then separate variables and integrate.)
(b) Then show that if $Ft \ll m_0 c$, one has the familiar expression

$$Ft = m_0 v.$$

impulse = momentum

26. Write in compact form the infinite series representations of

$$(a) \quad \cot \theta \qquad (b) \quad \ln(\sec \theta + \tan \theta).$$

27. The equation of state of a real gas can be expressed generally by a power series in the density as follows:

$$\frac{PV}{nRT} = \sum_{k=0}^{\infty} c_{k+1}(T) \left[\frac{n}{V} \right]^k .$$

The coefficients, $c_{k+1}(T)$, are referred to as the *virial coefficients*, and they can obviously be determined experimentally. They are important because they allow one to test the goodness of various theories of gases. Deduce the form of the second virial coefficient for a van der Waals gas, and then compute it for CO_2 at $87°C$ (see Exercise 11 of Chapter 2). Compare with the experimental value of -75 ml mole^{-1} (datum of K. E. MacCormack and W. G. Schneider as quoted in J. O. Hirschfelder, C. F. Curtiss, and R. B. Bird, *Molecular Theory of Gases and Liquids*, Wiley, New York, 1954, p. 202).

28. Make use of the identity

$$\sum_{k=1}^{\infty} \frac{1}{k^{2n}} = \frac{(-1)^{n+1}(2\pi)^{2n} B_{2n}}{2(2n)!}$$

and evaluate the infinite series $3^{-4} + 5^{-4} + 7^{-4} + 9^{-4} + \cdots +$.

29. Another commonly used equation of state for a gas is the *Dieterici equation*:

$$P(V - nb) = nRTe^{-an/RTV}$$

where a, b are the usual van der Waals constants. From this work out the form of the third virial coefficient (see Exercise 27 above).

30. Work out the Euler number E_6 and show that its value is indeed -61.

31. If $1 + 2^{-2} + 3^{-2} + 4^{-2} + \cdots + = \pi^2/6$, then what is the value of the sum of the series $3^{-2} + 5^{-2} + 7^{-2} + \cdots +$?

32. Calculate the percent error in estimating the value of 10! by the use of Stirling's formula.

33. Work through in detail all the steps in Example 42 in the expansion of the rotational partition function by means of the Euler–Maclaurin summation formula. Now suppose you have a diatomic molecule with a moment of inertia, I, equal to $3 \times 10^{-40} \mathrm{g\,cm^2}$. At what temperature will the second term in the expansion (the $1/3$) represent a 20% correction to the value given by the integral? At this same temperature how big of a correction will the third term in the expansion amount to?

34. The voltage from a *sawtooth generator* (see, for example, H. V. Malmstadt, C. G. Enke, and E. C. Toren, *Electronics for Scientists*, Benjamin, New York, 1962, pp. 235–236) has a period of 1 and may be represented by the equation $V(t) = 2t + 1$ $(0 < t < 1)$. Sketch what this output looks like, and then work out the Fourier series representation. Finally, take the first few terms of this series and plot the resulting approximate function.

35. Show that the set of functions $1/\sqrt{2T}$, $(1/\sqrt{T})\sin(n\pi x/T)$, $(1/\sqrt{T})\cos(n\pi x/T)$, etc. which was given in the text is an orthonormal set of functions.

36.* Let the arithmetic mean of the products of all distinct pairs of positive integers whose sum is S be denoted by M_S. Is the limit of M_S/S^2 as S approaches infinity equal to $1/6$?

37.* If the Taylor series expansion of a function $f(x,u)$ expanded in powers of u is

$$f(x,u) = P_0(x) + P_1(x)u + P_2(x)u^2 + \cdots +$$

then $f(x,u)$ is called a *generating function* for the sequence of functions $P_0(x)$, $P_1(x)$, $P_2(x),\ldots$. In the quantum mechanical description of the harmonic oscillator, functions known as the *Hermite polynomials* play an important role. They can be obtained from the generating function

$$f(x,u) = \exp(-u^2 + 2ux) = \sum_{n=0}^{\infty} \frac{H_n(x)u^n}{n!}.$$

(*a*) Deduce the second and fourth Hermite polynomials, $H_1(x)$ and $H_3(x)$.

(*b*) The Hermite polynomials can also be obtained from the differential relationship (referred to as a *Rodrigues' formula*)

$$H_n(x) = (-1)^n \exp(x^2) \frac{d^n}{dx^n} \exp(-x^2).$$

Show that $H_3(x)$ obtained in this way is identical with that from part (*a*) above. We will have more to say about the Hermite polynomials in the next chapter, where we view them as the solutions to a particular differential equation.

38.* Another set of functions that can be defined by means of a generating function are the *Laguerre polynomials*; they are useful in writing the wave functions for the hydrogen atom. Their generating function is

$$f(x,u) = \frac{e^{-xu(1-u)^{-1}}}{1-u} = \sum_{n=0}^{\infty} \frac{L_n(x)u^n}{n!}.$$

Deduce from this $L_3(x)$. We will meet the Laguerre polynomials again in the discussion of special functions in Chapter 7.

39.* In Exercise 24 at the end of Chapter 3 you showed that the heat capacity of a Debye crystal is given by

$$C_v = \frac{9R}{\tau^3}\left[4\int_0^{\tau} \frac{x^3 dx}{e^x - 1} - \frac{\tau^4}{e^{\tau} - 1} \right]$$

where $\tau = h\nu_{max}/kT$. At *very low temperatures* show that one has, approximately

$$C_v = \frac{234Rk^3T^3}{(h\nu_{max})^3}.$$

In what way is this consistent with the third law of thermodynamics?

40.* According to a theory known as the *Bloch–Grüneisen theory*, the electrical resistance of a monovalent metal is approximated by

$$\rho = C \frac{T^5}{\theta^6} \int_0^{\theta/T} \frac{x^5 dx}{(e^x - 1)(1 - e^{-x})}$$

where C is a collection of constants and θ is the so-called Debye temperature of the metal (also a constant). Show that for high T the resistance is roughly linear in T, and for very low T it depends on T^5.

41.* Recall from classical theory that a linear oscillator of reduced mass μ which vibrates in simple harmonic motion according to $F = -\beta(r - r_0)$ has potential energy $\frac{1}{2}\beta(r - r_0)^2$ and vibrational frequency $\nu_0 = (1/2\pi)\sqrt{\beta/\mu}$. Now let us suppose that we have a diatomic molecule whose equilibrium separation is r_0 and whose vibrational behavior we wish to approximate by that of a harmonic oscillator.

(a) Write, in the *general* case, the first three nonzero terms of the Taylor series expansion about $r = r_0$ of the potential energy function $U(r)$, and then derive from this a formula for ν_0 for a harmonic oscillator.

(b) P. M. Morse in 1929 proposed a potential energy function for diatomic molecules which led to predictions for the vibrational energy levels that were in good agreement with experimental spectra. Morse's equation is a function of the instantaneous internuclear spacing r, the dissociation energy D, the equilibrium separation r_0, and one empirical parameter, a.

$$U(r) = D\left\{1 - \exp[-a(r - r_0)]\right\}^2$$

Show that the vibrational frequency for *small* displacements is [on the basis of your answer to part (a)] given by

$$\nu_0 = \frac{a}{2\pi}\sqrt{\frac{2D}{\mu}} \quad .$$

(c) To get a feeling for typical values of a, calculate it for HCl given that $D = 102.0$ kcal mole,$^{-1}$ $r_0 = 1.275 Å$, and the wave number for the fundamental vibrational transition is 2990 cm^{-1} (data from G. Herzberg, *The Spectra of Diatomic Molecules*, 2nd ed., Van Nostrand, Princeton, N. J., 1950).

42.** In a previous problem (Exercise 28 of Chapter 3) you determined the second virial coefficient for a gas composed of spherically symmetric molecules interacting by a square-well potential. Another common potential is the *Sutherland* $(\infty,6)$ *potential*.

$$U(r) = \begin{cases} \infty & r < \sigma \\ -\varepsilon\left(\dfrac{\sigma}{r}\right)^6 & r > \sigma \end{cases}$$

Make a plot of this potential energy function and interpret ε and σ. Now use this potential to work out $B(T)$; write only the first three terms of the series. How does your $B(T)$.result compare in form with that for a van der Waals gas?

43.** The *Boyle temperature*, T_B, of a gas is that temperature at which the second virial coefficient $B(T)$ is zero. Using your three-term expression for $B(T)$ from above, estimate T_B for argon. Recent studies by A. E. Sherwood and J. M. Prausnitz (*J. Chem. Phys.*, **41**, 429 (1964)) give $\varepsilon = 0.606$ kcal mole.$^{-1}$ Compare your answer with the experimental Boyle temperature of $411°K$. Repeat your calculation for T_B using a four-term expression for $B(T)$ in order to see what effect an extra term in the series expansion has on the value of the temperature.

44.** Consider the function defined as follows:

$$f(x) = \begin{cases} 0 & \text{if } x = 0 \\ e^{-1/x^2} & \text{if } x \neq 0. \end{cases}$$

Is this function continuous at $x = 0$? Refer to the beginning of Chapter 2 for what is meant by continuity. Show that $f(x)$ has a first derivative at $x = 0$; what about higher derivatives? Now write out the Taylor series expansion of $f(x)$ about the point $x = 0$. Does the Taylor series expansion converge to the value of the function at $x = 0$? What about at other values of x?

45.** The difference between two quantities, both of which increase without bound, may or may not be finite. The nth harmonic sum, H_n, for example, and the natural logarithm, $\ln n$, both tend to infinity as $n \to \infty$. It is known, however, that their difference tends to some finite number, γ, as $n \to \infty$.

$$\lim_{n \to \infty} \left[1 + \tfrac{1}{2} + \tfrac{1}{3} + \tfrac{1}{4} + \cdots + \tfrac{1}{n} - \ln n \right] = \gamma$$

This number is called the *Euler–Mascheroni constant* and it occurs occasionally in applications. Show how to express γ as a series involving Bernoulli numbers, and that its value is about 0.578 (more exactly, 0.5772). Interestingly, it is not known whether γ is rational or irrational.

46.** Show mathematically that the peaks and troughs in Figure 4.7 actually consist of several local maxima and minima. Determine their number, their positions, and also the magnitude of their overshoots and undershoots.

FIVE

Differential Equations

1 SOME FIRST-ORDER TYPES

Some time around the turn of the seventeenth century Isaac Newton was studying the rate of cooling of substances. He discovered a simple reasonably accurate law that one can verify easily in the laboratory. I have done so by taking a 150-ml sample of methanol in a glass beaker, warming it to about 50°C, and then following its temperature in the interior as a function of time as the contents gradually cooled in a room whose temperature (T_0) was 23.2°C. The data presented in Table 5.1 were plotted as $\ln(T - T_0)$ versus t. The graph, that is shown in Figure 5.1, is a straight line with slope -6.60×10^{-2} min^{-1}. What does this tell us? The plot may be expressed by

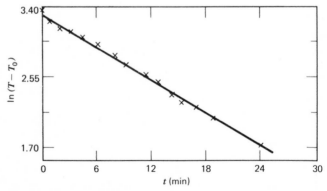

Fig. 5.1 Newton's law plot for a liquid.

the relation

$$\ln(T - T_0) = -kt + b$$

and if this is differentiated with respect to t one gets

$$\frac{dT}{dt} = -k(T - T_0).$$

This is *Newton's law of cooling*. It says that the rate of cooling of a substance is proportional to the instantaneous difference between the temperature of the substance and the external temperature.

Table 5.1   Newton's Law Cooling Data

$T(°C)$	t (min)	$T(°C)$	t (min)
51.0	0.0	36.3	11.0
49.3	1.0	35.1	12.5
47.0	2.0	34.0	14.0
46.0	3.0	33.0	15.5
43.7	4.5	32.1	17.0
41.6	6.0	31.3	18.5
39.7	7.5	28.8	24.0
38.2	9.0		

What we have here is historically one of the first differential equations to arise of Western science; Newton, of course, discovered it empirically.[1] It is almost a truism to say that since Newton's time nearly all of Western physical science has been formulated in the language of differential equations.

---

[1]"For the heat which heated iron gives up to cold bodies in contact with it in a given time, that is, the heat which iron loses in a certain time, is as the whole heat of the iron,..."

The word "heat" here means temperature today. This extract is taken from a manuscript of Newton's which was published with slight modifications and without his name in *Phil. Trans.*, **22**, 824–829 (1701) under the title "Scala Graduum Caloris. Caloris Descriptiones & Signa." It is one of his very few published works of a chemical nature, despite the fact that Newton was interested in chemistry all his life. See J. F. Scott (ed.), *The Correspondence of Isaac Newton*, Vol. IV (1694–1709), Cambridge University Press, Cambridge, 1967, pp. 363–365, for a translation from Latin into English of the article.

It should be pointed out that the law holds well only for small ranges of temperature. The proportionality constant k in the law is a function of the liquid and various mechanical aspects of the experiment such as the nature of the material which forms the container and the presence of convection currents.

The differential equation above is what is called a *first-order, linear, ordinary differential equation*. There is an extensive terminology for classifying differential equations because mathematicians eventually gave up hope of trying to find a general method for solving all the various types of differential equations. A brief breakdown, that is by no means as detailed as it could be and that is also not a perfect classification into mutually exclusive groups, is given in Figure 5.2. We do not attempt to say something about all of them, but instead look at some of the more frequently occurring types.

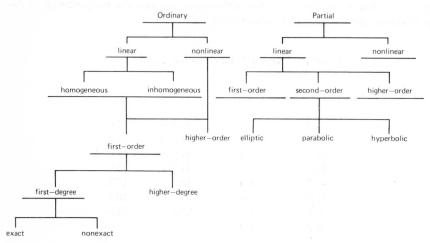

Fig. 5.2   Types of differential equations.

Differential equations that contain partial derivatives are called *partial differential equations*; otherwise, they are referred to as *ordinary*. The *order* of a differential equation is the order of the highest-ordered derivative present. The *degree* of a differential equation is the algebraic degree of its highest-ordered derivative after any rationalization of the equation has been performed. Thus the equation

$$\frac{d^2y}{dx^2} + xy = (1 - x)^{1/3} \frac{dy}{dx}$$

is of the second-order and first-degree, whereas the equation

$$\frac{d^2y}{dx^2} + xy = \left[(1 - x) \frac{dy}{dx} \right]^{1/3}$$

is of the second-order and third-degree because upon rationalization the equation becomes

$$\left(\frac{d^2y}{dx^2}\right)^3 + 3xy\left(\frac{d^2y}{dx^2}\right)^2 + 3x^2y^2\left(\frac{d^2y}{dx^2}\right) + x^3y^3 = (1-x)\frac{dy}{dx}.$$

Differential equations of the first-order and first-degree are obviously the simplest type possible, and we begin with them. This type of equation may be expressed in the form

$$\frac{dy}{dx} = f(x,y).$$

If $f(x,y)$ is linear in y, then the equation is a first-order, linear, differential equation; otherwise the equation is nonlinear. Newton's law of cooling is a linear equation. Mathematicians have investigated the conditions under which certain types of differential equations have solutions. We do not look at this question in much detail here but merely give for the first-order differential equation of the first degree a qualitative plausibility argument. The interested reader is referred to pertinent works in the Annotated Bibliography.

We begin by supposing that the function $f(x,y)$ possesses certain nice properties. First, it is bounded in some region R of the xy plane; this means that for all (x,y) in R, the function is equal to or less than some constant M, and does not go shooting off to infinity.

$$|f(x,y)| \leqslant M$$

Next, the function is continuous in R for x and y together. The definition of continuity of a function of two variables reads similarly to the definition of continuity of a function of one variable. If $(x_n,y_n),\ldots,(x_2,y_2)$, (x_1,y_1) is a sequence of points that approach a given fixed point (x_0,y_0), and if

$$\lim_{(x_n,y_n)\to(x_0,y_0)} f(x_n,y_n) = f(x_0,y_0)$$

regardless of how the initial sequence of points is constructed (that is, regardless of the direction of approach), then the function $f(x,y)$ is said to be continuous in x and y together at the point (x_0,y_0).

Let us now select some point (x_0,y_0) in R. At this point we compute the derivative; the derivative is uniquely determined because the differential equation reads

$$\frac{dy}{dx} = f(x,y).$$

Now we move away from (x_0, y_0) by a very short distance and in the direction specified by the derivative. At this new point, (x_1, y_1), we again compute the derivative and use this to move a short distance away to still another point. We may continue this process so long as we stay in R. The result is a curve made up of a series of short line segments. It is plausible to suppose that in the limit as these line segments become smaller and smaller, we will have a continuous, smooth curve $y = y(x)$ passing through the point (x_0, y_0) and one that is a solution to the differential equation. This limit can be shown to exist if the partial derivative $\partial f(x,y)/\partial y$ is bounded. Finally, since $f(x,y)$ is continuous and $y = y(x)$ exists and is also continuous, then the function of one variable $f[x, y(x)]$ is continuous and hence can be integrated so as to allow one to arrive at the form of $y(x)$.

Theorem 15. *In a region* R *let* f(x,y) *and* ∂ f(x,y)$/\partial$y *be bounded and continuous. Then through the point* (x_0, y_0) *interior to* R *there is a solution curve* y = y(x) *that satisfies the differential equation* y′ = f(x,y).

The content of this theorem is shown in Figure 5.3. Note that since the function $f(x,y)$ is bounded, it follows that $|dy/dx| \leqslant M$, and thus the solution curve must lie in the shaded portion. We emphasize that the conditions of Theorem 15 are extremely general.

An interesting class of first-order, first-degree, differential equations are those that are termed *exact*. Suppose, for generality, that

$$f(x,y) = -\frac{g(x,y)}{h(x,y)} .$$

Then the differential equation can be written

$$g(x,y)dx + h(x,y)dy = 0.$$

If the differential $g(x,y)dx + h(x,y)dy$ is expressible in the form $dU(x,y)$, then the original differential equation is termed exact and its solution is

$$U(x,y) = \text{constant}.$$

You will recognize that this is the same concept that was introduced in discussion of exact differentials in Section 2.3. The condition that $g(x,y)dx + h(x,y)dy$ be exact is

$$\frac{\partial g(x,y)}{\partial y} = \frac{\partial h(x,y)}{\partial x} .$$

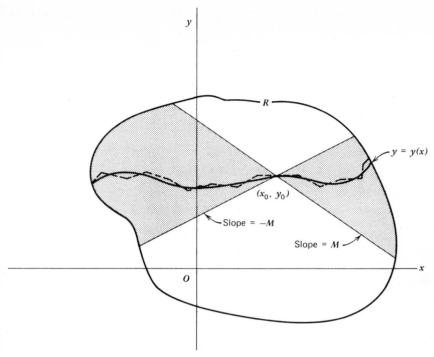

Fig. 5.3   Region of existence.

As a simple case consider the differential equation

$$\frac{dy}{dx} = \frac{x+2y}{y-2x}$$

which may be written in the form

$$(x+2y)dx + (2x-y)dy = 0.$$

In this form the differential equation is seen to be exact since

$$\frac{\partial}{\partial y}(x+2y) = \frac{\partial}{\partial x}(2x-y)$$

$$= 2.$$

Hence by the previous discussion there should be a function $U(x,y)$ such that

$$\frac{\partial U(x,y)}{\partial x} = x+2y \qquad \frac{\partial U(x,y)}{\partial y} = 2x-y.$$

To find $U(x,y)$ we integrate, holding y constant in the first case and holding x constant in the second case:

$$U(x,y) = \tfrac{1}{2}x^2 + 2xy + G(y)$$

$$U(x,y) = -\tfrac{1}{2}y^2 + 2xy + H(x).$$

Inspection shows that these are consistent if

$$G(y) = -\tfrac{1}{2}y^2 + \tfrac{1}{2}c$$

$$H(x) = \tfrac{1}{2}x^2 + \tfrac{1}{2}c$$

where c is a constant. Hence the solution to the differential equation is $U(x,y) = $ constant, or

$$y^2 - 4xy - x^2 = C.$$

If desired this can be solved for y explicitly to give

$$y = 2x + \sqrt{5x^2 + C} .$$

In some cases however the degree of the equation may prevent one from being able to solve for the dependent variable.

The solution above is referred to as a *general solution*; a general solution of a differential equation is a solution that contains a number of arbitrary (unspecified) constants equal to the order of the differential equation. A *particular solution* is one that does not contain any unspecified constants; it can be obtained from the general solution by assigning values to the arbitrary constants.[2] One way of accomplishing this is by imposing *boundary conditions* on the original differential equation. Thus in the example above if we impose the condition that $y(0) = 1$, then we have

$$y^2 - 4xy - x^2 = 1$$

and a particular solution of the differential equation is

$$y = 2x + \sqrt{5x^2 + 1} .$$

---

[2]Some solutions to a differential equation may not be obtainable from the general solution by assignment of values to the arbitrary constants. These are often referred to as *singular solutions*. A singular solution has the property, however, that its graph is tangent to every solution in the general solution family. Many differential equations arising in physical applications do not have a singular solution.

Exact differential equations are apt to arise in thermodynamics, because as was pointed out in Section 3.5 the thermodynamic differentials dE, dH, dS, dA, and dG are exact differentials. This in turn is a consequence of the path independence of the line integrals of these quantities (see Theorem 8).

A special case of the exact differential equation occurs when $g(x,y)$ is a function of x alone, and $h(x,y)$ is a function of y alone. The equation is then said to be of the *variables separable* type, and a general solution can be found immediately by integration. Variables separable differential equations are extremely common.

Example 45. The methylation of trimethylamine with methyl iodide follows the rate law

$$\frac{d[(CH_3)_3N]}{dt} = -k[(CH_3)_3N][CH_3I].$$

Solve the differential equation so as to find $[(CH_3)_3N]$ as a function of time.

Answer. The chemical reaction is

$$(CH_3)_3N + CH_3I \xrightarrow{k} (CH_3)_4N^+ + I^-$$
$$\quad A_0 \qquad\quad B_0$$

where A_0 and B_0 represent the initial concentrations of reactants. Let the variable x be the concentration of amine that has reacted. Then the differential equation becomes

$$\frac{d(A_0 - x)}{dt} = -k(A_0 - x)(B_0 - x)$$

or

$$\frac{-1}{(A_0 - x)(B_0 - x)}\, dx + k\, dt = 0.$$

This is clearly a variables separable equation. Integration by means of partial fractions (see Example 17) gives

$$\frac{1}{B_0 - A_0} \ln(A_0 - x) + \frac{1}{A_0 - B_0} \ln(B_0 - x) + kt = c.$$

To find the integration constant c we impose the boundary condition that $x = 0$ when $t = 0$. Then $c = [1/(A_0 - B_0)]\ln(B_0/A_0)$ and the solution to the equation becomes

$$kt = \frac{1}{A_0 - B_0} \ln \left[\frac{B_0(A_0 - x)}{A_0(B_0 - x)} \right].$$

If this is solved for the concentration of amine, we get

$$\ln[(CH_3)_3N] = (A_0 - B_0)kt + \ln[CH_3I] + \ln \frac{A_0}{B_0}.$$

According to this a plot of $\ln\{[(CH_3)_3N]/[CH_3I]\}$ versus time should give a straight line of slope $k(A_0 - B_0)$ (Figure 5.4). Since A_0 and B_0 are known, a plot made in this way would permit the evaluation of the experimental rate constant k.

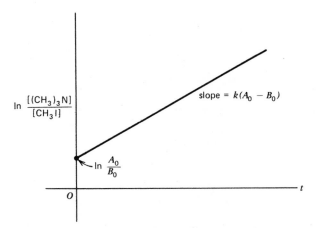

Fig. 5.4 Finding the rate constant of a second-order reaction.

Some differential equations that do not appear to be of the variables separable type can be made so by simple substitutions. These differential equations we shall call *reducible*. For example, consider the equation

$$\frac{dy}{dx} = \tfrac{1}{2}(2x + y)^2$$

which may be put in the form

$$(2x + y)^2 dx - 2dy = 0.$$

The substitution $u = 2x + y$ is suggested by the equation, and this leads to

$$(u^2 + 4)dx - 2\,du = 0$$

or

$$dx - \frac{2\,du}{u^2 + 4} = 0.$$

Integration can now be carried out directly to give

$$x - 2(\tfrac{1}{2})\tan^{-1}\tfrac{1}{2}u = -c,$$

and substitution for u gives as the final result

$$y = 2\tan(x + c) - 2x.$$

Another very special class of first-order, first-degree equations are those that are termed *homogeneous*. A differential equation of the form

$$g(x,y)dx + h(x,y)dy = 0$$

in which $g(x,y)$ and $h(x,y)$ are such that

$$g(tx,ty) = t^n g(x,y) \qquad h(tx,ty) = t^n h(x,y)$$

for some common n, is said to be homogeneous in x and y to the nth degree. Some examples of homogeneous differential equations follow:

$$xy^2\,dy - (x^3 + y^3)dx = 0 \quad \text{degree 3} \quad \text{nonexact}$$

$$(3\theta + 2\rho)\,d\theta + (2\theta - 4\rho)\,d\rho = 0 \quad \text{degree 1} \quad \text{exact.}$$

All homogeneous equations are reducible. To solve them we make use of a technique first employed by Leibniz in 1691. This consists in making the substitution $y = vx$, whereupon the equation is reduced to the variables separable type.

Consider the first homogeneous equation above, which is also a nonexact differential equation. Making the substitutions $y = vx$ and $dy = v\,dx + x\,dv$ leads to the equation

$$v^2x^3(v\,dx + x\,dv) - (x^3 + v^3x^3)\,dx = 0$$

and on rearranging terms this becomes

$$-\frac{dx}{x} + v^2\,dv = 0.$$

Direct integration gives as the solution, after substituting back for y,

$$y^3 = 3x^3 \ln cx.$$

We come finally to a very important class of differential equations, namely, the *linear differential equations*. A differential equation of order n is said to be linear if it is of degree 1 in the dependent variable and its derivatives. It has the general form

$$a_0(x)\frac{d^n y}{dx^n} + a_1(x)\frac{d^{n-1}y}{dx^{n-1}} + \cdots + a_n(x)y = Q(x)$$

where the coefficients $a_i(x)$ are functions of x only (or are constants). A first-order, linear, differential equation would then have the form

$$\frac{dy}{dx} + a(x)y = Q(x).$$

Nothing is stipulated about the functions $a(x)$ and $Q(x)$; they need not be linear in x. In fact, $a(x)$ and $Q(x)$ will show quite a functional variation.

Fortunately, there is a powerful theorem that provides a general method of attack.

Theorem 16 (Superposition Theorem). *The general solution of the linear differential equation*

$$\frac{dy}{dx} + a(x)y = Q(x)$$

can be obtained by adding together a particular solution of it to a general solution of the related equation

$$\frac{dy}{dx} + a(x)y = 0.$$

The related equation mentioned above is called the *complementary equation* and its general solution is referred to in this context as the *complementary solution*. Since the complementary equation will always be of the variables separable type, obtaining the complementary solution is easy and straightforward. The crux of the problem is obtaining a particular solution of the original equation. Sometimes this can be done by inspection or trial and error. Thus in the equation

$$x\frac{dy}{dx} + 2y = x^3$$

it is evident that a particular solution would be a cubic in x. Call this ax^3. Then it follows that

$$x(3ax^2) + 2(ax^3) = x^3$$

and hence $a = \frac{1}{5}$. The complementary equation is

$$\frac{dy}{dx} + 2\frac{y}{x} = 0$$

and its general solution is given by $y = c/x^2$. Therefore, by the superposition theorem the general solution of the original linear equation is

$$y = \frac{1}{5}x^3 + cx^{-2}.$$

When inspection or trial and error prove inconvenient there is a general method of attack that is valid for first-order, linear, differential equations. Consider once again the general form for this type of equation

$$\frac{dy}{dx} + a(x)y = Q(x)$$

and let us first solve, instead,

$$\frac{dy}{dx} + a(x)y = 0.$$

Separation of the variables gives the equation

$$\frac{dy}{y} = -a(x)dx$$

whose solution is

$$ye^{\int a(x)\,dx} = c.$$

We note that the differential of the left-hand side of this equation is

$$e^{\int a(x)\,dx}[dy + ya(x)\,dx].$$

Now multiply both sides of the original equation by the factor $e^{\int a(x)\,dx}$ to give

$$e^{\int a(x)\,dx}[dy + ya(x)\,dx] = Q(x)e^{\int a(x)\,dx}.$$

But the left side of this is an exact differential, and so according to previous discussion on exact differential equations, the solution of the original equation must be

$$
ye^{\int a(x)\,dx} = \int Q(x)e^{\int a(x)\,dx}\,dx + c \;.
$$

We can look on this result as follows: the factor $e^{\int a(x)\,dx}$ is a multiplicative factor that transforms a first-order, linear differential equation into an exact differential equation. Such a factor is called an *integrating factor*.

Example 46.   The isotope $^{70}_{34}\mathrm{Se}$ undergoes β^+ decay to give $^{70}_{33}\mathrm{As}$; the $^{70}_{33}\mathrm{As}$, in turn, undergoes β^+ decay to give stable $^{70}_{32}\mathrm{Ge}$. The decay constant for the selenium decay is $0.0158\ \mathrm{min}^{-1}$ and for the arsenic decay it is $0.0133\ \mathrm{min}^{-1}$. Assume these two processes are the only ones occurring. If one starts with N_0 atoms of $^{70}_{34}\mathrm{Se}$, how many atoms of $^{70}_{33}\mathrm{As}$ will be present after 10 min?

Answer.   The nuclear chemical processes under consideration are

$$
^{70}_{34}\mathrm{Se} \rightarrow\, ^{70}_{33}\mathrm{As} + e^+ + \gamma
$$

$$
^{70}_{33}\mathrm{As} \rightarrow\, ^{70}_{32}\mathrm{Ge} + e^+ + \gamma.
$$

Beta decay of isotopes is a first-order process, that is, it depends only on the number of atoms of substance present. Since arsenic is being made in one process and consumed in another, the differential equation is

$$
\frac{dN^{\mathrm{As}}}{dt} = W_{\mathrm{Se}}N_{\mathrm{Se}} - W_{\mathrm{As}}N_{\mathrm{As}}
$$

where, for example, W_{Se} is the decay constant for the selenium isotope. We also know that the selenium itself follows the differential equation

$$
-\frac{dN^{\mathrm{Se}}}{dt} = W_{\mathrm{Se}}N_{\mathrm{Se}}
$$

and integration of this gives

$$
\int_{N_{\mathrm{Se}}}^{N_0} \frac{dN^{\mathrm{Se}}}{N_{\mathrm{Se}}} = \int_t^0 - W_{\mathrm{Se}}\,dt
$$

or

$$N_{Se} = N_0 \exp(-W_{Se}t).$$

Therefore, the original differential equation becomes

$$\frac{dN^{As}}{dt} + W_{As}N_{As} = W_{Se}N_0 \exp(-W_{Se}t)$$

where in terms of our earlier notation we have

$$a(x) \equiv W_{As} \qquad Q(x) \equiv W_{Se}N_0 \exp(-W_{Se}t).$$

We have then

$$e^{\int a(x)dx} = \exp\left(\int W_{As}dt\right) = \exp(W_{As}t)$$

$$\int Q(x)e^{\int a(x)dx}dx = \int W_{Se}N_0 \exp(-W_{Se}t)\exp(W_{As}t)\,dt$$

$$= \frac{W_{Se}N_0}{W_{As} - W_{Se}}\exp[(W_{As} - W_{Se})t].$$

The solution to the differential equation, then, is

$$N_{As}\exp(W_{As}t) = \frac{W_{Se}N_0}{W_{As} - W_{Se}}\exp[(W_{As} - W_{Se})t] + c.$$

At time $t = 0$ one has $N_{As} = 0$. Hence the constant c is

$$c = \frac{-W_{Se}N_0}{W_{As} - W_{Se}},$$

and so finally

$$N_{As} = \frac{W_{Se}N_0}{W_{As} - W_{Se}}[\exp(-W_{Se}t) - \exp(-W_{As}t)]$$

$$= \frac{0.0158N_0}{(0.0133 - 0.0158)}(e^{-0.158} - e^{-0.133})$$

$$= \boxed{0.136 \, N_0 \text{ atoms}}.$$

Partly in order to illustrate once again the solution of a linear differential equation and also to illustrate the way in which the language of mathematics can be used in the formulation of the description of some problem or physical system, let us consider a simplified mathematical model for the sodium–potassium pump. In the higher animals there is a continual flux into and out of their erythrocytes of Na^+ and K^+ ions. The *primary sodium–potassium pump* is what biochemists term an active mediated transport system, and it tends to maintain high internal K^+ ion concentrations and low internal Na^+ ion concentrations. Outward transport of Na^+ ions into the plasma is postulated to be the driving force for the transport of K^+ ions (needed for protein synthesis by ribosomes and needed for maximal activity of pyruvate kinase in glycolysis) into the erythrocytes. Let us suppose that an investigator studying some aspect of the kinetics of the sodium–potassium pump by using radioactive ^{42}K desires a model of the process. We assume that the erythrocytes (E) and the plasma (P) together constitute for this process a closed system (see Figure 5.5). At any time let [E] be the concentration of ^{42}K in the erythrocytes and [P] be the concentration of ^{42}K in the blood plasma. Our investigator supposes that the radiolabel is transported into the erythrocytes by a first-order process

$$\text{rate in} = k_1[P],$$

and that it is transported out of the erythrocytes by a first-order process

$$\text{rate out} = k_2[E].$$

Then since the sum of [E] and [P] is a constant, C, we may write for the net increase in ^{42}K concentration in the E chamber

$$\frac{d[E]}{dt} = k_1[P] - k_2[E]$$

$$= k_1 C - (k_1 + k_2)[E].$$

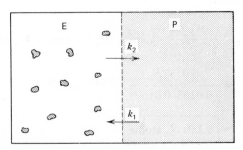

Fig. 5.5 Model system for the sodium–potassium pump.

This first-order linear differential equation can be solved readily by the integrating factor method. The result is (B is a constant)

$$[E] = \frac{k_1 C}{k_1 + k_2} + Be^{-(k+k)t}.$$

This expression shows how the concentration in the E chamber varies with the time. As time increases, the concentration of ^{42}K in the E chamber does not grow indefinitely because the limit of $[E]$ as t approaches infinity is just $k_1 C / (k_1 + k_2)$. We may designate this concentration as $[E]_\infty$. The constant of integration can be evaluated from a boundary condition. Thus if the experiment is carried out in such a way that at time $t = 0$, the concentration in the E chamber is zero, then it follows that $B = -k_1 C / (k_1 + k_2)$.

As far as actual mathematics is concerned, we are through. However, our experimenter's radioimmunoassay may be more suited for measuring $[P]$ than $[E]$. In the equation above we could simply replace $[E]$ by $C - [P]$, but this equation would not lend itself to easy graphical treatment. If we let $[P]_\infty$ be $C - [E]_\infty$, then some simple manipulations (follow through on this) give

$$\ln\left(\frac{[P]}{[P]_\infty} - 1\right) = -(k_1 + k_2)t + \ln\frac{k_1}{k_2}.$$

From this expression one sees that a plot of $\ln\{([P]/[P]_\infty) - 1\}$ versus time would give a straight line of slope $-(k_1 + k_2)$ and of intercept $\ln(k_1/k_2)$.

The common first-order differential equations are summarized in Table 5.2. The practical approach you should follow when you meet with any of these equations is to (1) classify the equation according to type, (2) use the standard method of attack indicated in the table for that type, and (3) make use of any known boundary conditions.

Table 5.2 First-Order Differential Equations

Type of equation	Method of solution
Exact	Partial integration of the coefficients of dx and dy
Variables separable	Direct integration
Reducible	Substitution followed by direct integration
Homogeneous	Substitute $y = vx$, followed by direct integration
Linear	Complementary solution plus particular solution; integrating factor

2   THE LAPLACE TRANSFORM

Transformations of variables are very common in mathematics. We do this, for example, in solving the general cubic $ax^3 + 3bx^2 + 3cx + d = 0$ by first writing $x = (1/a)(z - b)$. We do this in integrating certain functions as, for instance $\int [dx/(a^2 + x^2)]$, where we let $x = a\tan\theta$. This section describes another kind of transformation that was extensively exploited by Heaviside in the years 1887–1898 as an operational means of solving certain types of differential equations.[3]

The transformation to be described is one of a class of integral transformations of the general form

$$F(s) = \int_a^b f(x) K(s,x) \, dx$$

where $F(s)$ is said to be the *transform* of $f(x)$ with respect to the *kernel* $K(s,x)$. Table 5.3 lists some of the common transforms; you have already had some experience with one of them, the Fourier transform in Chapter 3. In this table the quantity $J_n(sx)$ is a Bessel function of the first kind of order n. We consider Bessel functions briefly in Chapter 7.

Our interest in Laplace[4] transforms stems from their powerful use in

Table 5.3   Integral Transforms

$K(s,x)$	a	b	Transform
$\sin sx$	0	π	Finite sine
$\cos sx$	0	π	Finite cosine
x^{s-1}	0	∞	Mellin
e^{-sx}	0	∞	Laplace
e^{-isx}	$-\infty$	∞	Fourier
$xJ_n(sx)$	0	b	Finite Bessel or Hankel

[3]The Englishman Oliver Heaviside (1850–1925) started out in life as a telegraph and telephone engineer. He retired to country life in 1874 where he began to write mainly about electromagnetic theory. Much of what Heaviside did infuriated the pure mathematicians because although he most often got correct results, his methods seemed to lack rigor and a solid foundation. See M. Kline, *Mathematical Thought from Ancient to Modern Times*, Oxford University Press, New York, 1972, p. 787.

[4]After the French mathematician and physicist Marquis Pierre Simon de Laplace (1749–1827). Laplace, author of the famous multivolume work *Mécanique céleste* which summed up Newton's laws of motion as applied to the solar system, was a colorful character in contrast to his contemporary Lagrange.

solving differential equations that (*1*) are linear and may be of order greater than 1, and (*2*) have associated one or more prescribed initial conditions. Other than this the only constraints would be those for which the defining integral converges:

$$L\{f(x)\} = F(s) = \int_0^\infty f(x)e^{-sx}\,dx.$$

These conditions are that $f(x)$ be piecewise continuous (see Section 4.5) and of *exponential order*. A function $f(x)$ is said to be of exponential order for $x > X$ if we can find constants a and M such that $|f(x)| \leqslant Me^{ax}$. Qualitatively, this says that after a certain point $x = X$ our function $f(x)$ does not increase faster than an exponential function. A great many functions are of this type.

In terms of the notation above we can call $f(x)$ the *inverse Laplace transform* of $F(s)$ and write

$$L^{-1}\{F(s)\} = f(x).$$

The inverse Laplace transform can be set up as an integral, but this involves the process of contour integration in the complex plane, a subject we do not consider in this book. Instead, we look upon finding inverse Laplace transforms as the reverse of finding Laplace transforms from tables, in much the same way as we look upon integration as the use of tables of derivatives in a reverse manner. In special cases it may turn out that if a Laplace transform exists, and is therefore unique, the inverse Laplace transform may not be unique. The difficulty occurs at the end points of the piecewise continuous segments. Since most functions we will be dealing with are not only piecewise continuous but also continuous over the entire range of integration, we assume that for all practical purposes the inverse transform is unique.

Theorem 17. *If a function* f(x) *is piecewise continuous for all finite intervals in the domain* x > 0, *and if* f(x) *is of exponential order as* x *tends to infinity, then the Laplace transform defined by the definite integral*

$$F(s) = \int_0^\infty f(x)e^{-sx}\,dx$$

exists for some range of s, *and further,* $lim_{s\to\infty}$F(s) = 0.

The range of s mentioned in the theorem is often $s > 0$ or $s > a$, but many tables of Laplace transforms do not explicitly state the valid range of s for each transform.

As an illustration of what a transform looks like, let us work it out for $f(x) = x^n$. We have by definition

$$L(x^n) = F(s) = \int_0^\infty x^n e^{-sx} dx$$

$$= \frac{-x^n}{s e^{sx}} \Big|_0^\infty + \frac{n}{s} \int_0^\infty x^{n-1} e^{-sx} dx$$

$$= 0 + \frac{n}{s} L(x^{n-1}).$$

Similarly, one has

$$L(x^{n-1}) = \frac{n-1}{s} L(x^{n-2}),$$

and continuing the argument down to x^0 yields

$$L(x^n) = \frac{n!}{s^{n+1}}.$$

This expression will be defined for all values of s greater than zero. We see here clearly that the first term in each integration by parts always vanishes because e^{sx} increases faster than x^n, that is,

$$\lim_{x \to \infty} \frac{x^n}{e^{sx}} = 0.$$

For another illustration we work out the Laplace transform for the first derivative of a function. Again, making use of integration by parts, we have

$$L\{ f'(x) \} = F(s) = \int_0^\infty e^{-sx} \left(\frac{df}{dx} \right) dx$$

$$= e^{-sx} f(x) \Big|_0^\infty + s \int_0^\infty e^{-sx} f(x) dx$$

$$= -f(0) + s L\{ f(x) \}.$$

This expression will also be defined for all positive values of s. This expresses the Laplace transform of the derivative in terms of the transform of the function. For a derivative of order n the general expression is

$$L\{ f^n(x) \} = s^n L\{ f(x) \} - \left(s^{n-1} x_0 + s^{n-2} x_1 + \cdots + x_{n-1} \right)$$

where $x_n = \dfrac{d^n f(x)}{dx^n}$ evaluated at $x = 0$

and $x_0 = f(x)$ evaluated at $x = 0$.

It is not possible to work out transforms for powers of derivatives, so the use of Laplace transforms for solving differential equations is restricted to first-order equations. Table 5.4 lists 30 of the more common Laplace transforms; more extensive tabulations can be found in handbooks or specialized monographs (see Annotated Bibliography). Unless otherwise indicated, assume that $s > 0$. The functions in entries 27 and 28 of the table are the Dirac delta function and the Heaviside step function, respectively, both of which have been mentioned before in this book. Entry 29 is the Laplace transform of a Bessel function of the first kind and of order n. Finally, we recognize the expression in the function column for entry 30 as a convolution integral, first mentioned at the end of Chapter 3. Figure 5.6 shows the graphs of transforms 2, 5, 17, and 25.

Table 5.4   Some Laplace Transforms

$f(x)$	$L\{f(x)\} = F(s)$
1. n	n/s
2. x^n $(n = 1, 2, \ldots)$	$n!/s^{n+1}$
3. x^n $(n > -1)$	$\Gamma(n+1)/s^{n+1}$
4. e^{nx}	$1/(s-n)$ $(s > n)$
5. $\sin nx$	$n/(s^2 + n^2)$
6. $\cos nx$	$s/(s^2 + n^2)$
7. $\sinh nx$	$n/(s^2 - n^2)$ $(s > |n|)$
8. $\cosh nx$	$s/(s^2 - n^2)$ $(s > |n|)$
9. $\dfrac{d^n f(x)}{dx^n}$	$s^n L\{f(x)\} - \displaystyle\sum_{i=1}^{n} s^{i-1} \left[\dfrac{d^{n-i} f}{dx^{n-i}} \right]_{x=0}$
10. $x^{n-1} e^{mx}$ $(n > 0)$	$\Gamma(n)/(s-m)^n$ $(s > m)$
11. $e^{-nx} \sin px$	$p/[(s+n)^2 + p^2]$ $(s > -n)$
12. $e^{-nx} \cos px$	$(s+n)/[(s+n)^2 + p^2]$ $(s > -n)$
13. $e^{-nx} \sinh px$	$p/[(s+n)^2 - p^2]$ $(s > -n)$
14. $e^{-nx} \cosh px$	$(s+n)/[(s+n)^2 - p^2]$ $(s > -n)$
15. $x \sin nx$	$2ns/(s^2 + n^2)^2$
16. $x \cos nx$	$(s^2 - n^2)/(s^2 + n^2)^2$
17. $\dfrac{\sin nx}{x}$	$\tan^{-1}\left(\dfrac{n}{s}\right)$
18. $(e^{nx} - e^{mx})/(n - m)$	$1/[(s-n)(s-m)]$ $\begin{array}{l}(s > n) \\ (s > m)\end{array}$

Table 5.4 (*Continued*)

$f(x)$	$L\{f(x)\} = F(s)$
19. $\sin nx - nx \cos nx$	$2n^3/(s^2 + n^2)^2$
20. $\dfrac{\cos nx - \cos mx}{m^2 - n^2}$	$s/[(s^2 + n^2)(s^2 + m^2)]$
21. $\dfrac{n \sin mx - m \sin nx}{nm(n^2 - m^2)}$	$1/[(s^2 + n^2)(s^2 + m^2)]$
22. $\cos^2 nx$	$(s^2 + 2n^2)/[s(s^2 + 4n^2)]$
23. $\dfrac{e^{-nx}}{m-n} + \dfrac{e^{-mx}}{n-m}$	$1/[(s+n)(s+m)]$ $\quad\begin{array}{l}(s > -n)\\(s > -m)\end{array}$
24. $\dfrac{k}{2\sqrt{\pi x^3}} \exp\left(\dfrac{-k^2}{4x}\right) \quad (k > 0)$	$e^{-k\sqrt{s}}$
25. $\operatorname{erfc}\left(\dfrac{k}{2\sqrt{x}}\right) \quad (k \geqslant 0)$	$\dfrac{1}{s}e^{-k\sqrt{s}}$
26. $\dfrac{1}{\sqrt{\pi x}} \exp\left(\dfrac{-k^2}{4x}\right) \quad (k \geqslant 0)$	$\dfrac{1}{\sqrt{s}}e^{-k\sqrt{s}}$
27. $\dfrac{d^n}{dx^n} \delta(x - a)$	$s^n e^{-as}$
28. $H(x-a) = \begin{cases} 0 & x < a \\ \frac{1}{2} & x = a \\ 1 & x > a \end{cases}$	$\dfrac{1}{s}e^{-as}$
29. $J_n(x)$	$1/\left[\sqrt{(s^2+1)}\left\{s + \sqrt{(s^2+1)}\right\}^n\right]$
30. $\displaystyle\int_0^x W(t)f(x-t)\,dt$	$F(s)L\{W(x)\}$

Additional transforms can be derived directly from the definition or from transforms given in the table. It is simply necessary to realize that since transforms are integrals, they follow the same algebraic laws as regards addition and multiplication by a constant:

$$L\{f(x) + g(x)\} = L\{f(x)\} + L\{g(x)\}$$
$$L\{af(x)\} = aL\{f(x)\}.$$

Similar statements hold for finding inverse Laplace transforms. In this way the contents of Table 5.4 may be built up considerably.

Let us now use Laplace transforms to solve an interesting differential equation.

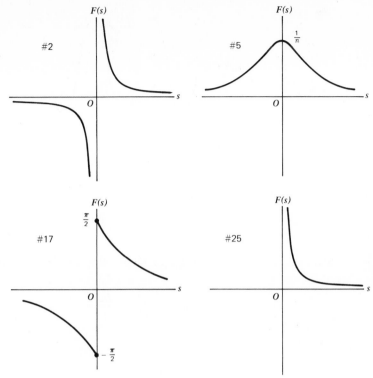

Fig. 5.6   Graphs of four Laplace transforms.

Example 47.   A simplified model for a chemical bond might be one where a given atom of interest vibrates according to a Hooke's law restoring force plus a sinusoidally time-varying force such as might arise from oscillating electric fields that originate from other atoms that are present. Investigate this model mathematically.

Answer.   The equation of motion of the atom is (see Figure 5.7)

$$m\frac{d^2x}{dt^2} + kx = F_0 \sin \omega t$$

where x is the displacement from the equilibrium position, k is the Hooke's law constant, and F_0 is the maximum amplitude of the sinusoidal force. For initial conditions we suppose that the displacement and the velocity are zero:

$$x(0) = x'(0) = 0.$$

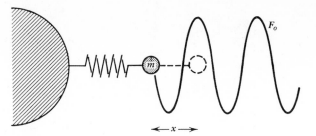

Fig. 5.7   Model for a chemical bond.

Writing the equation in the form

$$\frac{d^2x}{dt^2} + \beta^2 x = K \sin \omega t$$

with $\beta^2 = k/m$ and $K = F_0/m$ and taking the transform of both sides

$$s^2 L(x) - sx(0) - x'(0) + \beta^2 L(x) = \frac{K\omega}{s^2 + \omega^2},$$

we have

$$L(x) = F(s) = \frac{K\omega}{(s^2 + \omega^2)(s^2 + \beta^2)}$$

$$= \frac{K\omega}{\beta^2 - \omega^2} \left(\frac{1}{s^2 + \omega^2} - \frac{1}{s^2 + \beta^2} \right)$$

Then in view of the linearity of the inverse Laplace transform, we have from transform no. 5

$$x = L^{-1}\{F(s)\}$$

$$= \frac{K\omega}{\beta^2 - \omega^2} \left[L^{-1} \left(\frac{1}{s^2 + \omega^2} \right) - L^{-1} \left(\frac{1}{s^2 + \beta^2} \right) \right]$$

$$= \frac{K\omega}{\beta^2 - \omega^2} \left[\frac{\sin \omega t}{\omega} - \frac{\sin \beta t}{\beta} \right].$$

This is the solution if $\beta^2 \neq \omega^2$. In the case of equality

$$L(x) = F(s) = \frac{K\omega}{(s^2 + \omega^2)^2}$$

and hence from transform no. 19

$$x = L^{-1}\{F(s)\}$$

$$= \frac{K}{2\omega^2}[\sin \omega t - \omega t \cos \omega t].$$

Consider first the case $\beta^2 \neq \omega^2$. The expression in brackets for x cannot exceed $[(1/\omega) + (1/\beta)]$. Consequently the upper limit for the displacement is necessarily finite:

$$x_{max} = \frac{K\omega}{\beta^2 - \omega^2}\left(\frac{1}{\omega} + \frac{1}{\beta}\right)$$

$$= \frac{K}{\beta(\beta - \omega)}.$$

The oscillator is thus a bounded oscillator. However, now consider the case of equality $\beta^2 = \omega^2$. As t grows very large the second term in the brackets oscillates wildly from very large negative values to very large positive values; the oscillation can, in fact, be made as large as one likes. The same picture is conveyed also by looking at the velocity:

$$v = \frac{dx}{dt}$$

$$= \frac{Kt \sin \omega t}{2}.$$

This function clearly shows that as t increases without bound the velocity is alternately very positive and very negative. Such an oscillator could not remain physically stable for long; accordingly, the condition $\beta^2 = \omega^2$ is sometimes referred to as the *condition of resonance*.

Laplace transforms can be used to solve systems of linear differential equations. We can illustrate this by incompletely working out an example from kinetics. Consider the unimolecular reaction

$$A \rightarrow B$$

that is presumed to proceed according to the *Lindemann–Hinshelwood mechanism*:

$$A + M \xrightarrow{k_1} A^* + M$$

$$A^* + M \xrightarrow{k_{-1}} A + M$$

The substance M is any molecule that can serve to activate A to A^* or to deactivate A^* to A by collision; it might be A itself or some added inert gas. In the present situation we assume that its concentration is constant. Then we have

$$\frac{dA^*}{dt} = k_1[A][M] - k_{-1}[A^*][M] - k_2[A^*]$$

$$\frac{dA}{dt} = k_{-1}[A^*][M] - k_1[A][M].$$

We now proceed to take the Laplace transform of both sides of both equations. This is valid because although each equation contains two dependent variables, each of these is a function of the same independent variable (namely, the time, t) and this is the variable of integration.

$$sL(A^*) - A^*(0) = k_1[M]L(A) - (k_{-1}[M] + k_2)L(A^*)$$

$$sL(A) - A(0) = k_{-1}[M]L(A^*) - k_1[M]L(A)$$

This is a pair of simultaneous equations and it may be solved for the two unknowns $L(A^*)$ and $L(A)$. Since A is the starting material one would normally be more interested in this. Thus from the above we find after introducing the conditions $A(0) = [A_0]$ and $A^*(0) = 0$

$$L(A) = F(s) = \frac{A_0(s + k_2 + k_{-1}[M])}{s^2 + s\{k_2 + [M](k_1 + k_{-1})\} + k_1k_2[M]}.$$

Although this expression is complex, an inverse Laplace transform will exist, and so in principle the concentration of A can be ascertained as a function of time. Some simplification could be achieved by solving the equations under conditions where something is known about the relative values of the three rate constants.[5]

Finally it is useful to point out that a table of Laplace transforms is actually a practical compilation of definite integrals. Thus if one needs to know the integral

$$\int_0^\infty e^{-5x}\sinh 3x\,dx,$$

reference to transform no. 13 shows that the value is $3/(25-9)$ or $\frac{3}{16}$.

[5]Kinetic problems like this one and more complicated ones are taken up in the book N. M. Rodiguin and E. N. Rodiguina, *Consecutive Chemical Reactions*, Van Nostrand, Princeton, N.J., 1964.

3 SOME SECOND-ORDER TYPES AND POWER SERIES SOLUTIONS

Differential equations of order greater than one present special problems since only in certain cases can they be integrated exactly to give closed expressions for the solutions. In many cases it becomes necessary to express the answers as infinite series, infinite continued fractions, or definite integrals. Some of the most important second-order differential equations are of this type. In Table 5.5 we list the names and forms of the better-known ones; all have applications in various branches of science.

In this section we work through sketchily a problem in chemistry that involves one of these equations. This will show how the mathematics is handled, and it will also show how considerations of the chemical physics involved must enter. The problem is the quantum mechanical solution of the harmonic oscillator in one dimension. This is a model for a chemical bond constrained to vibrate along a single direction or axis. For a harmonic oscillator with a force constant of k (recall Exercise 41[*] of Chapter 4; the force constant was given the symbol β there) the potential energy is $\frac{1}{2}kx^2$ if the oscillator is centered about the origin. Schrödinger's equation for this system is then

$$\frac{d^2\psi}{dx^2} + \frac{2m}{\hbar^2}\left(E - \tfrac{1}{2}kx^2\right)\psi = 0.$$

Table 5.5 Some Second-Order Differential Equations

Name	Form	Remarks
Weber's equation	$\dfrac{d^2y}{dx^2} + \left(n + \tfrac{1}{2} - \tfrac{1}{4}x^2\right)y = 0$	
Mathieu's equation	$\dfrac{d^2y}{dx^2} + (a - 2b\cos 2x)y = 0$	$a, b = $ constant
Bessel's equation of order n	$x^2\dfrac{d^2y}{dx^2} + x\dfrac{dy}{dx} + (x^2 - n^2)y = 0$	$n = $ constant
Hermite's equation	$\dfrac{d^2y}{dx^2} - 2x\dfrac{dy}{dx} + 2ny = 0$	$n = $ nonnegative integer
Associated Laguerre equation	$x\dfrac{d^2y}{dx^2} + (a + 1 - x)\dfrac{dy}{dx} + ny = 0$	$a, n = $ nonnegative integers
Laguerre equation	$x\dfrac{d^2y}{dx^2} + (1 - x)\dfrac{dy}{dx} + ny = 0$	$n = $ nonnegative integer

Table 5.5 (*Continued*)

Name	Form	Remarks
Associated Legendre equation	$(1-x^2)\dfrac{d^2y}{dx^2} - 2x\dfrac{dy}{dx}$ $+ \left\{ n(n+1) - \dfrac{m^2}{1-x^2} \right\} y = 0$	$\lvert m \rvert = $ integer $\leqslant n$ $n = $ nonnegative integer
Legendre equation	$(1-x^2)\dfrac{d^2y}{dx^2} - 2x\dfrac{dy}{dx}$ $+ n(n+1)y = 0$	$n = $ nonnegative integer
Hypergeometric equation	$x(1-x)\dfrac{d^2y}{dx^2} + \{\gamma - (\alpha+\beta+1)x\}\dfrac{dy}{dx}$ $- \alpha\beta y = 0$	$\alpha, \beta, \gamma \neq$ negative integers
Kummer's confluent hypergeometric equation	$x\dfrac{d^2y}{dx^2} + (c-x)\dfrac{dy}{dx} - ay = 0$	

Let us first see what solutions to this equation should look like in the limit of large x. For x sufficiently large the term $\frac{1}{2}kx^2$ will dominate the constant E, and the differential equation will reduce to

$$\frac{d^2\psi}{dx^2} = \frac{km}{\hbar^2} x^2\psi.$$

Without attempting to solve this equation exactly, we may note that an approximate solution of it is $\psi = \exp(-\frac{1}{2}\sqrt{km/\hbar^2}\, x^2)$, since differentiation of this gives

$$\frac{d^2\psi}{dx^2} = x^2\left(\frac{km}{\hbar^2}\right)\exp\left[-\tfrac{1}{2}\sqrt{km/\hbar^2}\, x^2\right] - \sqrt{\frac{km}{\hbar^2}}\;\exp\left[-\tfrac{1}{2}\sqrt{km/\hbar^2}\, x^2\right]$$

and for large x the second term will be much smaller than the first term.

Our procedure now is to assume that solutions to the original differential equation can be given by the product of the above exponential times suitable functions such that the behavior of the product at large x approaches that of the exponential. Now make the substitution $\sqrt{km/\hbar^2}\, x^2 = \alpha x^2 = z^2$, and insert this into the differential equation to give

$$\alpha\frac{d^2\psi}{dz^2} + \frac{2mE}{\hbar^2}\psi - \alpha z^2\psi = 0.$$

Assume that ψ can be expressed in the form $\psi(z) = \exp(-\tfrac{1}{2}z^2)H(z)$; if this is put into the differential equation above and the exponential factor is divided throughout, then a new differential equation results:

$$\frac{d^2H}{dz^2} - 2z\frac{dH}{dz} + 2H\left(\frac{\lambda}{2\alpha} - \tfrac{1}{2}\right) = 0$$

$$\frac{2mE}{\hbar^2} = \lambda.$$

This, it will be recognized from Table 5.5, is *Hermite's differential equation*.[6]

Now we are ready to proceed with the actual power series solution. We assume that $H(z)$ can be expanded as a power series in z.

$$H(z) = \sum_{i=0}^{\infty} a_i z^i$$

Differentiation once and twice yields the series

$$H'(z) = \sum_{i=0}^{\infty} i a_i z^{i-1} \qquad H''(z) = \sum_{i=0}^{\infty} i(i-1)a_i z^{i-2}$$

and rewriting Hermite's equation we have

$$\sum_{i=0}^{\infty} \left[i(i-1)a_i z^{i-2} - 2i a_i z^i + 2n a_i z^i \right] = 0$$

where $n = (\lambda/2\alpha) - \tfrac{1}{2}$. For both $i=0$ and $i=1$, the first term in the brackets vanishes, and so since i is just a dummy index and not a variable we may make the substitution $j = i - 2$ *in the first term only*, and $j = i$ in the second and third terms:

$$\sum_{j=0}^{\infty} \left[(j+1)(j+2)a_{j+2} - 2j a_j + 2n a_j \right] z^j = 0.$$

This equation must hold for all values of z, and this can only be if the expression in brackets is identically zero. It follows then that

$$a_{j+2} = \frac{2(j-n)}{(j+1)(j+2)} a_j$$

[6]After Charles Hermite (1822–1901), who for many years was professor of mathematics at the Sorbonne; Hermite is famous for having proved that e is a transcendental number.

and at this point we see that a_0 and a_1 are arbitrary. All the even a's are determined from a_0 and the *recursion relation* above, and all the odd a's determined from a_1 and the recursion relation.

So far, then, we have the function $H(z)$ expressed (at this point) as an infinite series.

$$H(z) = a_0 + a_1 z - n a_0 z^2 + \left(\frac{1-n}{3}\right) a_1 z^3 - \cdots +$$

At this point chemical physics enters the picture; it says that valid wave functions must be finite even in the limit as z approaches infinity. The requirement of finiteness is necessary if we are to maintain the interpretation (first introduced to you in beginning chemistry courses) of the square of the wave function as a probability density. In fact we already used this requirement once before in discussing the asymptotic behavior of the wave function for large x, for there we deliberately chose the sign in the exponential to be negative rather than positive in order that the function would tend to a finite limit as x increased without bound.

From the recursion relation we have for the ratio of two consecutively alternate terms

$$\lim_{j \to \text{large}} \frac{a_{j+2} z^{j+2}}{a_j z^j} = \lim_{j \to \text{large}} \frac{2(j-n)z^2}{(j+1)(j+2)} \sim \frac{2}{j} z^2.$$

Now consider the function $\exp(z^2)$. From material in the last chapter we can expand this function as

$$\exp(z^2) = 1 + z^2 + \frac{z^4}{2!} + \cdots + \frac{z^n}{\left(\frac{n}{2}\right)!} + \frac{z^{n+2}}{\left(\frac{n+2}{2}\right)!} + \cdots$$

and here the limit of the ratio of consecutive terms is equal to

$$\lim_{n \to \text{large}} \frac{z^{n+2}/\left[\frac{1}{2}(n+2)\right]!}{z^n/\left(\frac{1}{2}n\right)!} = \lim_{n \to \text{large}} \frac{\left(\frac{1}{2}n\right)! z^2}{\left[\frac{1}{2}(n+2)\right]!} \sim \frac{2}{n} z^2.$$

Hence we see that for large j the function $H(z)$ increases about as rapidly as the function $\exp(z^2)$, and thus the wave functions

$$\psi = \exp\left(-\tfrac{1}{2}z^2\right) H(z)$$

behave roughly as $\exp(+\tfrac{1}{2}z^2)$ after a sufficient number of terms. Such wave functions would be inadmissible physically since their value would tend to infinity as z increased without bound.

A way out of the dilemma is to make $H(z)$ a finite polynomial by terminating the series after some j. From the recursion relation we can see that this will occur when $j - n = 0$, or equivalently,

$$\lambda = (2j + 1)\alpha.$$

At the same time we note that if the j at which the series is stopped is odd, then a_0 must be set equal to zero so that no terms beyond j can occur, and similarly, if the j is even then $a_1 = 0$. The resulting *Hermite polynomials* $H_n(z)$ thus obtained are either even or odd functions of z.

The first Hermite polynomial $(n = 0)$ is obviously just a_0. But it is clearly seen that appealing to the differential equation

$$\frac{d^2 H_0(z)}{dz^2} - 2z \frac{dH_0(z)}{dz} + 2(0)H_0(z) = 0$$

will not allow us to evaluate a_0 since any constant will be a solution. Similarly, the second Hermite polynomial $(n = 1)$ is just $a_1 z$, but the value of a_1 is completely arbitrary as is seen by direct substitution:

$$0 - 2z \frac{dH_1(z)}{dz} + 2(1)H_1(z) = 0$$

or

$$-2z(a_1) + 2a_1 z = 0.$$

This arbitrariness is true for the first term of all of the $H_n(z)$ polynomials. However it can be shown that the particular Hermite polynomials obtained from a generating function (recall Exercise 37[*] Chapter 4) satisfy the Hermite differential equation. The same polynomials can also be obtained from what is called a *Rodrigues' formula* (see Chapter 7). If either of these two methods is employed, the following partial list of Hermite polynomials results.

Table 5.6 Hermite Polynomials

$H_0(z) = 1$	$H_1(z) = 2z$
$H_2(z) = 4z^2 - 2$	$H_3(z) = 8z^3 - 12z$
$H_4(z) = 16z^4 - 48z^2 + 12$	$H_5(z) = 32z^5 - 160z^3 + 120z$
$H_6(z) = 64z^6 - 480z^4 + 120z^2 - 120$	$H_7(z) = 128z^7 - 1344z^5 + 3360z^3 - 1680z$

To complete the description of the harmonic oscillator wave functions, it is necessary to evaluate what is called the *normalization constant* for each. This is that value of N such that the integral

$$\int_{-\infty}^{\infty} \psi^2(x)\, dx = \int_{-\infty}^{\infty} \left[N\exp(-\tfrac{1}{2}\alpha x^2) H_n(\sqrt{\alpha}\,x) \right]^2 dx$$
$$= 1$$

has the value shown. This is another requirement from the chemical physics of the problem, namely, if the harmonic oscillator is in the state associated with the (quantum) number n, then the probability that its displacement x lies anywhere in the range $-\infty$ to $+\infty$ must obviously be unity. For the case of $n = 0$, this implies that

$$N^2 \int_{-\infty}^{\infty} \exp(-\alpha x^2)\, dx = 1.$$

From material in Chapter 3 the definite integral is found to have the value $\sqrt{\pi/\alpha}$. Hence we find that $N = \sqrt[4]{\alpha/\pi}$.

For the case of $n = 1$, normalization requires

$$N^2 \int_{-\infty}^{\infty} 4\alpha \exp(-\alpha x^2) x^2\, dx = \frac{4N^2}{\sqrt{\alpha}} \int_0^{\infty} e^{-u} u^{(3/2)-1}\, du$$

$$= \frac{4N^2}{\sqrt{\alpha}} \Gamma(\tfrac{3}{2})$$

$$= 2N^2 \sqrt{\frac{\pi}{\alpha}}$$

$$= 1.$$

Thus we find that $N = \sqrt[4]{\alpha/4\pi}$. The first four harmonic oscillator wave functions are collected in Table 5.7, and are shown graphically in Figure 5.8.

Table 5.7   Harmonic Oscillator Wave Functions

$$\psi_0(x) = \sqrt[4]{\frac{\alpha}{\pi}}\ \exp(-\tfrac{1}{2}\alpha x^2)$$

$$\psi_1(x) = \sqrt[4]{\frac{4\alpha^3}{\pi}}\ x\exp(-\tfrac{1}{2}\alpha x^2)$$

$$\psi_2(x) = \sqrt[4]{\frac{\alpha}{4\pi}}\ (2\alpha x^2 - 1)\exp(-\tfrac{1}{2}\alpha x^2)$$

$$\psi_3(x) = \sqrt[4]{\frac{\alpha^3}{9\pi}}\ x(2\alpha x^2 - 3)\exp(-\tfrac{1}{2}\alpha x^2)$$

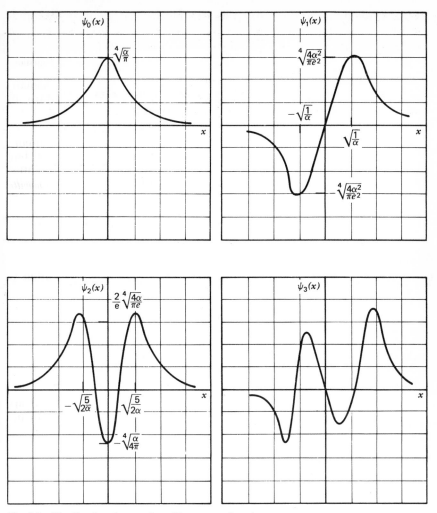

Fig. 5.8 The first four harmonic oscillator wave functions.

Two main but related points have emerged from this examination of the harmonic oscillator. First, it has been found that the solutions must be expressed as finite polynomials; this is not general as many second-order differential equations have to be solved in terms of infinite series. Second, solutions exist only for certain values of the constant E (in the differential equation as first written, or equivalently, of the constant n in the equation as written at a later point). These are the eigenvalue-eigenfunction pairs; that is, corresponding to each allowed value of E, referred to as an *eigenvalue*, there is a particular function $\psi(x)$, referred to as an *eigenfunction*, that together with the E satisfies the differential equation. It is precisely eigenvalue–

eigenfunction differential equations such as this that provide the mathematical background for quantization phenomena such as we first learn in beginning chemistry classes regarding electron behavior in hydrogen.

Eigenvalue–eigenfunction problems are extremely common. It is important to see that the harmonic oscillator problem is not an isolated case, but may in fact be subsumed under a more widely occurring class of differential equations. The general differential equation is called the *Sturm–Liouville equation*,[7] usually written as

$$\frac{d}{dx}\left[f(x)\frac{dy}{dx} \right] + [g(x) + nh(x)]\, y = 0$$

where n is a real constant. Instead of initial conditions, the equation is usually subjected to boundary conditions in the form

$$ay(x_1) + b\left(\frac{dy}{dx} \right)_{x_1} = 0$$

$$cy(x_2) + d\left(\frac{dy}{dx} \right)_{x_2} = 0$$

and then solved by means of power series. The constants a, b, c, d are supplied by the nature of the particular problem, and x_1 and x_2 are the extreme values of the range of the independent variable.

Rather than work through another example of a power series solution to a Sturm–Liouville equation, we take this opportunity to point out an important property of the solutions to any Sturm–Liouville equation (such as, for example, of the harmonic oscillator wave functions). To simplify the treatment we consider the special case where $b = d = 0$, or $y(x_1) = y(x_2) = 0$. Let us look at two different eigenvalue–eigenfunction pairs.

$$\frac{d}{dx}\left[f(x)\frac{dy_1}{dx} \right] + [g(x) + n_1 h(x)]y_1 = 0$$

$$\frac{d}{dx}\left[f(x)\frac{dy_2}{dx} \right] + [g(x) + n_2 h(x)]y_2 = 0.$$

Multiply the top equation by y_2 and the bottom by $-y_1$, add, then proceed

[7]After J. C. F. Sturm (1803–1855) and J. Liouville (1809–1882).

to integrate both sides between the limits x_1 and x_2.

$$(n_2 - n_1)\int_{x_1}^{x_2} y_1 y_2 h(x)\,dx = \int_{x_1}^{x_2} f(x)\left[y_2\frac{d^2y_1}{dx^2} - y_1\frac{d^2y_2}{dx^2}\right]dx$$

$$+ \int_{x_1}^{x_2} f'(x)\left[y_2\frac{dy_1}{dx} - y_1\frac{dy_2}{dx}\right]dx$$

Consider the first term of the first integral on the right; it may be integrated by parts:

$$\int_{x_1}^{x_2} f(x)y_2\left(\frac{d^2y_1}{dx^2}\right)dx = f(x)y_2\frac{dy_1}{dx}\bigg|_{x_1}^{x_2} - \int_{x_1}^{x_2}\left(\frac{dy_1}{dx}\right)[f(x)y_2' + y_2 f'(x)]\,dx.$$

The first term on the right vanishes because of the boundary condition. If now the second term of the first integral in the master equation above is similarly integrated by parts, and then all terms are collected, it is found that there is complete cancellation. Hence we have the result

$$\boxed{\int_{x_1}^{x_2} y_1 y_2 h(x)\,dx = 0}$$

which says that the two eigenfunctions y_1 and y_2 are orthogonal (this term was introduced in Section 4.5) with respect to the weighting function $h(x)$ on the interval $[x_1, x_2]$. Sometimes $h(x)$ is equal to a constant; in that case we have

$$\int_{x_1}^{x_2} y_i(x)y_j(x)\,dx = 0 \qquad (i \neq j).$$

This, in fact, is the case with the harmonic oscillator wave functions. The results above are also true under the broader boundary conditions given earlier. Some examples of Sturm–Liouville equations are given in Table 5.8.

From entries 4 and 5 in the table we can conclude that the hydrogenic orbitals in a one-electron system are automatically orthogonal as a con-

Table 5.8   Some Sturm–Liouville Equations

Equation	$f(x)$	$g(x)$	$h(x)$	n	y
1. Harmonic oscillator equation	1	$\dfrac{-mkx^2}{\hbar^2}$	$\dfrac{2m}{\hbar^2}$	E	$\psi(x)$
2. Legendre's equation	$1-x^2$	0	1	$n(n+1)$	y
3. Schrödinger equation in one dimension	$\dfrac{\hbar^2}{2m}$	$-V(x)$	1	E	$\psi(x)$
4. Schrödinger radial equation for hydrogen	r^2	$\dfrac{2mrZe^2}{\hbar^2}-l(l+1)$	$\dfrac{2mr^2}{\hbar^2}$	E	$R(r)$
5. Schrödinger θ-equation for hydrogen	$\sin\theta$	$\dfrac{-m^2}{\sin\theta}$	$\sin\theta$	$l(l+1)$	$\Theta(\theta)$

sequence of the form of the differential equation plus the boundary condition. In multi-electronic atoms and in molecules the orbitals are usually *constructed* to be mutually orthogonal for reasons of mathematical convenience since the differential equation contains so many independent variables that are tightly coupled, thus preventing a rigorous separation into individual differential equations of the Sturm–Liouville type.

When a series solution of a second-order differential equation is not desired, other approaches are possible. Numerous methods exist for solving differential equations by purely numerical means. Other times an approximate solution that is good in a particular range of the independent variable is sufficient. The following is illustrative of the sort of approximate treatment that one can pursue. Consider the following one-dimensional, second-order differential equation:

$$\frac{d^2y}{dx^2} + k^2y = 0.$$

If k is a constant, the general solution is $Ae^{ikx} + Be^{-ikx} = y$. In other words the real and imaginary parts of particular solutions are cosine and sine waves of wavelength $2\pi/k$.

Now suppose in the equation above that $k = k(x)$, that k is positive, and that for all x of interest k is nearly a constant, that is, it is *slowly* varying. We can express a new, approximate solution as $y = e^{if(x)}$. If we substitute this into the differential equation, we get

$$\frac{d}{dx}\left[ie^{if(x)}f'(x)\right] + k^2(x)e^{if(x)} = 0$$

$$ie^{if(x)}f''(x) + f'(x)iie^{if(x)}f'(x) + k^2(x)e^{if(x)} = 0$$

or

$$[f'(x)]^2 - if''(x) = k^2(x).$$

The first level of approximation is to set $f''(x)$ equal to zero because $f(x)$ should be close to kx, that is, it should be close to linear and thus its second derivative would vanish. Therefore, we have

$$[f'(x)]^2 = k^2(x)$$

$$f'(x) = \pm k(x)$$

$$f(x) = \pm \int k(x)dx$$

and the approximate solution to the differential equation is

$$y \cong e^{\pm i\int k(x)dx}.$$

A better approximation is to now tack on a small correction to $f'(x)$, say $e(x)$:

$$f'(x) = \pm k(x) + e(x).$$

Differentiation of this and substitution into the equation relating $f'(x)$ and $f''(x)$ to $k(x)$ gives

$$[\pm k(x) + e(x)]^2 - i[\pm k'(x) + e'(x)] = k^2(x).$$

Since $e(x)$ is supposed to be small the quantities $e'(x)$ and $[e(x)]^2$ should probably be smaller. If these terms are neglected, then we get

$$k^2(x) \pm 2k(x)e(x) \mp ik'(x) = k^2(x)$$

or

$$e(x) = \frac{ik'(x)}{2k(x)} .$$

Therefore, we have

$$f(x) = \pm \int k(x)\,dx + \tfrac{1}{2}i \int \frac{k'(x)}{k(x)}\,dx$$

or

$$y \cong e^{i\int k(x)\,dx} / \sqrt{k(x)}$$

and if we revert back to sines and cosines, the approximate general solution can be written as

$$\boxed{\, y \cong A[k(x)]^{-\frac{1}{2}}\sin\left(\int k(x)\,dx\right) + B[k(x)]^{-\frac{1}{2}}\cos\left(\int k(x)\,dx\right) \,} .$$

In the scientific literature this procedure is known as the *WKB method*.[8]

As an illustration of the results let $k(x) = 5 - (1/x)$. Then as one particular solution to the differential equation we have

$$y \cong \frac{\sin(5x - \ln x)}{\sqrt{(5 - \frac{1}{x})}} .$$

This function is graphed in Figure 5.9, where it is compared with the reference function $y = (\sqrt{5}/5)\sin 5x$. The similarity of the two curves is evident.

[8]After G. Wentzel, H. A. Kramers, and L. Brillouin, who in 1926 independently published descriptions as well as extensions of the method.

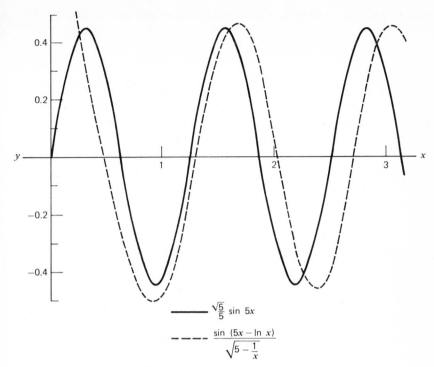

$$\underline{\hspace{2cm}} \quad \frac{\sqrt{5}}{5}\ \sin\ 5x$$

$$\underline{\ }\ \underline{\ }\ \underline{\ }\ \underline{\ } \quad \frac{\sin\ (5x-\ln\ x)}{\sqrt{5-\frac{1}{x}}}$$

Fig. 5.9   Illustration of the WKB method.

4   PARTIAL DIFFERENTIAL EQUATIONS

Partial differential equations can arise whenever one has a function of two or more independent variables and when the partial derivatives of the function with respect to these variables is important. Since characteristics of most real systems in Nature do depend on more than one variable, partial differential equations should be quite common. They should occur in thermodynamics where any of the state variables such as internal energy E for a real system would be expected to depend on at least two independent variables (such as pressure and temperature). They should occur in the treatment of transport properties such as diffusion or spin magnetization where the property in question would be expected to depend on one or more structural characteristics of the system and on time.

Like ordinary differential equations, partial differential equations may be classed by their order, that is, the order of the highest derivative. Second-order partial differential equations are particularly common in chemistry; a famous example of such an equation is Fick's second law of diffusion:

$$\frac{\partial C}{\partial t} = D \frac{\partial^2 C}{\partial x^2}.$$

It relates the time rate of change of concentration of some species at some point in a diffusive medium to the rate of change of the concentration gradient at that point. The term linear in partial differential equations also has the same meaning that it has in ordinary differential equations. A partial differential equation is said to be linear if it is of the first degree in the dependent variable and its derivatives. Fick's law of diffusion above is linear. The general linear partial differential equation of second order in two independent variables is, therefore,

$$A \frac{\partial^2 f}{\partial x^2} + B \frac{\partial^2 f}{\partial x \, \partial y} + C \frac{\partial^2 f}{\partial y^2} + D \frac{\partial f}{\partial x} + E \frac{\partial f}{\partial y} + Ff = G$$

where $A, B, \ldots, G$ are functions of x and y; they need not be linear in these variables. If the function G is identically zero, we say the partial differential equation is *homogeneous*. An important property of linear, homogeneous differential equations, whether they be ordinary or partial, can be stated somewhat in the nature of a superposition theorem much like Theorem 16.

Theorem 18. (Principle of Superposition). *Any linear combination of two solutions of a linear, homogeneous, differential equation is also a solution of the differential equation.*

Clearly, the theorem can be extended to combinations of three or more solutions as well.

As an application of the theorem we note that the Schrödinger equation (see earlier discussion on the harmonic oscillator, as well as Exercises 31*, 35*, and 37*) in quantum mechanics is a linear, second-order, homogeneous, partial differential equation. One-electron wave functions satisfying the equation for an atom, say, are the familiar $1s$, $2s$, etc., orbitals. If we wish to construct hybrid orbitals on this atom by making linear combinations of the original solutions, then Theorem 18 guarantees us that any such combination like

$$\psi_{sp^2} = c_1 \phi_{2s} + c_2 \phi_{2p_x} - c_3 \phi_{2p_z}$$

will also be a valid solution of the Schrödinger equation.

There is an important difference between ordinary and partial differential equations. A solution of an ordinary differential equation of order n has, in general, n arbitrary constants, but a solution of a partial differential equation of order n has, in general, n arbitrary *functions*. In many applied situations, however, one is not interested in obtaining general solutions to partial differential equations, but rather just particular solutions satisfying certain auxiliary conditions. For example, because of the nature of the solutions, different types of boundary specifications are found to work best for the general, linear, second-order partial differential equation of two variables, depending on whether the *discriminant*, $B^2 - 4AC$, is positive, negative, or zero. By analogy with the terminology used in Section 1.3, the differential equation is classified as

$$\text{hyperbolic if } B^2 - 4AC > 0$$

$$\text{elliptic if } B^2 - 4AC < 0$$

$$\text{parabolic if } B^2 - 4AC = 0.$$

These types are illustrated by the following examples:

One-dimensional wave equation	$\dfrac{\partial^2 \psi}{\partial x^2} = \dfrac{1}{c^2} \dfrac{\partial^2 \psi}{\partial t^2}$	hyperbolic	$B^2 - 4AC = \dfrac{4}{c^2}$
Two-dimensional Laplace equation	$\dfrac{\partial^2 \psi}{\partial x^2} + \dfrac{\partial^2 \psi}{\partial y^2} = 0$	elliptic	$B^2 - 4AC = -4$
One-dimensional diffusion equation	$\dfrac{\partial^2 \psi}{\partial x^2} = \dfrac{1}{D} \dfrac{\partial \psi}{\partial t}$	parabolic	$B^2 - 4AC = 0.$

In the space remaining we do not pursue ways of obtaining general solutions; further, we restrict ourselves to one common technique for handling second-order equations. The interested reader who wishes to know more about first-order equations and about general methods of solution is referred to other works (books by Sneddon and other authors as cited in the Annotated Bibliography).

It happens that many second-order partial differential equations can be attacked by means of a device called the *separation of variables*. We may illustrate this by first working one example in the abstract and then by solving the one-dimensional diffusion equation.

Example 48. Solve the equation $(\partial^2 z / \partial x^2) = (\partial^2 z / \partial y^2) + 2(\partial z / \partial x)$ by means of the separation of variables.

Answer. We want to assume that a solution has the form $z = X(x)Y(y)$, and then see if the equation is solvable. Substitution of this into the above gives

$$y\frac{d^2X}{dx^2} = X\frac{d^2Y}{dy^2} + 2Y\frac{dX}{dx}.$$

Division of both sides by XY and rearrangement yields

$$\frac{1}{X}\frac{d^2X}{dx^2} - \frac{2}{X}\frac{dX}{dx} = \frac{1}{Y}\frac{d^2Y}{dy^2}.$$

Now this equation is an equality for all permissible values of x and y; but x and y, supposedly, are independent variables. Therefore, the only way the equality can persist is if both sides are equal to some constant, say, $-k^2$ (this choice is merely one of convenience). We therefore have two separate second-order, ordinary differential equations. One of these is

$$\frac{d^2Y}{dy^2} = -k^2Y$$

and solutions for this can be written as $Y = e^{iky}$, e^{-iky}. The other equation is

$$\frac{d^2X}{dx^2} - 2\frac{dX}{dx} + k^2X = 0.$$

One neat way to solve this is to think of it as a factorable quadratic equation

$$(D^2 - 2D + k^2)X = 0$$

where $D \equiv d/dx$. This quadratic equation can be factored as

$$\left[D - \left(1 + \sqrt{1-k^2}\,\right)\right]\left[D - \left(1 - \sqrt{1-k^2}\,\right)\right]X = 0$$

and hence we must have separately

$$\left[D - \left(1 + \sqrt{1-k^2}\,\right)\right]X = 0 \text{ and } \left[D - \left(1 - \sqrt{1-k^2}\,\right)\right]X = 0.$$

The solutions to these first-order equations are

$$X = c_1\exp\left[\left(1 + \sqrt{1-k^2}\,\right)x\right]$$

$$X = c_2\exp\left[\left(1 - \sqrt{1-k^2}\,\right)x\right].$$

With two possible solutions for Y and two possible solutions for X, this gives four possible ways of expressing z. One of these is

$$z = c\exp\left[\left(1 + \sqrt{1 - k^2}\,\right)x + iky\right]$$

and by Theorem 18 combinations of this with any of the other three possibilities will also be solutions.

Let us now work in detail another example, where in this case physical considerations dictate how we may select boundary conditions and employ them to obtain a particular solution. This example concerns the physical phenomenon of diffusion. Diffusion is a process that operates to equalize the concentrations of a given solute throughout all regions of a single phase. Fick's laws of diffusion (after A. Fick, who published them in 1855) relate the flow rate of the diffusing substance with the concentration gradient responsible for this flow. *Fick's first law of diffusion* says that the flow rate J is proportional to the concentration gradient. The flow rate is the quantity of substance passing through a reference surface (such as a plane) of unit area in unit time. The law may be formulated as

$$J = -D\frac{\partial C}{\partial x}$$

and if J has units of moles $cm^{-2}sec^{-1}$, then the *coefficient of diffusion*, D, has units of cm^2sec^{-1}. For one substance diffusing into another, there is an equation like this for both substances; their coefficients of diffusion, in general, would be unequal.

Fick's first law is not very practical to work with experimentally because in order to get D by measurement of J, one has to have a fixed concentration gradient. It is easier to look at the time rate of change of the concentration. Consider a small volume element in solution bounded by two parallel planes of area A and located at x and $x + dx$. The amount of diffusing substance passing the first plane per unit time is $A(J)_x = -AD(\partial C/\partial x)$. The amount of substance passing the second plane per unit time is $A(J)_{x+dx} = -AD(\partial C/\partial x) + Ad[-D(\partial C/\partial x)]$. Hence the net increase in the amount of substance in the volume element accumulated during a unit time period is

$$A(J)_x - A(J)_{x+dx} = A\frac{\partial}{\partial x}\left(D\frac{\partial C}{\partial x}\right)dx.$$

To rewrite this, we observe that $A \, dx$ is a volume differential, dV, and if both sides are divided by this, the left-hand side then has units of moles per volume per time, that is, a time-rate of change of concentration. The above equation can thus be written as

$$\frac{\partial C}{\partial t} = \frac{\partial}{\partial x}\left(D \frac{\partial C}{\partial x}\right).$$

The coefficient of diffusion is strictly not a constant; it varies with the concentration, but if one operates in dilute solutions where it is nearly a constant, then we have *Fick's second law of diffusion* in its more common form:

$$\frac{\partial C}{\partial t} = D \frac{\partial^2 C}{\partial x^2}.$$

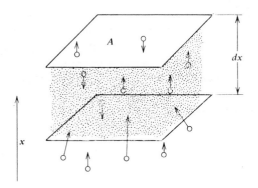

Fig. 5.10 Diffusion.

The first law of diffusion is thus a first-order partial differential equation, and the second law of diffusion is a second-order partial differential equation.

Before proceeding let us look at some experimental values for the diffusion coefficient. Data for some representative substances are collected in Table 5.9. It is one of the obligations of modern-day kinetic molecular theory and of present theories of the liquid and solid states to interpret data such as these. The data themselves show some interesting features. In the gaseous phase the coefficient D is about 10^3–10^4 times larger than in condensed phases. In the latter there appears to be little variation with respect to solute charge or mass except in extreme cases such as highly charged macromolecules. Although not evident by the data in the table, there should be some dependence of the solute diffusion coefficient on temperature and on the solvent.

Table 5.9 Some Coefficients of Diffusion

Substance[a]	D $(10^5$ $cm^2sec^{-1})$	Remarks	Substance[a]	D $(10^5$ $cm^2sec^{-1})$	Remarks
He	138,500	STP	I_2	2.697	20°C in CS_2
CO_2	10,300	STP	$Na^+_{(aq)}$	1.30	25°C $(0.05M)$
Hg	1.63	25°C	$Cd^{2+}_{(aq)}$	1.99	25°C $(0.00015M)$
Na^+	13.75	952°C	$I^-_{(aq)}$	1.88	25°C $(0.05\ M)$
H_2O	2.13	25°C	Ribonuclease[b]	0.119	25°C in water
Sucrose	5.23	25°C in water	Serum album-in[b]	0.0594	25°C in water

[a] Data taken from Landolt-Börnstein, *Zahlenwerte und Funktionen*, Band II., Teil 5a, "Transportphänomene," Springer-Verlag, Berlin, 1969, pp. 516–653.
[b] From C. Tanford, *Physical Chemistry of Macromolecules*, Wiley, New York, 1967, p. 358.

An understanding of diffusion and a knowledge of diffusion coefficients are essential in many chemical situations. In the analytical technique known as *chronoamperometry*, for example, a current is measured as a function of time following the sudden application of an electrical potential of sufficient magnitude to cause an electrode reaction (such as a reduction). If the electroactive species is transported by diffusion and not by convection, the diffusion coefficient can be evaluated from the current-time relationship. To see this we recall that for the process $A^{n+} + ne^- \rightarrow B$

current = no. of Coulombs of charge arriving at
the electrode per second

= no. of electrons
involved per second $\times$ charge on the electron

= $N_0 \times$ no. of moles of A^{n+}
involved per second $\times (n \times e)$

= $N_0 \times$ area of the
electrode, A $\times$ diffusion
flow, J $\times ne$

$$\therefore \boxed{\ i = ADnF \left(\frac{\partial C}{\partial x} \right)_{x=0}\ }$$

from Fick's first law. The quantity F is the Faraday (96,500 C mole^{-1}). Since the concentration gradient evaluated at the electrode is a function of the initial concentration C_0, a knowledge of D plus a measurement of the current i with time permit the determination of C_0.

Example 49. A cation M^+ moving in one direction toward a cathode where it picks up an electron obeys Fick's second law of diffusion. Find a solution to the differential equation.

Answer. Assume the concentration has the form $C(x,t) = X(x)T(t)$. Substitution into the partial differential equation representing Fick's second law and division of both sides by $X(x)T(t)$ gives

$$\frac{1}{X(x)} \frac{d^2X}{dx^2} = \frac{1}{D} \frac{1}{T(t)} \frac{dT}{dt}.$$

In this equation the left side is a function of x only, and the right side is a function of t only. The equality must hold for all pairs (x,t), which implies that both sides are equal to a constant, say $-k^2$. We then have

$$\frac{d^2X}{dx^2} = -k^2X$$

and thus

$$X(x) = a\sin kx + b\cos kx.$$

Also,

$$\frac{dT}{dt} = -k^2DT$$

and thus

$$T(t) = e^{-k^2Dt}.$$

A general solution, therefore, is

$$\boxed{C(x,t) = (a\sin kx + b\cos kx)\exp(-k^2Dt)}.$$

Before proceeding we note that this example and the preceding one prompt the question: how do we know that the solution is one where the variables are separated? The answer is that we don't know, but that we assume a separation of variables as a possible way of trying to solve the differential equation, and if a solution so obtained can be made to satisfy all prescribed boundary conditions there is no reason to discard the solution. It should be stressed again that the boundary conditions usually arise from physical and not mathematical considerations.

In the example above a reasonable set of boundary conditions might be the following:

(*a*) The electroactive species is reduced at a rate that is so fast that the effective concentration of the species at the electrode is close to zero during the entire electrolysis, or stated in mathematical terms, $C(0,t)=0$ for $t>0$.

(*b*) Before reduction of M^+ commences the concentration of M^+ everywhere in the solution (neglecting adsorption at the electrode) is some constant value, or $C(x,0)=C_0$.

Consideration of boundary condition (*a*) leads to the conclusion that in the general solution $b=0$; this leaves us with the product of a sine function times an exponential. Physically such an expression cannot be correct. The sine function can assume negative values, but a negative concentration is meaningless. In order for boundary condition (*b*) to hold one must have in the expression several sines. There is still a problem, however, since $\sin kx$ has no limit as x approaches infinity. This means that we cannot assume our vessel to be infinitely large; we must specify some upper limit for x at which $C(x,t)=0$.

Suppose we take this upper limit to be $x=2$. Then we have at $t=0$ the relation $C(x,t)=0=a\sin 2k$, and hence, $k=\tfrac{1}{2}n\pi$, where $n=1, 2, 3,\ldots$. The general solution is now

$$C(x,t)=\sum_{n=1}^{\infty}\left(a_n\sin\tfrac{1}{2}n\pi x\right)e^{-\tfrac{1}{4}n^2\pi^2 Dt}$$

and to find the a_n's we note that at $t=0$ this is just a Fourier sine series provided that

$$a_n=\tfrac{2}{2}\int_0^2 C_0\sin\tfrac{1}{2}n\pi x\, dx$$

$$=4\frac{C_0}{n\pi}.$$

Therefore, the final general solution is given by

$$C(x,t)=\frac{4C_0}{\pi}\sum_{n=1}^{\infty}\frac{(\sin\tfrac{1}{2}n\pi x)\exp\left(-\tfrac{1}{4}n^2\pi^2 Dt\right)}{n}$$

$$=\frac{4C_0}{\pi}\left[\sin\tfrac{1}{2}\pi x\,\exp\left(-\tfrac{1}{4}\pi^2 Dt\right)+\tfrac{1}{3}\sin\tfrac{3}{2}\pi x\,\exp\left(-\tfrac{9}{4}\pi^2 Dt\right)+\cdots+\right].$$

As a quick check consider the point $(1,0)$. The series in the brackets is then just the alternating series $1-\tfrac{1}{3}+\tfrac{1}{5}-\tfrac{1}{7}+\cdots-$. From formula 5 of Section 4.3 this series is $\tan^{-1}1$ or $\tfrac{1}{4}\pi$; hence $C(1,0)=(4C_0/\pi)\times\tfrac{1}{4}\pi=C_0$, in agreement with boundary condition (*b*).

Suppose we change our model slightly and operate with a vessel that is very large (in an approximate sense, infinitely large). Then we must replace the boundary condition that says the concentration goes to zero at the edge, by one that says that at an infinite distance from the cathode the concentration of ion remains sensibly constant at a value of C_0 during the electrolysis. It is clear from the argument above that one then cannot use the separation of variables technique to solve the partial differential equation representing Fick's second law of diffusion.

To proceed we make use of material presented earlier. Let us take the Laplace transform *with respect to t* of both sides of Fick's second law:

$$\int_0^\infty e^{-st}\frac{\partial^2 C}{\partial x^2}\,dt = \frac{1}{D}\int_0^\infty e^{-st}\frac{\partial C}{\partial t}\,dt.$$

Since in the left integral the partial differentiation is with respect to x and the integration is with respect to t, we assume that we may interchange the order of the two operations. This gives for the left side

$$\frac{d^2}{dx^2}\int_0^\infty e^{-st}C\,dt = \frac{d^2}{dx^2}L\{C(x,t)\}.$$

The integral on the right side above is just an application of transform no. 9 in Table 5.4. If we let $L\{C(x,t)\} = F(x,s)$, then we have

$$\frac{d^2F}{dx^2} = \frac{sF}{D} - \frac{C_0}{D}$$

and the solution of this second-order ordinary differential equation is

$$F(x,s) = Ae^{-\sqrt{s/D}\,x} + Be^{+\sqrt{s/D}\,x} + \frac{C_0}{s}.$$

To evaluate the arbitrary constants A and B we recall that $C(0,t)=0$. The Laplace transform of this gives $F(0,s)=0$, and hence $0 = A + B + (C_0/s)$. Our new boundary condition that we instituted for this particular model is $C(\infty,t) = C_0$; the Laplace transform of this yields $F(\infty,s) = C_0/s$. This implies that $B=0$. Hence we have that $A = -C_0/s$, and therefore

$$F(x,s) = \frac{C_0}{s} - \frac{C_0}{s}e^{-\sqrt{s/D}\,x}.$$

From transforms 1 and 25 we find that the inverse Laplace transform of this is

$$C(x,t) = C_0 - C_0\,\text{erfc}\left[\frac{x}{2\sqrt{Dt}}\right]$$

and from material given in Chapter 3 we can rewrite this finally as

$$C(x,t) = \frac{2C_0}{\sqrt{\pi}} \int_0^{x/2\sqrt{Dt}} \exp(-u^2)\,du \; .$$

This solution is clearly one where the variables are not separated. A plot of $C(x,t)$ versus $t^{-1/2}$ for constant x is shown in Figure 5.11a.

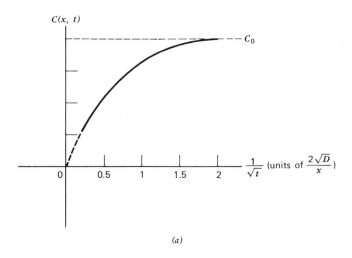

(a)

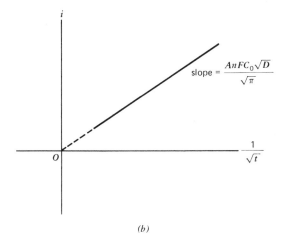

(b)

Fig. 5.11 Plot of (a) concentration, and (b) current versus $t^{-1/2}$.

Finally, we inquire about the current–time relationship in our chronoamperometry experiment. Differentiation of the above expression with respect to x according to Theorem 6 gives

$$C'(x,t) = \frac{C_0}{\sqrt{\pi Dt}} \exp\left(-x^2/4Dt\right)$$

and insertion into the expression for the current i yields

$$i = \frac{AnFC_0\sqrt{D}}{\sqrt{\pi}} \frac{1}{\sqrt{t}}.$$

Hence according to this model a plot of current versus reciprocal square root of time should be linear. From the slope of a plot such as the one in Figure 5.11b one can determine D if C_0 is known, or alternatively, determine C_0 if D is known. As in any experimental science, of course, the selection and development of a suitable model is to be guided by the results of experiment.

EXERCISES

1. Solve the following first-order differential equations:

(a) $\dfrac{dy}{dx} + \dfrac{3e^x}{1+e^x} \dfrac{\tan y}{\sec^2 y} = 0$ $[y(\ln 3) = \tfrac{1}{4}\pi]$

(b) $\left(x + y\sin\dfrac{y}{x}\right)dx - x\sin\dfrac{y}{x}\,dy = 0$

(c) $\dfrac{dy}{dx} = \dfrac{2(x-y)}{1-x}$

(d) $2r(r\sin 2\theta + \cos 2\theta)\,d\theta + (\sin 2\theta - 2r\cos 2\theta)\,dr = 0$

(e) $1 + 2xy\dfrac{dy}{dx} = ye^{-y^2}\dfrac{dy}{dx}$

(f) $\dfrac{dy}{dx}\left\{-xy\dfrac{dy}{dx} + 2x^2 + y^2\right\} = 2xy$

(g) $\dfrac{dy}{dx} + \dfrac{2y}{x} = 3 + x^2$

(h) $\dfrac{dy}{dx} = 2 - \dfrac{1}{x}\dfrac{dz}{dx};\quad x\dfrac{dz}{dx} - \dfrac{dy}{dx} = -z$

2. According to an absorption law due to Lambert,[9] the rate of change of the intensity of light transmitted by a thin transparent layer with respect to the thickness of the layer is proportional to the intensity of light transmitted. Express this as a differential equation and solve. State as much as you can regarding the nature of the constants in your solution.

3. A differential equation encountered by E. Rutherford in his study of the scattering of α particles from metal nuclei is

$$\frac{d\theta}{dr} + \frac{b}{r^2}\sqrt{1 - \frac{2q}{r} - \frac{b^2}{r^2}} = 0$$

where b and q are constants. Determine the scattering angle θ as a function of the distance r subject to the boundary condition $\theta = 0°$ at $r = \infty$.

4. Quantum chemistry, insofar as it begins with the Schrödinger equation, may be said to be the physical application of the mathematical eigenvalue–eigenfunction problem. This is a very general type of problem which says the following: Let $\hat{O}$ be some known differential operator; it is required to find functions $f(x)$, called eigenfunctions, and numbers E, called eigenvalues, such that

$$\hat{O}f(x) = Ef(x).$$

In quantum chemistry $\hat{O}$ may be a Hamiltonian, the allowed $f(x)$'s wave functions, and the E's allowed energy values. Show that $f(x) = Ce^{-ax}$ is an eigenfunction of the operator

$$\hat{O} = \frac{d^2}{dx^2} + 2\frac{d}{dx} - 2a$$

and find the corresponding eigenvalue.

5. Various differential equations have come down to us associated with the names of certain individuals. For example, we have
   (a) the Bernoulli equation,

$$\frac{dy}{dx} + f(x)y = g(x)y^n,$$

[9] After Johann Heinrich Lambert (1728–1777), who was born in Mulhouse, Alsace (then part of Switzerland), and who was the author of the famous work *Photometria*. This work was later issued in German in the series of Ostwald's *Klassiker*.

after Jakob Bernoulli (1654–1705). Show that this equation becomes linear if the substitution $z = y^{1-n}$ is made.

(b) the Riccati equation,

$$\frac{dy}{dx} + ay^2 = bx^n,$$

after Count Jacopo Francesco Riccati (1676–1754). Show that the Riccati equation becomes

$$\frac{d^2z}{dx^2} - abzx^n = 0$$

upon making the substitution $y = z'/az$. The equation may be solved by means of Bessel functions.

(c) the Clairaut equation,

$$y = x\frac{dy}{dx} + f\left(\frac{dy}{dx}\right),$$

after Alexis C. Clairaut (1713–1765). Show how simplification results by just differentiating this equation and letting the derivative dy/dx be represented by the variable p.

6. Should the function $\exp(x^2)$ have a Laplace transform? Explain.

7. Verify entry number 17 in the table of Laplace transforms (Hint: you may want to refer back to certain material in Chapter 3.)

8. Recalling the special properties of differentials such as dS, dE, dG, etc., and the mathematical statement of the second law of thermodynamics (refer back to Table 2.3 if necessary), formulate a statement of the second law in terms of vocabulary from Section 5.1.

9. P. Schweitzer and R. M. Noyes [*J. Am. Chem. Soc.*, **93**, 3561 (1971)] recently found that the reaction of iodine with bromine in 96% aqueous sulfuric acid

$$\underset{A_0 - x}{I_2} + \underset{B_0 - x}{Br_2} \underset{k_{-1}}{\overset{k_1}{\rightleftharpoons}} 2IBr$$

follows the rate law

$$\frac{1}{2}\frac{d[IBr]}{dt} = k[I_2]_0\left\{[I_2][Br_2] - \frac{[IBr]^2}{K}\right\}$$

where $[I_2]_0$ is a constant (the initial concentration of iodine) and K is also a constant (the equilibrium constant for the reaction). Solve this differential equation and express [IBr] as a function of time.

10. Consider the second-order, nonlinear, differential equation

$$xy\frac{d^2y}{dx^2} + x\left(\frac{dy}{dx}\right)^2 - y\frac{dy}{dx} = 0.$$

(a) Make the change of variable $x = e^t$ and after applying the chain rule show that the above equation assumes the form $y'' = f(y, y')$, where y' now means dy/dt.

(b) To solve an equation of this form assume $y' = p(y)$; then it follows that $y'' = p'(y)p(y)$ and the resulting equation becomes a first-order equation. Solve this for the example above and eventually express y as a function of x.

11. Second-order, nonlinear, differential equations of the form $y'' = f(x, y')$ may be solved by making the substitution $y' = p(x)$. Apply this to solving the equation

$$(1 - x^2)\frac{d^2y}{dx^2} + x\frac{dy}{dx} = x.$$

12. Solutions to differential equations are sometimes given as indefinite integrals. Show that

$$y = \frac{1}{c}\int_0^x f(a)\sin c(x - a)\,da$$

is a solution to the differential equation

$$\frac{d^2y}{dx^2} + c^2y = f(x).$$

13. Show that if the substitutions $\varepsilon = \frac{1}{2}x$ and $y = \exp(-\frac{1}{2}\varepsilon^2)f(\varepsilon)$ are made in Weber's differential equation, then Hermite's differential equation results, and thus in the quantum mechanical treatment of the one-dimensional harmonic oscillator one could equally well have solved Weber's equation instead of Hermite's equation in order to get the wave functions.

14. Work through all the steps leading from Schrödinger's equation for the harmonic oscillator to the Hermite differential equation. Also show that the oscillator has a *zero-point energy*, that is, a nonzero energy even when the quantum number n is zero. The existence of a zero-point energy is a purely quantum mechanical phenomenon.

15. Write out the first five or six derivatives of the simple function $\exp(-x^2)$. By inspection ascertain a relation that connects the $(n+1)$st derivative with lower derivatives. The similarity of this relation to the Hermite differential equation underlies the Rodrigues' formula given in Exercise $37^*(b)$ of Chapter 4.

In that exercise you were also given the generating function for the Hermite polynomials. From the generating function derive the following relationship:

$$\frac{H_n'(x)}{n!} = \frac{2H_{n-1}(x)}{(n-1)!}.$$

16. Work through all the steps leading to the statement of the orthogonality of the eigenfunctions of a Sturm–Liouville equation. Then show that wave functions $\psi_1(x)$ and $\psi_2(x)$ for the harmonic oscillator are indeed orthogonal.

17. The zero overlap between an s orbital on one atom and a p-π orbital on an adjacent atom is sometimes qualitatively rationalized by noting the equal contributions of the positive and negative lobes of the p orbital. To show that sketches like this can be pushed too far, work out the overlap integral S by direct integration for a $1s$ and $2s$ orbital of

$$S = \int \psi_{1s} \psi_{2s} \, d\tau$$

hydrogen *located on the same center*, and thus show, as Sturm–Liouville theory would tell us, that the overlap here is zero even though pictorially the two orbitals would appear to overlap perfectly well (see Figure 5.12*b*).

18. Find the general power series solution to $(d^2y/dx^2) + x(dy/dx) + 2y = x$. Apply a test for convergence to the terms in your series. Making use of material in Chapter 4, see if you can simplify part of your answer.

19. There is a convolution theorem for Laplace transforms which is exactly analogous to the corresponding theorem for Fourier transforms (refer to the end of Chapter 3). Let $f(x)$ and $g(x)$ have Laplace transforms $F(s)$ and $G(s)$, and let $h(x)$ be the convolution integral

$$h(x) = \int_0^x f(x-z) g(z) \, dz = \int_0^x f(z) g(x-z) \, dz.$$

Then according to the convolution theorem we have

$$H(s) = F(s)G(s).$$

Use this relation to invert the transform $H(s) = (1/s)e^{-a\sqrt{s}}$.

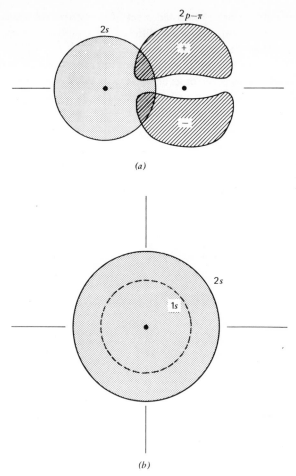

Fig. 5.12 Overlap of (a) an s and a p orbital, and (b) two s orbitals.

20. By substituting the final exponential form of the answer back into the original differential equation

$$\frac{d^2y}{dx^2} + k^2y = 0,$$

show that the Wentzel–Kramers–Brillouin approximation will be a good one if the derivatives of $k(x)$ are close to zero. In the illustrative example verify that the numerical error for reasonably large x (say, $x > 2$) is about $\dfrac{\sqrt{5}}{25} x^{-3}$, that is, about 0.011 at $x = 2$.

21. Suppose that we have obtained a set of particular solutions $y_1(x), y_2(x)$, $y_3(x), \ldots, y_n(x)$ to an nth-order differential equation. From the text we know that any linear combination of any of them is also a solution. What we would like to know is if any members of the set are already linear combinations of some of the others (this is a feature that we do not want). It is known that for a linear, ordinary nth-order *homogeneous* differential equation the n particular solutions of some test set will be linearly independent of each other if their *Wronskian*[10] W is different from zero.

$$
W = \begin{vmatrix}
y_1 & y_2 & y_3 & \cdots & y_n \\
y_1' & y_2' & y_3' & \cdots & y_n' \\
y_1'' & y_2'' & y_3'' & \cdots & y_n'' \\
\vdots & \vdots & & & \\
y_1^{n-1} & y_2^{n-1} & \cdots & \cdots & y_n^{n-1}
\end{vmatrix}
$$

Are x and e^x linearly independent solutions of the differential equation

$$
\frac{d^2y}{dx^2} + \frac{x}{1-x}\frac{dy}{dx} - \frac{y}{1-x} = 0 ?
$$

Are the wave functions $\psi_1(x)$ and $\psi_2(x)$ of the harmonic oscillator linearly independent of each other?

22. To illustrate the difference between ordinary and partial differential equations of order n, verify that $z = xf(y) + g(y)$ is a general solution of the second-order partial differential equation

$$
\frac{\partial^2 z}{\partial x^2} = 0
$$

where $f(y)$ and $g(y)$ are arbitrary functions.

23. By substitution show that the function $C(x,t) = \exp(-k^2 t)\sin(kx/\sqrt{D})$ is a solution to the one-dimensional second diffusion law of Fick. Will the more general function

$$
C(x,t) = \sum_{n=1}^{N} a_n \exp(-k^2 n^2 t)\sin\frac{knx}{\sqrt{D}},
$$

where $a_1, a_2, \ldots, a_N$ are constants, also be a solution?

[10]After the Polish-born mathematician Josef Maria Hoëné-Wronski (1778–1853).

24. Solve the partial differential equation $\dfrac{\partial^2 z}{\partial x^2} = x^2 e^{-y}$.

25. Consider the hyperbolic partial differential equation

$$\frac{\partial^2 \psi}{\partial x^2} - \frac{\partial^2 \psi}{\partial y^2} = 1.$$

Now let $x = \omega + z$ and $y = \omega - z$. Show that the differential equation becomes

$$\frac{\partial^2 \psi}{\partial \omega \, \partial z} = 1.$$

By a suitable transformation hyperbolic equations can generally be put in this convenient form.

26.* In their study of solutions of electrolytes P. Debye and E. Hückel were required to solve the differential equation

$$\frac{1}{r^2} \frac{d}{dr}\left(r^2 \frac{d\phi}{dr} \right) = \frac{e^2 \phi}{kT\varepsilon\varepsilon_0} \sum_i c_i Z_i^2$$

where $\phi = \phi(r)$ is the electrical potential of an ion at a point r units away, and all other quantities are constants. Find the general solution to this equation after making the substitution $u(r) = r\phi(r)$.

27.* The Bessel function of the first kind and of order zero is an infinite series.

$$J_0(x) = \sum_{m=0}^{\infty} \frac{(-1)^m}{m!\, m!}\left(\frac{x}{2} \right)^{2m}$$

Proceed to find the Laplace transform of this by direct integration; assume that there is no problem in reversing the order of summation and integration. Your result will be another infinite series; write out the first three terms of this series. Now use the binomial theorem to write out the first three terms in the expansion of $(x+y)^{-1/n}$, and by making suitable identifications between these two series, show that the transform of $J_0(x)$ reduces to a simple algebraic form.

28.* Consider a simple nuclear magnetic spin system where the spin quantum number I can assume only the values of $\pm \frac{1}{2}$ (see Figure 5.13). Let $N_{\pm \frac{1}{2}}$ be the instantaneous populations of the two levels and define n as the surplus of spins in the lower energy state, $(N_{+\frac{1}{2}} - N_{-\frac{1}{2}})$. If a large collection of such spins at equilibrium is suddenly perturbed, the collection will relax according to the differential equation

$$\frac{dn}{dt} = \frac{n_0 - n}{T_1}$$

where n_0 is the surplus at equilibrium and T_1 is the *spin-lattice relaxation time*.

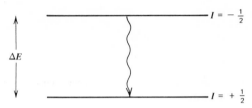

Fig. 5.13   A two-level spin system.

(a) Solve this differential equation for n in terms of t.

(b) If the collection of spins is present in a static radiation field when the perturbation is applied, then another term is required.

$$\frac{dn}{dt} = \frac{n_0 - n}{T_1} - 2nW$$

Here W is a constant; it is a function of the static field strength, and represents the probability of an induced transition from the upper to the lower state. Solve for n now in terms of t.

(c) If $\Delta E \ll kT$, what can you say about n_0? Try to be quantitative. (Hint: think back to Exercise 34* at the end of Chapter 2.)

29.* Find the eigenfunctions and eigenvalues for the operator d^2/dx^2 for the region $0 \leqslant x \leqslant a$ if the eigenfunctions $\psi(x)$ also satisfy the boundary relations $\psi(x) = 0$ at $x = a$, and $d\psi(x)/dx = 0$ at $x = 0$.

30.* Consider the linear, homogeneous differential equation

$$\frac{d}{dx}\left[f(x)\frac{dy}{dx} \right] + g(x)y = 0$$

and let $y_1(x)$ and $y_2(x)$ be two linearly independent solutions of it. After eliminating $g(x)$ from these two solutions, show that

$$y_1(x)y_2'(x) - y_2(x)y_1'(x) = \frac{\text{constant}}{f(x)}$$

and thus only at points where $f(x)$ is unbounded can the Wronskian (see Exercise 21) of two linearly independent solutions of the equation vanish.

31.* The Schrödinger equation for the deuteron, written as an angle-independent equation, is in polar coordinates

$$\frac{-\hbar^2}{2\mu r^2}\left[r^2\frac{d^2\psi}{dr^2} + 2r\frac{d\psi}{dr} \right] + V(r)\psi = E\psi$$

where μ is the reduced mass (recall Exercise 42* of Chapter 1) of the neutron–proton pair (each being assumed to have identical mass M). In one simple version of the theory the potential $V(r)$ is taken to be a square-well potential (see Figure 5.14), and one looks for solutions of the form $\psi = \phi(r)/r$, subject to the requirements that $\lim_{r\to 0}\psi$ be finite and $\lim_{r\to\infty}\psi = 0$.

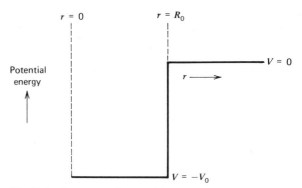

Fig. 5.14 A square-well potential.

(a) Write the Schrödinger equation in terms of $\phi(r)$ for the two regions $r < R_0$ and $r > R_0$, and find solutions for both regions.
(b) We now require that these two solutions join smoothly at the boundary $r = R_0$. Show that this means that R_0 and V_0 must satisfy the relation

$$\cot\frac{R_0}{\hbar}\sqrt{M(E+V_0)} = -\sqrt{\frac{-E}{E+V_0}}\ .$$

32.* A very widely occurring class of equations in science are the so-called *integral equations*. They appear, for example, in all molecular theories of the liquid state. An example of an integral equation is

$$\frac{df(x)}{dx} + af(x) = b - \frac{a^2}{4} \int_0^x f(t)\,dt.$$

Here the unknown is a function which is contained in an integrand.
(a) Show by integration by parts that the Laplace transform of an
integral $\int_0^z g(x)\,dx$ is given by $\frac{1}{s} L\{g(x)\}$.
(b) Use this result to solve the integral equation above, given that
$f(0) = 1$. Check your answer by substitution.

33.* In a nuclear magnetic resonance experiment a macroscopic sample of
nuclei bathed in an external static magnetic field H_0 and also subjected
to a rotating magnetic field H_1 acquires a magnetization that changes
with time. The magnetization $\mathbf{M}$ is defined as the magnetic moment $\mathbf{p}$
of the bulk sample divided by the volume; $\mathbf{M}$ is a vector because the
magnetic dipole moment is a vector. The variations with time of the
components of $\mathbf{M}$ are given by the famous *Bloch equations*[11]:

$$\frac{dM_x}{dt} = \gamma(M_y H_0 - M_z H_1 \sin \omega t) - \frac{M_x}{T_2}$$

$$\frac{dM_y}{dt} = -\gamma(M_x H_0 - M_z H_1 \cos \omega t) - \frac{M_y}{T_2}$$

$$\frac{dM_z}{dt} = -\gamma(M_x H_1 \sin \omega t + M_y H_1 \cos \omega t) - \frac{M_z - M_0}{T_1}.$$

The T's are constants referred to as relaxation times; the quantities γ,
ω, H_0, and H_1 are also constants. Show how Laplace transforms could
in principle be used to solve these coupled differential equations, but do
not actually carry the work through to completion as the inverse
transforms will be extremely messy. Assume the experiment is done by
starting with the sample equilibrated in the H_0 field, and then turning
on the H_1 field at time $t = 0$; then $M_x(0) = M_y(0) = 0$ and $M_z(0) = M_0$.

34.* In some instances an electrochemical cell may be shaped in the form of
a long circular cylinder with the electrode in the center in the form of a
long, thin cylindrical rod. For this situation show that Fick's second law

[11]After Felix Bloch (1905–   ), who received the Nobel prize in physics in 1952 for his work in
magnetic resonance.

of diffusion (x and y variables, only) should be written as

$$\frac{\partial C}{\partial t} = D \left[\frac{\partial^2 C}{\partial r^2} + \frac{1}{r}\frac{\partial C}{\partial r} + \frac{1}{r^2}\frac{\partial^2 C}{\partial \phi^2} \right].$$

Investigate whether or not the equation in this form is separable.

35.* The Schrödinger equation for the hydrogen atom is

$$\left[\frac{-\hbar^2}{2m}\nabla^2 - \frac{e^2}{\sqrt{x^2+y^2+z^2}} \right]\psi = E\psi$$

where ∇^2 is the Laplacian operator

$$\frac{\partial^2}{\partial x^2} + \frac{\partial^2}{\partial y^2} + \frac{\partial^2}{\partial z^2}.$$

Convince yourself that this equation is not separable, that is, that the assumption that $\psi(x,y,z) = X(x)Y(y)Z(z)$ does not lead to three separate, ordinary differential equations. If the Laplacian is written in terms of a spherical polar coordinate system centered on the nucleus, the wave equation becomes

$$\frac{1}{r^2\sin^2\theta}\frac{\partial^2\psi}{\partial\phi^2} + \frac{1}{r^2\sin\theta}\frac{\partial}{\partial\theta}\left(\sin\theta\frac{\partial\psi}{\partial\theta}\right)$$

$$+\frac{1}{r^2}\frac{\partial}{\partial r}\left(r^2\frac{\partial\psi}{\partial r}\right) + \frac{2me^2}{r\hbar^2}\psi = -\frac{2mE}{\hbar^2}\psi.$$

Show that in this form the equation is separable. This is one justification for using this particular coordinate system. Solve the ordinary differential equation in ϕ, but do not attempt to solve the other two equations (we will take a closer look at them in Chapter 7).

36.* Laplace's equation is a description of the gravitational potential in a region if there is no matter in that region. Does Newton's formula for the gravitational potential energy, $V = -GM_1M_2/r$, satisfy the three-dimensional Laplace equation? How about the solution $V = -GM_1M_2 \times \ln[(r+z)/(r-z)]$? Why would this solution be *physically* unacceptable?

37.* The Schrödinger equation for a system of n electrons may be written as

$$\left[\frac{-\hbar^2}{2m} \sum_{i=1}^{n} \nabla_i^2 - Ze^2 \sum_{i=1}^{n} \frac{1}{r_i} + \frac{e^2}{2} \sum_{i=1}^{n} \sum_{j=1}^{n} \frac{1}{r_{ij}} \right] \psi = E\psi$$

where the wave function ψ is a function of the coordinates of all n electrons. Convince yourself that this equation is not separable into n one-electron wave equations where $\psi = \phi_1 \phi_2 \cdots \phi_n$. Early workers in molecular orbital theory such as F. Hund, D. R. Hartree, and R. S. Mulliken made what is called the *orbital approximation*. It amounts to representing the $1/r_{ij}$ electron–electron interaction terms above as a sum of "effective" one-electron potentials:

$$\frac{e^2}{2} \sum_{i=1}^{n} \sum_{j=1}^{n} \frac{1}{r_{ij}} \cong \sum_{k=1}^{n} V_i.$$

Is the wave equation now separable?

38.** Complete the analysis of the Lindemann–Hinshelwood mechanism by working out exactly the ratio $[A]/[A_0]$. You will need to know the Laplace transform

$$\frac{ne^{-nx} - me^{-mx}}{n - m} \rightarrow \frac{s}{(s+n)(s+m)}.$$

Show that your expression reduces to $A = A_0 e^{-kt}$, where k is a constant, if the second step in the mechanism is very slow, that is, $k_{-1} \ll k_1$.

SIX

Matrices, Vectors, and Tensors

MATRICES

1 TYPES OF AND OPERATIONS WITH MATRICES

All the material in this chapter is related and belongs to the branch of mathematics called linear algebra. This subject is much more general than the contents of this chapter would suggest, and we do not attempt to give a decent definition here. In much of linear algebra one is concerned with transformations among linear equations; our interest is mainly with the mechanics of such transformations and, to a much lesser extent, with the theoretical underpinning of the subject. In spite of this restriction the sheer volume of material, even after much pruning, is large. Rather than separate what is logically related material into two distinct chapters, the contents of Chapter 6 are subdivided into a part on matrices, with its own set of exercises at the end of Section 6.2, and a second part on vectors and tensors, with its set of exercises at the end of 6.6.

The concept of a matrix is an extremely easy one to grasp. A matrix is nothing more than a pattern or ordered arrangement of elements; the multiplication table is an example of a matrix. Matrices originated roughly 125 years ago in the research of the British mathematicians Arthur Cayley (1821–1895) and James J. Sylvester (1814–1897). Cayley's approach was motivated by the following general problem. Suppose we have a linear transformation of the type

$$x' = ax + by$$

$$y' = cx + dy$$

that converts the coordinates of a point in one xy-coordinate system into the corresponding coordinates in a new (primed) system. Now let us change coordinate system still again:

$$x'' = Ax' + By'$$
$$y'' = Cx' + Dy'.$$

We would like to know the relation between the unprimed coordinate system and the doubly primed system. Simple algebra gives the following results:

$$x'' = A(ax + by) + B(cx + dy)$$
$$y'' = C(ax + by) + D(cx + dy)$$

or

$$x'' = (Aa + Bc)x + (Ab + Bd)y$$
$$y'' = (Ca + Dc)x + (Cb + Dd)y.$$

What Cayley said was that the first transformation can be completely characterized by the array of numbers

$$\begin{pmatrix} a & b \\ c & d \end{pmatrix}$$

and the second transformation by the array

$$\begin{pmatrix} A & B \\ C & D \end{pmatrix}.$$

It is therefore convenient to suppose that these arrays can be operated with, much like real numbers, to give as their product, for example,

$$\begin{pmatrix} A & B \\ C & D \end{pmatrix}\begin{pmatrix} a & b \\ c & d \end{pmatrix} = \begin{pmatrix} Aa + Bc & Ab + Bd \\ Ca + Dc & Cb + Dd \end{pmatrix}$$

where the product is to be interpreted as the array that completely characterizes a direct transformation from the first to the third coordinate system. This in fact provides the rationale for the way in which matrix multiplication is defined. Although the above equations pertain to operations in the plane, Cayley and Sylvester were able to extend their work to higher dimensional space. Matrices provided mathematicians and physical scientists with a powerful tool for dealing with n-dimensional spaces, in spite of the fact that for n larger than three geometric visualization is denied us.

In the British mathematical Forum
Young Cayley was present to bore'em;
He spent much of his time
Drawing matrices sublime,
But his theory of n-space did floor'em.

adapted from
LEO MOSER

Let us dispense now with some general matters. First, we emphasize again that a matrix is nothing more than a two-dimensional array of elements or numbers; a matrix is not itself a number and cannot be evaluated as can determinants (see Chapter 1). Second, because of the two-dimensionality of a matrix, two indices are required to specify the location of any particular element in the matrix.

In this book we follow the convention of always giving the row index first and the column index second for any element.

A matrix **A** will be said to have elements a_{ij}. Thus in the matrix

$$\mathbf{A} = \begin{pmatrix} 2 & 0 & 4 & -1 \\ 9 & 0 & 7 & 3 \\ 1 & -2 & 5 & -4 \end{pmatrix} \begin{matrix} \leftarrow\text{row 1} \\ \leftarrow\text{row 2} \\ \leftarrow\text{row 3} \end{matrix}$$

$$\begin{matrix} \uparrow \qquad\qquad\quad \uparrow \\ \text{column 1} \qquad \text{column 4} \end{matrix}$$

the element a_{23} is 7, and $a_{32} = -2$. Third, as the example above shows, matrices need not be square arrays (as determinants always are). Matrices are, in general, rectangular; special cases are a *row matrix* such as $(2\ 0\ 4\ -1)$, and a *column matrix* such as

$$\begin{bmatrix} 2 \\ 9 \\ 1 \end{bmatrix}.$$

Some general properties of matrices can be summarized in the following statements:

1. Two matrices can be said to be *equal* only if they have identical corresponding dimensions and if their corresponding elements are identical.
2. The sum of an $m \times n$ matrix **A** with elements a_{ij} and another $m \times n$

matrix $\mathbf{B}$ with elements b_{ij} is the $m \times n$ matrix $\mathbf{C}$ with elements $c_{ij} = a_{ij} + b_{ij}$:

$$\begin{pmatrix} 1 & 2 & 1 \\ 0 & 4 & 7 \end{pmatrix} + \begin{pmatrix} 4 & -2 & 3 \\ 5 & -2 & 1 \end{pmatrix} = \begin{pmatrix} 5 & 0 & 4 \\ 5 & 2 & 8 \end{pmatrix}.$$

3. The *Cayley product* of an $m \times n$ matrix $\mathbf{A}$ with an $n \times p$ matrix $\mathbf{B}$ is the $m \times p$ matrix $\mathbf{C}$ where $c_{ij} = \sum_{k=1}^{n} a_{ik} b_{kj}$.

This rule is the same as was used in the example in the opening paragraphs of this section; here is another example:

$$\begin{pmatrix} 2 & 3 \\ 1 & 1 \\ 4 & -2 \end{pmatrix} \begin{pmatrix} -3 & 1 & 7 \\ 4 & 0 & 2 \end{pmatrix} = \begin{bmatrix} 2(-3)+3(4) & 2(1)+3(0) & 2(7)+3(2) \\ 1(-3)+1(4) & 1(1)+1(0) & 1(7)+1(2) \\ 4(-3)-2(4) & 4(1)-2(0) & 4(7)-2(2) \end{bmatrix}$$

$$= \begin{pmatrix} 6 & 2 & 20 \\ 1 & 1 & 9 \\ -20 & 4 & 24 \end{pmatrix}.$$

The multiplication is always done in the order row × column. In other words, to get the element for the third row and second column in the product matrix, multiply the elements in the third row of matrix $\mathbf{A}$ by the elements in the 2nd column of matrix $\mathbf{B}$ and add. This also implies that for multiplication to be meaningful the number of columns in matrix $\mathbf{A}$ has to be the same as the number of rows in matrix $\mathbf{B}$.

4. The zero matrix $\mathbf{O}$ is one where all elements are zero; the unit matrix $\mathbf{1}$ is a square matrix where all elements along the left diagonal are 1, and all other elements are zero.

$$\mathbf{O} = \begin{pmatrix} 0 & 0 \\ 0 & 0 \end{pmatrix} \qquad \mathbf{1} = \begin{pmatrix} 1 & 0 & 0 \\ 0 & 1 & 0 \\ 0 & 0 & 1 \end{pmatrix}$$

These definitions lead to the nice results

$$\mathbf{AO} = \mathbf{OA} = \mathbf{O}$$
$$\mathbf{A1} = \mathbf{1A} = \mathbf{A}.$$

5. If $\mathbf{A}$, $\mathbf{B}$, and $\mathbf{C}$ are square matrices such that $\mathbf{AB} = \mathbf{C}$, then one also has $\det \mathbf{A} \times \det \mathbf{B} = \det \mathbf{C}$. A matrix $\mathbf{A}$ is said to be *singular* if and only if $\det \mathbf{A} = 0$.

Properties 1–4 are actually definitions; property 5 is a demonstrable theorem.

Nearly all of the rules of a normal algebra quoted in Section 1.1 hold for matrices. One that does not, however, is the commutative law of multiplication. Consider the coordinate transformations given at the beginning of this section. If the two matrices there are multiplied in the reverse order, one gets the result

$$\begin{pmatrix} a & b \\ c & d \end{pmatrix}\begin{pmatrix} A & B \\ C & D \end{pmatrix} = \begin{pmatrix} aA + bC & aB + bD \\ cA + dC & cB + dD \end{pmatrix}$$

and it is seen that these are not the same elements as given before. This is very interesting, actually, because it says that matrices do not multiply exactly the same as real numbers. Thus, for comparison,

$$a \times b - b \times a = 0$$

but

$$\mathbf{AB} - \mathbf{BA} \neq 0$$

except in special cases. Whether you realize it or not, you have been exposed to other cases of potential noncommutation. Consider the operators x and d^2/dx^2 and permit them to operate successively on some general function $f(x)$:

$$x\frac{d^2}{dx^2} f(x) - \frac{d^2}{dx^2}[xf(x)] = -2\frac{d}{dx} f(x).$$

Clearly, it makes a difference in which order the operations x and d^2/dx^2 are performed. We say that the *commutator* $[x, d^2/dx^2]$ of the two operators is $-2(d/dx)$. More explicitly, the commutator $[\hat{A}, \hat{B}]$ of the two operators $\hat{A}$ and $\hat{B}$ is the new operator $\hat{A}\cdot\hat{B} - \hat{B}\cdot\hat{A}$, and we evaluate its effect on some function $f(x)$ by means of the expression $\hat{A}\{\hat{B}\cdot f(x)\} - \hat{B}\{\hat{A}\cdot f(x)\}$.

Example 50. The three Pauli spin matrices used in describing electron spin are

$$\mathbf{S}_x = \tfrac{1}{2}\hbar\begin{pmatrix} 0 & 1 \\ 1 & 0 \end{pmatrix} \quad \mathbf{S}_y = \tfrac{1}{2}\hbar\begin{pmatrix} 0 & -i \\ i & 0 \end{pmatrix} \quad \mathbf{S}_z = \tfrac{1}{2}\hbar\begin{pmatrix} 1 & 0 \\ 0 & -1 \end{pmatrix}.$$

Investigate their commutation properties.

Answer. We have by Cayley multiplication

$$\mathbf{S}_x\mathbf{S}_y = \tfrac{1}{4}\hbar^2\begin{pmatrix} 0 & 1 \\ 1 & 0 \end{pmatrix}\begin{pmatrix} 0 & -i \\ i & 0 \end{pmatrix} = \tfrac{1}{4}\hbar^2\begin{pmatrix} i & 0 \\ 0 & -i \end{pmatrix}$$

$$\mathbf{S}_y\mathbf{S}_x = \tfrac{1}{4}\hbar^2\begin{pmatrix} 0 & -i \\ i & 0 \end{pmatrix}\begin{pmatrix} 0 & 1 \\ 1 & 0 \end{pmatrix} = \tfrac{1}{4}\hbar^2\begin{pmatrix} -i & 0 \\ 0 & i \end{pmatrix}$$

and hence

$$S_x S_y + S_y S_x = O.$$

Matrices that behave in this way are said to *anticommute*. Similar results are obtained for the other two possible combinations. The square of any of the spin matrices is interesting.

$$S_x S_x = \tfrac{1}{4}\hbar^2 \begin{pmatrix} 0 & 1 \\ 1 & 0 \end{pmatrix}\begin{pmatrix} 0 & 1 \\ 1 & 0 \end{pmatrix} = \tfrac{1}{4}\hbar^2 \begin{pmatrix} 1 & 0 \\ 0 & 1 \end{pmatrix} = S_y S_y = S_z S_z$$

We can therefore indicate the anticommutation of the spin matrices in the following shorthand way:

$$S_i S_j + S_j S_i = \tfrac{1}{2}\hbar^2 \delta_{ij} 1$$

where the symbol δ_{ij} is the so-called *Kronecker delta*[1]; it has the value 1 when $i = j$, and the value 0 when $i \neq j$.

Another interesting result that follows from the definition of Cayley multiplication is that if $AB = O$, it does not necessarily follow that either A or B has to be equal to O. See if you can think of a simple example in support of this statement.

Certain types of matrices are given special names. The *transpose* of an $m \times n$ matrix is a new matrix formed from the first by interchanging the rows and the columns; it has dimensions $n \times m$. Thus the transpose of the 3×2 matrix

$$\begin{bmatrix} 2 & 1 \\ 0 & 3 \\ -4 & 1 \end{bmatrix}$$

is the 2×3 matrix

$$\begin{pmatrix} 2 & 0 & -4 \\ 1 & 3 & 1 \end{pmatrix}.$$

If the transpose operation is repeated again, the original matrix is restored. It is also not hard to show that the transpose of the product of two matrices is the product of the transposes written in reverse order

$$\text{transpose } (AB) = \text{transpose } B \times \text{transpose } A$$

[1] After the German mathematician Leopold Kronecker (1823–1891).

The *classical adjoint* of a square matrix is the ·transpose of the matrix of minors of the elements of the matrix. Recall from Section 1.2 that the minor associated with the ijth element of a determinant is that determinant resulting from striking out the ith row and the jth column. Consider the following matrix:

$$\mathbf{A} = \begin{bmatrix} 2 & 0 & 1 \\ -1 & 3 & 2 \\ 4 & 2 & -1 \end{bmatrix}.$$

The matrix of minors for this matrix is (remember there is an alternation of signs)

$$\begin{bmatrix} \begin{vmatrix} 3 & 2 \\ 2 & -1 \end{vmatrix} & -\begin{vmatrix} -1 & 2 \\ 4 & -1 \end{vmatrix} & \begin{vmatrix} -1 & 3 \\ 4 & 2 \end{vmatrix} \\ -\begin{vmatrix} 0 & 1 \\ 2 & -1 \end{vmatrix} & \begin{vmatrix} 2 & 1 \\ 4 & -1 \end{vmatrix} & -\begin{vmatrix} 2 & 0 \\ 4 & 2 \end{vmatrix} \\ \begin{vmatrix} 0 & 1 \\ 3 & 2 \end{vmatrix} & -\begin{vmatrix} 2 & 1 \\ -1 & 2 \end{vmatrix} & \begin{vmatrix} 2 & 0 \\ -1 & 3 \end{vmatrix} \end{bmatrix}$$

and the transpose of this matrix is

$$\begin{bmatrix} \begin{vmatrix} 3 & 2 \\ 2 & -1 \end{vmatrix} & -\begin{vmatrix} 0 & 1 \\ 2 & -1 \end{vmatrix} & \begin{vmatrix} 0 & 1 \\ 3 & 2 \end{vmatrix} \\ -\begin{vmatrix} -1 & 2 \\ 4 & -1 \end{vmatrix} & \begin{vmatrix} 2 & 1 \\ 4 & -1 \end{vmatrix} & -\begin{vmatrix} 2 & 1 \\ -1 & 2 \end{vmatrix} \\ \begin{vmatrix} -1 & 3 \\ 4 & 2 \end{vmatrix} & -\begin{vmatrix} 2 & 0 \\ 4 & 2 \end{vmatrix} & \begin{vmatrix} 2 & 0 \\ -1 & 3 \end{vmatrix} \end{bmatrix}.$$

Hence the classical adjoint of the original matrix is

$$\mathrm{adj}\, \mathbf{A} = \begin{bmatrix} -7 & 2 & -3 \\ 7 & -6 & -5 \\ -14 & -4 & 6 \end{bmatrix}.$$

The classical adjoint of a matrix is important because it is related to the problem of finding an inverse to a matrix.

Theorem 19. *The inverse of a matrix* $\mathbf{A}$ *is a unique matrix* $\mathbf{B}$ *having the property* $\mathbf{AB} = \mathbf{BA} = 1$, *and it is given by the expression*

$$\mathbf{B} = \mathbf{A}^{-1} = \frac{\mathrm{adj}\, \mathbf{A}}{\det \mathbf{A}}$$

provided that $\mathbf{A}$ *is not a singular matrix.*

Example 51. Extract the inverse of the matrix **A** above.

Answer. Theorem 19 shows that an inverse will exist if **A** is not singular. Expanding the determinant, we have

$$\det \mathbf{A} = \begin{vmatrix} 2 & 0 & 1 \\ -1 & 3 & 2 \\ 4 & 2 & -1 \end{vmatrix} = -6 + 0 - 2 - 12 + 0 - 8 = -28.$$

The inverse matrix is therefore $-\dfrac{1}{28} \operatorname{adj} \mathbf{A}$, or

$$\mathbf{A}^{-1} = \frac{1}{28} \begin{bmatrix} 7 & -2 & 3 \\ -7 & 6 & 5 \\ 14 & 4 & 6 \end{bmatrix}.$$

You may verify that the product $\mathbf{A}\mathbf{A}^{-1}$ is indeed **1**.

In practical applications it often happens that very large matrices have to be inverted; for these cases the above procedure becomes too time-consuming. Here is a procedure easily programmable for high-speed computers. Suppose we have a nonsingular square matrix **A** of elements a_{ij}. The *characteristic matrix* associated with **A** is the matrix

$$\begin{bmatrix} a_{11} - x & a_{12} & a_{13} & a_{14} & \cdots \\ a_{21} & a_{22} - x & a_{23} & a_{24} \\ a_{31} & a_{32} & a_{33} - x & a_{34} \\ a_{41} & a_{42} & a_{43} & a_{44} - x & \cdots \\ \vdots & & & \vdots \end{bmatrix}$$

and if the determinant of this is expanded, one has the *characteristic polynomial*

$$c_0 x^n + c_1 x^{n-1} + c_2 x^{n-2} + \cdots + c_n.$$

An important theorem in linear algebra says that if in the characteristic polynomial we replace x by the original matrix **A**, then the resulting matrix polynomial will be identical to the zero matrix.

Theorem 20 (Cayley–Hamilton Theorem). *Every square matrix satisfies its own characteristic equation, that is, if*

$$c_0 x^n + c_1 x^{n-1} + c_2 x^{n-2} + \cdots + c_n$$

is the characteristic polynomial associated with the $n \times n$ *matrix* $\mathbf{A}$, *then the following identity holds*:

$$c_0\mathbf{A}^n + c_1\mathbf{A}^{n-1} + c_2\mathbf{A}^{n-2} + \cdots + c_n\mathbf{1} = \mathbf{O}.$$

The desired result follows from taking the matrix equation in the theorem, multiplying both sides by $c_n^{-1}\mathbf{A}^{-1}$, and transposing:

$$\mathbf{A}^{-1} = \frac{-\left(c_0\mathbf{A}^{n-1} + c_1\mathbf{A}^{n-2} + \cdots + c_{n-1}\mathbf{1}\right)}{c_n}.$$

Use of this formula entails expansion of just one determinant, and repeated multiplication of the same matrix $\mathbf{A}$.

Example 52. Find the inverse of matrix $\mathbf{A}$ given in Example 51 by making use of the Cayley–Hamilton theorem.

Answer. The characteristic matrix is

$$\begin{pmatrix} 2-x & 0 & 1 \\ -1 & 3-x & 2 \\ 4 & 2 & -1-x \end{pmatrix}$$

and on expansion the characteristic equation is seen to be

$$x^3 - 4x^2 + 7x + 28 = 0.$$

Since $\mathbf{A}$ is a 3×3 matrix, the only power of $\mathbf{A}$ needed is the second:

$$\mathbf{A}^2 = \begin{pmatrix} 2 & 0 & 1 \\ -1 & 3 & 2 \\ 4 & 2 & -1 \end{pmatrix}\begin{pmatrix} 2 & 0 & 1 \\ -1 & 3 & 2 \\ 4 & 2 & -1 \end{pmatrix} = \begin{pmatrix} 8 & 2 & 1 \\ 3 & 13 & 3 \\ 2 & 4 & 9 \end{pmatrix}.$$

Hence from Theorem 20 we have for the inverse of $\mathbf{A}$

$$\mathbf{A}^{-1} = \frac{-\left[\begin{pmatrix} 8 & 2 & 1 \\ 3 & 13 & 3 \\ 2 & 4 & 9 \end{pmatrix} - 4\begin{pmatrix} 2 & 0 & 1 \\ -1 & 3 & 2 \\ 4 & 2 & -1 \end{pmatrix} + \begin{pmatrix} -7 & 0 & 0 \\ 0 & -7 & 0 \\ 0 & 0 & -7 \end{pmatrix}\right]}{28}$$

$$= \frac{-1}{28}\begin{pmatrix} -7 & 2 & -3 \\ 7 & -6 & -5 \\ -14 & -4 & 6 \end{pmatrix}.$$

Another kind of matrix of special importance in quantum mechanics is the Hermitian matrix (after Charles Hermite). Consider a square matrix in which some of the off-diagonal elements may be complex numbers. Now take the complex conjugate of all elements and then form the transpose matrix; this matrix is referred to as the *Hermitian adjoint* of the original matrix. If this matrix is identical to the original matrix, then the original matrix is said to be *Hermitian*. Thus the matrix

$$\begin{pmatrix} -1 & i & 4 \\ -i & 3 & 2-i \\ 4 & 2+i & 2 \end{pmatrix}$$

is Hermitian because its complex conjugate is the matrix

$$\begin{pmatrix} -1 & -i & 4 \\ i & 3 & 2+i \\ 4 & 2-i & 2 \end{pmatrix}$$

and the transpose of this is the original matrix. We will have more to say about Hermitian matrices later.

An important operation connecting two square matrices is one known as a *similarity transformation*. This amounts to the transformation of matrix **A** into matrix **B** by means of any nonsingular matrix **C**.

$$\mathbf{B} = \mathbf{C}^{-1}\mathbf{A}\mathbf{C}$$

Matrices **A** and **B** are said to be *similar*. From property 5 given earlier for matrices and from Theorem 19 it is not hard to see that they will have equal determinants. It can also be shown that the sum of the elements of the left diagonal, known as the *trace* or *spur* of the matrix, is an invariant quantity (i.e., a constant) and will therefore be the same in the two cases. If we start with a matrix **A** and discover a matrix **C** such that matrix **B** obtained by the above prescription contains nonzero elements along the diagonal and zero everywhere else, then **B** is a *diagonal matrix* and it is called the *classical canonical form* of matrix **A**.

2 MATRICES AS OPERATORS; TRANSROTATION

More than once in the preceding pages it has been hinted that matrices can be looked on as more than just an abstract array of numbers. For example, in Example 50 matrices were used to represent the physical quantities spin angular momentum components. Another example was that used in the opening theme of this chapter; thus suppose we have two coordinate systems

(Figure 6.1) connected by the relations

$$x' = ax + by$$
$$y' = cx + dy.$$

In general, x' and y' need not be perpendicular. If they are, however, the two systems are related through the counterclockwise rotation angle θ. For example, let P be a point in the $x'y'$ system. Then from the diagram one has

$$OB = OA + AB$$
$$x' = \frac{x}{\cos\theta} + y'\tan\theta$$

and

$$OD = OC + CD$$
$$\frac{y}{\cos\theta} = y' + x'\tan\theta.$$

These can be rearranged to give the relations

$$x' = x\cos\theta + y\sin\theta$$
$$y' = -x\sin\theta + y\cos\theta.$$

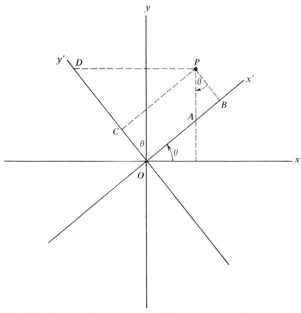

Fig. 6.1 Two coordinate systems with a common origin.

This linear transformation is said to be an *orthogonal transformation* because since the perpendicularity of the axes is maintained during rotation, the length of a vector is unchanged by the operation, that is,

$$x^2 + y^2 = x'^2 + y'^2.$$

We can certainly think of coordinate rotation as a real, physical operation, and accordingly it makes sense to say that the matrix

$$\begin{pmatrix} \cos\theta & \sin\theta \\ -\sin\theta & \cos\theta \end{pmatrix}$$

"stands for" the operation of rotation, or that this matrix is the *operator* for rotation in the plane. Actually, one sees that the operation described here is a counterclockwise rotation about the z axis; since the z and z' coordinates would be the same, the above matrix can be written more completely as a 3×3 matrix:

$$\begin{bmatrix} \cos\theta & \sin\theta & 0 \\ -\sin\theta & \cos\theta & 0 \\ 0 & 0 & 1 \end{bmatrix}.$$

For a clockwise rotation one would replace θ by $-\theta$; since $\cos\theta = \cos(-\theta)$ and $\sin\theta = -\sin(-\theta)$, it is seen that the matrix for clockwise rotation will just be the transpose of the matrix for counterclockwise rotation. Still neater is the fact that the product of the counterclockwise matrix and its transpose is a unit matrix:

$$\begin{bmatrix} \cos\theta & \sin\theta & 0 \\ -\sin\theta & \cos\theta & 0 \\ 0 & 0 & 1 \end{bmatrix} \begin{bmatrix} \cos\theta & -\sin\theta & 0 \\ \sin\theta & coa\theta & 0 \\ 0 & 0 & 1 \end{bmatrix} = \begin{bmatrix} 1 & 0 & 0 \\ 0 & 1 & 0 \\ 0 & 0 & 1 \end{bmatrix}.$$

In other words, the transpose of the original matrix is also equal to its inverse. Whenever this happens, the original matrix is said to be an *orthogonal matrix*. In the particular example above, this is just what we should expect since a clockwise rotation by θ should exactly undo the change caused by a counterclockwise rotation by θ.

What if the origin is translated to some new position and the directions of the axes remain unchanged? In Figure 6.2 let the origin of the $x'y'$ system be at (h, k). Then from the figure one has for a general point P

$$x' = x - h \qquad \text{and} \qquad y' = y - k.$$

As written this cannot be conveniently put into matrix notation. To get around this, one can define for the point (x, y) a dummy third coordinate,

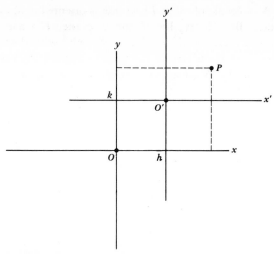

Fig. 6.2 Translation of a coordinate system.

giving it a constant value of 1 in both the xy and $x'y'$ systems. One then has the transformation

$$x' = x + Oy - h \cdot 1$$
$$y' = Ox + y - k \cdot 1$$
$$1 = Ox + Oy + 1 \cdot 1$$

and the translation matrix in the plane then becomes

$$\begin{pmatrix} 1 & 0 & -h \\ 0 & 1 & -k \\ 0 & 0 & 1 \end{pmatrix}.$$

In general, one can say that every linear transformation of the plane (translation, rotation, or both) may be expressed by the operator

$$\begin{bmatrix} a & b & e \\ c & d & f \\ 0 & 0 & 1 \end{bmatrix}.$$

Thus in the particular case of a counterclockwise rotation about the z axis, one has $e = f = 0$, $a = d = \cos\theta$, and $b = -c = \sin\theta$. It will be appreciated that a more complete matrix would be needed to describe transrotations in three-dimensional space.

Example 53. A molecule of methyl bromide is oriented as shown in Figure 6.3. The fragment Br—C—H$_a$ lies in the xy plane. The axes are rotated clockwise about the z axis until the x' axis coincides with the C—H$_a$ bond. The $x'y'$ system is then translated in the positive x' direction until the origin coincides with atom H$_a$. What are the coordinates of a general point in the new $x''y''$ system?

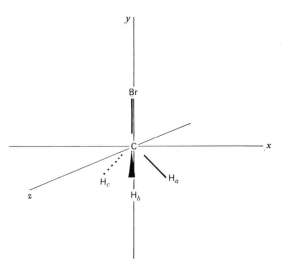

Fig. 6.3 A methyl bromide molecule.

Answer.   Rotation is performed first and translation second. Therefore, we have the matrix equation

$$\mathbf{x}'' = \mathbf{TRx}$$

or

$$\begin{bmatrix} x'' \\ y'' \\ 1 \end{bmatrix} = \begin{bmatrix} 1 & 0 & -h \\ 0 & 1 & -k \\ 0 & 0 & 1 \end{bmatrix} \begin{bmatrix} \cos\theta & -\sin\theta & 0 \\ \sin\theta & \cos\theta & 0 \\ 0 & 0 & 1 \end{bmatrix} \begin{pmatrix} x \\ y \\ 1 \end{pmatrix}$$

$$= \begin{bmatrix} (x\cos\theta - y\sin\theta - h) \\ (x\sin\theta + y\cos\theta - k) \\ 1 \end{bmatrix}.$$

Hence for a general point in the $x''y''$ plane one has for the coordinates

$$\boxed{\begin{aligned} x'' &= x\cos\theta - y\sin\theta - h \\ y'' &= x\sin\theta + y\cos\theta - k \end{aligned}}.$$

Thus for the bromine atom in this system where C—Br $= 1.939\text{Å}$, C—H $= 1.095\text{Å}$, and $\angle$ Br—C—H $= 107.2°$,

$$x'' = 0 - 1.939\sin 17.2° - 1.095$$
$$y'' = 0 + 1.939\cos 17.2° - 0$$

and finally

$$(x'', y'') = (-1.669, 1.852).$$

One begins to see that the great convenience in using matrices is that they allow us to express a lot of information in a very compact form. Thus if we have the following system of linear equations such as might arise in a problem in molecular orbital theory:

$$c_{11}x_1 + c_{12}x_2 + c_{13}x_3 + c_{14}x_4 = a_1$$
$$c_{21}x_1 + c_{22}x_2 + c_{23}x_3 + c_{24}x_4 = a_2$$
$$c_{31}x_1 + c_{32}x_2 + c_{33}x_3 + c_{34}x_4 = a_3$$
$$c_{41}x_1 + c_{42}x_2 + c_{43}x_3 + c_{44}x_4 = a_4$$

this is equivalent to the following matrix multiplication:

$$\begin{bmatrix} c_{11} & c_{12} & c_{13} & c_{14} \\ c_{21} & c_{22} & c_{23} & c_{24} \\ c_{31} & c_{32} & c_{33} & c_{34} \\ c_{41} & c_{42} & c_{43} & c_{44} \end{bmatrix} \begin{bmatrix} x_1 \\ x_2 \\ x_3 \\ x_4 \end{bmatrix} = \begin{bmatrix} a_1 \\ a_2 \\ a_3 \\ a_4 \end{bmatrix}$$

or more elegantly as just

$$CX = A.$$

This notation is obviously less cluttered than that of the linear equations.

For example any row or column matrix of numbers can be looked on as a vector, with the elements of the matrix being the components of the vector in some suitable space. The row matrix $(2 \quad 1 \quad -3)$, for instance, might stand for the vector $2\mathbf{i} + \mathbf{j} - 3\mathbf{k}$ in ordinary xyz space. Now it is observed that any square matrix $\mathbf{A}$ has certain associated characteristic vectors $\mathbf{C}_i$ or *eigenvectors* such that the only effect of the operation of $\mathbf{A}$ on vectors in these directions is to change their length by a multiplicative factor k_i:

$$\mathbf{AC}_i = k_i \mathbf{C}_i.$$

This kind of situation is highly reminiscent of the eigenvalue–eigenfunction problem mentioned in Section 5.3 and in Exercise 4 of Chapter 5. The scalar k_i above is in fact called the *eigenvalue* belonging to the eigenvector $\mathbf{C}_i$. Now just as in the eigenvalue problems with differential operators there will in general be several column eigenvectors $\mathbf{C}_i$ that belong to the matrix $\mathbf{A}$. The total set of all such eigenvectors can be arranged as a square matrix to give the matrix equation

$$\mathbf{AC} = \mathbf{Ck}$$

and if we multiply both sides of this on the left by $\mathbf{C}^{-1}$ we have

$$\mathbf{C}^{-1}\mathbf{AC} = \mathbf{k}$$

$$= \begin{bmatrix} k_1 & 0 & 0 & \cdots \\ 0 & k_2 & 0 & \cdots \\ 0 & 0 & k_3 & \cdots \\ \vdots & & & \end{bmatrix}.$$

What this shows is that by using a matrix of eigenvectors and its inverse, it is possible to carry out a similarity transformation on any square $n \times n$ matrix $\mathbf{A}$ that possesses n eigenvectors, to give a diagonal matrix. This process is referred to as *diagonalization* of the matrix.

We now inquire how one goes about finding the associated eigenvalues and eigenvectors. If we rearrange a previous equation to give

$$\mathbf{AC}_i - k_i \mathbf{C}_i = \mathbf{O}$$

then it is easy to see that k is an eigenvalue of $\mathbf{A}$ if the matrix $(\mathbf{A} - k\mathbf{1})$ is singular. However we know that a matrix is singular if its determinant is zero. Therefore the eigenvalues can be found by setting the determinant

$$\begin{vmatrix} a_{11} - k & a_{12} & a_{13} & \cdots \\ a_{21} & a_{22} - k & a_{23} & \\ a_{31} & a_{32} & a_{33} - k & \cdots \\ \vdots & & \vdots & \end{vmatrix}$$

equal to zero, expanding to give a polynomial in k, and solving for the possible values of k. You will recognize this determinant as the determinant of the characteristic matrix introduced in the last section. Therefore we conclude that diagonalization of a matrix is equivalent to finding the eigenvalues of that matrix, and the eigenvalues are given by simply solving the characteristic equation.

The matrix eigenvalue–eigenvector problem occurs in numerous places in chemistry; it can be expected to show up where some quantity has been quantized to give a discrete spectrum rather than a continuous range of values. In the next several paragraphs we present an application to vibrational spectroscopy. This treatment is somewhat oversimplified, and the interested student is urged to consult standard works for more complete coverage.[2] In this simplified version only planar molecules are considered, and each atom is permitted only one degree of freedom, that is, each atom is constrained to vibrate along a single direction (this direction may be different for different atoms in the molecule). The vibration is assumed to obey Hooke's law (recall Example 47; see also Exercise 41[*] of Chapter 4).

$$\mathbf{F} = -\mathbf{KX}$$

This says that a force applied to atom i and leading to a unit displacement X_j of atom j is counterbalanced by a restoring force at atom i of magnitude $-K_{ij}$. The matrix $\mathbf{K}$ thus plays the role of an "elastic constant." Simple arguments can be used to convince oneself that the $\mathbf{K}$ matrix should be symmetric $(K_{ij} = K_{ji})$. Each atom also obeys Newton's second law of motion:

$$m\ddot{\mathbf{X}} = \mathbf{F}.$$

At this point we have to decide in what manner the vibrations of the atoms vary with time in order that an expression can be given to the acceleration in the above equation. A common assumption is that the atoms undergo simple harmonic motion in phase with each other, but that the vibrations may have different amplitudes. Such vibrations are called *normal modes of vibration*. If the Hooke's law force constant is defined in a standard way, then solution of Newton's second law of motion yields the result

$$X_i = A_i \sin(2\pi\nu t + \delta)$$

with ν being the frequency of the vibration and A_i and δ being constants of integration. The cases considered here involve vibrating atoms of the same

[2]Such as L. A. Woodward, *Introduction to the Theory of Molecular Vibrations and Vibrational Spectroscopy*, Oxford University Press, London, 1972; K. Nakamoto, *Infrared Spectra of Inorganic and Coordination Compounds*, 2nd ed., Wiley-Interscience, New York, 1970.

mass m, which for simplicity we may take to be of unit magnitude. Then differentiation and substitution in the first two equations yield

$$\mathbf{KX} = 4\pi^2\nu^2\mathbf{X}.$$

Example 54. What vibrational (in-plane stretching) frequencies are possible for (a) a linear triatomic molecule AB_2, and (b) a trigonal planar molecule AB_3, where in both cases A is a very heavy atom that is presumed to be stationary?

Answer. The basic equation above is seen to be an eigenvalue–eigenvector problem if we rewrite it as

$$(\mathbf{K} - 4\pi^2\nu^2\mathbf{1})\mathbf{X} = \mathbf{O}.$$

Permissible values for the vibrational frequency ν are obtained from the determinantal equation

$$\det(\mathbf{K} - 4\pi^2\nu^2\mathbf{1}) = 0.$$

(a) AB_2 (see Figure 6.4a).
Owing to the symmetry of the molecule it is apparent that a unit force on atom 1 will displace it, say, R units and atom 2, say, S units. A unit force on atom 2 will displace atom 1 by S and atom 2 by R units. The **K** matrix thus has the form

$$\mathbf{K} = \begin{pmatrix} k_{11} & k_{12} \\ k_{12} & k_{11} \end{pmatrix}$$

and the determinantal equation, accordingly, becomes

$$\begin{vmatrix} k_{11} - 4\pi^2\nu^2 & k_{12} \\ k_{12} & k_{11} - 4\pi^2\nu^2 \end{vmatrix} = 0.$$

This has two roots; the frequencies work out to be

$$\boxed{\nu = \frac{1}{2\pi}\sqrt{k_{11} \pm k_{12}}}\ .$$

(b) AB_3 (see Figure 6.4b).
Here a unit force on atom 1 will displace it, say, R units and atoms

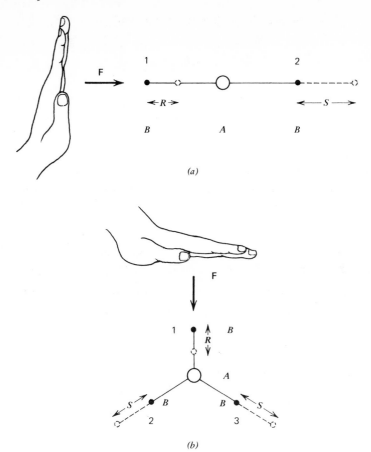

Fig. 6.4 Vibrations of two simple molecules.

2 and 3, say, S units. The **K** matrix has the form

$$\mathbf{K} = \begin{bmatrix} k_{11} & k_{12} & k_{12} \\ k_{12} & k_{11} & k_{12} \\ k_{12} & k_{12} & k_{11} \end{bmatrix}$$

and the determinantal equation becomes

$$\begin{vmatrix} k_{11} - 4\pi^2\nu^2 & k_{12} & k_{12} \\ k_{12} & k_{11} - 4\pi^2\nu^2 & k_{12} \\ k_{12} & k_{12} & k_{11} - 4\pi^2\nu^2 \end{vmatrix} = 0.$$

This has three roots; the frequencies work out to be

$$
\nu = \begin{bmatrix} \dfrac{1}{2\pi}\sqrt{k_{11} - k_{12}} \\[2mm] \dfrac{1}{2\pi}\sqrt{k_{11} - k_{12}} \\[2mm] \dfrac{1}{2\pi}\sqrt{k_{11} + 2k_{12}} \end{bmatrix}.
$$

According to this, two eigenfunctions belong to the same eigenvalue, and we say that the eigenvalue (or more loosely, the vibration) is *twofold degenerate*. The result is that our spectrum contains only two peaks instead of the expected three.

What do the two observable modes of vibration look like? To answer this we have to work out the eigenvectors. If in the AB_3 case we insert the frequency $\dfrac{1}{2\pi}\sqrt{k_{11} - k_{12}}$ back into the original matrix equation, three identical linear equations are obtained:

$$
k_{12}X_1 + k_{12}X_2 + k_{12}X_3 = 0.
$$

This is soluble by letting $X_1 = 0$, $X_2 = +1$, and $X_3 = -1$. Figure 6.5a shows what this would look like; in this mode the molecule is clearly stretching in an asymmetric manner.

If the frequency $(1/2\pi)(k_{11} + 2k_{12})^{1/2}$ is inserted into the matrix equation, there are obtained the three equations

$$
k_{12}X_2 + k_{12}X_3 = 2k_{12}X_1
$$
$$
k_{12}X_1 + k_{12}X_3 = 2k_{12}X_2
$$
$$
k_{12}X_1 + k_{12}X_2 = 2k_{12}X_3
$$

and this system of equations is consistent with $X_1 = X_2 = X_3 = +1$. This mode of vibration is shown in Figure 6.5b; it is a symmetric mode.

Experimentally, it is observed that the vibrational spectra of linear AB_2 and trigonal planar AB_3 molecules are relatively simple. The former contain two bands that can be assigned to the symmetric and asymmetric stretching modes (see Table 6.1); a third band, that is not covered by the above theory, must be assigned to the degenerate bending vibrational mode. Trigonal planar AB_3 molecules show in their spectra a symmetric and an asymmetric vibrational frequency, as well as two other frequencies, one for an in-plane

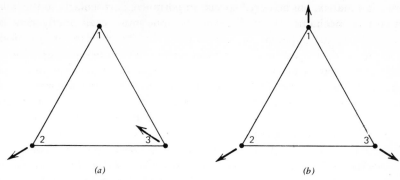

Fig. 6.5 (*a*) An asymmetric stretching; and (*b*) a symmetric stretching of a trigonal planar molecule.

Table 6.1 Vibrational Data for Some Simple Molecules

Molecule	ν_1 (sym)(cm^{-1})	ν_2 (bend)(cm^{-1})	ν_3 (asym)(cm^{-1})	ν_4 (bend)(cm^{-1})
HgCl$_2$[a]	360	70	413	
XeF$_2$[b]	513	213	564	
LaF$_3$[c]	528	130	497	81
HgF$_2$[d]	588	171	641	
BH$_3$[e]		1125	2808	1604

[a] As a gas; W. Klemperer and L. Lindeman, *J. Chem. Phys.*, **25**, 397 (1956).
[b] As a gas; K. Nakamoto, *Infrared Spectra of Inorganic and Coordination Compounds*, 2nd ed., Wiley-Interscience, New York, 1970, p. 83.
[c] In a neon matrix; R. H. Hauge, J. W. Hastie, and J. L. Margrave, *J. Less-Common Metals*, **23**, 359 (1971).
[d] A. Snelson in H. E. Hallam (ed.), *Vibrational Spectroscopy of Trapped Species*, J. Wiley, New York, 1973, p. 233.
[e] This elusive substance was prepared by thermolysis of the adduct BH$_3$·CO and the trapping of the borane in an argon matrix at 5°K; see A. Kaldor and R. F. Porter, *J. Am. Chem. Soc.*, **93**, 2140 (1971).

bending mode and one for an out-of-plane bending mode. The simple theory above cannot account, of course, for the intensities of bands or for the operation of various selection rules; quantum mechanics is needed for this.

We have previously seen that matrices representing the operation of rotation in the plane must be orthogonal, and matrices used in the description of molecular vibrations are symmetric. A third type of matrix, the

Hermitian matrix, has achieved special importance, partricularly in the field of quantum mechanics. To understand this, one must recall briefly some of the historical development of the subject. In the version of quantum mechanics as developed by the Austrian scientist Erwin Schrödinger (1887–1961) one starts with a second-order partial differential equation (see Exercise 35* at the end of Chapter 5) and from this the discreteness of Nature follows from the continuity of the wave function and the boundary conditions placed on it (also see Exercise 31* at the end of Chapter 5). In this brand of quantum mechanics physical observables are represented by differential operators $\hat{O}$. According to Dirac, one of the postulates of quantum mechanics is that the average value of $\hat{O}$ in a series of measurements made on a collection of systems in identical states ψ is to be given by

$$\langle \hat{O} \rangle = \frac{\int \psi^* \hat{O} \psi \, d\tau}{\int \psi^* \psi \, d\tau}.$$

If the wave function ψ is an eigenfunction of $\hat{O}$, one has the usual identity

$$\hat{O}\psi = k\psi$$

and therefore the average value of the physical quantity represented by $\hat{O}$ is just

$$\langle \hat{O} \rangle = \frac{\int \psi^* k\psi \, d\tau}{\int \psi^* \psi \, d\tau} = k.$$

We see then that the average value of an operator $\hat{O}$ for a state represented by an eigenfunction of $\hat{O}$ is the corresponding eigenvalue. If the physical quantity corresponding to $\hat{O}$ can be measured, it must be real; hence eigenvalues of a quantum mechanical operator corresponding to an observable are real numbers. Operators that permit only real eigenvalues are thus seen to be especially important.

And what kind of operators are these? The answer is Hermitian operators. Suppose eigenfunctions ψ_1 and ψ_2 belong to the eigenvalues k_1 and k_2:

$$\hat{O}\psi_1 = k_1\psi_1$$
$$\hat{O}\psi_2 = k_2\psi_2.$$

Let us multiply the first equation by ψ_2^* on the left; next let us take the complex conjugate of both sides of the second equation, and then multiply by ψ_1 on the left. We now integrate both these new equations and subtract to get

$$\int \psi_2^* \hat{O}\psi_1 \, d\tau - \int \psi_1 \hat{O}^* \psi_2^* \, d\tau = k_1 \int \psi_2^* \psi_1 \, d\tau - k_2^* \int \psi_1 \psi_2^* \, d\tau.$$

If the two inegrals on the left side are equal, then the operator $\hat{O}$ is said to be Hermitian. In such a case, then, it would follow that

$$0 = (k_1 - k_2^*) \int \psi_1 \psi_2^* \, d\tau.$$

Two important conclusions follow readily from this relation.

1. If the wave functions ψ_1 and ψ_2 are identical, then $\psi_1 \psi_2^*$ is always positive. The integral then cannot vanish and one must have $k_1 = k_2^* = k_1^*$. This is possible only if k_1 and k_2 are real.

Hermitian differential operators have real eigenvalues.

2. If $(k_1 - k_2^*)$ does not equal zero, then the integral of the product $\psi_1 \psi_2^*$ must be zero; in other words, ψ_1 and ψ_2^* are orthogonal (recall the definition of orthogonality given in Section 4.5).

Eigenfunctions of Hermitian operators corresponding to different eigenvalues are orthogonal.

All this became clear during the years following Schrödinger's development. At the same time, however, Werner Heisenberg gave up the idea of trying to describe Nature against a background fabric of continuity, and he began working directly with discrete collections of data from quantal transitions. The natural mathematical tool to use to organize such data was matrices. Heisenberg's results were identical to those obtained by other workers using the differential equation approach, so that apparently the matrix approach and the differential equation approach were merely two different representations for the same thing. What gives Hermitian matrices special importance is that a matrix representation of an Hermitian operator is also Hermitian. For such matrices the two statements above have their counterparts, namely, the eigenvalues of an Hermitian matrix are real, and if **A** is an Hermitian matrix, then the eigenvectors of **A** associated with distinct eigenvalues are mutually orthogonal vectors. Note that for use in quantum mechanics we are not asking that the elements of our matrix operators be real, but only that the eigenvalues of the matrices be real since these will be the values of experimentally measurable things such as position, energy, and angular momentum. For example, in Example 50 the matrix representing the y component of electron spin angular momentum contains two imaginary elements; nevertheless, as is easily shown, the eigenvalues of S_y are real ($\pm \frac{1}{2}\hbar$).

To be more specific, suppose one has a coordinate system with a certain set of elements $e_1, e_2, e_3, \ldots, e_n$ as the *basis set*. What this means is that any function defined in this coordinate system can be written in terms of the basis.

$$f = a_1 e_1 + a_2 e_2 + a_3 e_3 + \cdots +$$

$$= \sum_i a_i e_i$$

The basis functions e_i may be just ordinary Cartesian unit vectors pointing along the x, y, z directions, or something more abstract such as a complete set of orthonormal functions (see Section 4.5). If some particular operator $\hat{O}$ acts on e_j, the result can certainly be expressed as some combination of all of the available basis functions including e_j itself.

$$\hat{O}e_j = \sum_k a_{kj} e_k$$

The question is, how do we find the a_{kj} coefficients? This is done in a manner resembling the procedure we used earlier for finding coefficients in a Fourier series expansion of some function. Let us multiply both sides on the left by e_i^*, and in the case where the basis consists of functions, integrate both sides:

$$\int e_i^* \hat{O}e_j = \int e_i^* \sum_k a_{kj} e_k.$$

Because the basis functions are mutually orthogonal, all terms on the right will vanish except the one where $k = i$. The integral on the left then reduces to

$$\int e_i^* \hat{O}e_j = a_{ij}.$$

We can arrange these a_{ij} coefficients in the form of a matrix, and this matrix will then be the matrix representation of the operator $\hat{O}$ in the coordinate system spanned by the e_i:

$$\begin{bmatrix} \int e_1^* \hat{O} e_1 & \int e_1^* \hat{O} e_2 & \int e_1^* \hat{O} e_3 & \cdots \\[2mm] \int e_2^* \hat{O} e_1 & \int e_2^* \hat{O} e_2 & \int e_2^* \hat{O} e_3 & \cdots \\[2mm] \int e_3^* \hat{O} e_1 & \int e_3^* \hat{O} e_2 & \int e_3^* \hat{O} e_3 & \cdots \\[2mm] \vdots & & & \cdots \int e_n^* \hat{O} e_n \end{bmatrix}.$$

Any of the quantum mechanical operators such as the Pauli spin matrices in Example 50 can be constructed in this way provided one has a suitable orthonormal basis set available.

The only complete set of orthonormal functions that you have been exposed to is the countably infinite set of sines and cosines used in writing down Fourier series. Let this set be arranged in the order shown below.

e_1	0	e_4	$\dfrac{1}{\sqrt{T}} \cos \dfrac{n\pi x}{T}$
e_2	$\dfrac{1}{\sqrt{2T}}$	e_5	$\dfrac{1}{\sqrt{T}} \sin \dfrac{2n\pi x}{T}$
e_3	$\dfrac{1}{\sqrt{T}} \sin \dfrac{n\pi x}{T}$	e_6	$\dfrac{1}{\sqrt{T}} \cos \dfrac{2n\pi x}{T}$

$$\vdots$$

Example 55. Find the matrix representation of the operator $\hat{O} = d^2/dx^2$ in the coordinate system spanned by sines and cosines; the interval of orthonormality is $(-T, T)$.

Answer. First we work out the effect of the operator $\hat{O}$ on each of the basis functions e_i:

$$\hat{O} e_1 = 0 \qquad \hat{O} e_2 = 0 \qquad \hat{O} e_3 = -\frac{n^2\pi^2}{T^2} e_3$$

$$\hat{O} e_4 = -\frac{n^2\pi^2}{T^2} e_4 \qquad \hat{O} e_5 = -\frac{4n^2\pi^2}{T^2} e_5.$$

Therefore, it is seen that the off-diagonal matrix elements consist of integrals of products of unlike basis functions, and so these elements are all zero because of orthogonality (these integrals were really worked out in Section 4.5). The diagonal matrix elements consist of integrals of squares of basis functions:

$$\int_{-T}^{T} e_1 \hat{O} e_1 \, dx = \int_{-T}^{T} e_2 \hat{O} e_2 \, dx = 0$$

$$\int_{-T}^{T} e_3 \hat{O} e_3 \, dx = \left(\frac{-n^2\pi^2}{T^3} \right) \int_{-T}^{T} \sin^2\left(\frac{n\pi x}{T} \right) dx$$

$$= \left(\frac{-n^2\pi^2}{T^2} \right)$$

$$\int_{-T}^{T} e_4 \hat{O} e_4 \, dx = \left(\frac{-n^2\pi^2}{T^3} \right) \int_{-T}^{T} \cos^2\left(\frac{n\pi x}{T} \right) dx$$

$$= \left(\frac{-n^2\pi^2}{T^2} \right)$$

$$\int_{-T}^{T} e_5 \hat{O} e_5 \, dx = \left(\frac{-4n^2\pi^2}{T^3} \right) \int_{-T}^{T} \sin^2\left(\frac{2n\pi x}{T} \right) dx$$

$$= \left(\frac{-4n^2\pi^2}{T^2} \right).$$

The resulting matrix, that is of infinite dimensions, is thus a diagonal matrix:

$$\mathbf{O} = \frac{-n^2\pi^2}{T^2} \begin{bmatrix} 0 & & & & & \\ & 0 & & & 0 & \\ & & +1 & & & \\ & & & +1 & & \\ & 0 & & & +4 & \\ & & & & & +4 \\ & & & & & & \ddots \end{bmatrix}.$$

It seems to me in the highest degree improbable that our joint speculations should not eventually find their embodiment in chemical doctrine proper, and I think that young chemists desirous to raise their science to its proper rank would act wisely in making themselves masters, betimes, of the theory of algebraical forms.

J. J. SYLVESTER

EXERCISES

1. Perform the indicated operations:

(a) $\begin{pmatrix} 2 & 4 \\ 3 & -3 \\ 0 & 5 \end{pmatrix} - \begin{pmatrix} 3 & 9 \\ 2 & 0 \\ -4 & -5 \end{pmatrix}$

(e) $\begin{pmatrix} 2 & 0 & 4 \\ -1 & 1 & -2 \\ 1 & 3 & 1 \end{pmatrix}^{-1}$

(b) $(1 \quad 3 \quad 2)\begin{pmatrix} 7 \\ -3 \\ 1 \end{pmatrix}$

(f) $\displaystyle\sum_j \sum_i \delta_{ij} a_{ij}$ in $\begin{pmatrix} 3 & 7 & 9 \\ 2 & 4 & 0 \\ 5 & 3 & -6 \end{pmatrix}$

(c) $\begin{pmatrix} 2 & 0 & 0 \\ 0 & 2 & 0 \\ 0 & 0 & 2 \end{pmatrix}\begin{pmatrix} 2 & 1 & -1 \\ 4 & -3 & 0 \\ 5 & 2 & 4 \end{pmatrix}$

(g) $\begin{pmatrix} a & b \\ c & d \end{pmatrix}\begin{pmatrix} 2 & 1 \\ 3 & 2 \end{pmatrix} = \begin{pmatrix} 3 & 2 \\ 1 & 4 \end{pmatrix}$

(find a, b, c, and d)

(d) $\text{adj}\begin{pmatrix} -8 & 2 & 0 \\ 3 & -4 & 1 \\ 6 & 5 & 1 \end{pmatrix}$

(h) $\det\begin{pmatrix} x-1 & 0 & 0 \\ 0 & x-4 & 0 \\ 0 & 0 & x+2 \end{pmatrix} = 0$

(find x)

2. Construct an example, as suggested in the text, to show that if one has $\mathbf{AB} = \mathbf{O}$, then both $\mathbf{A}$ and $\mathbf{B}$ can be different from $\mathbf{O}$.

3. Take another look at the Pauli spin matrices and see if you can find any simple relationships between the product of two of the spin matrices, $\mathbf{S}_i \mathbf{S}_j$, and the third matrix, $\mathbf{S}_k$.

4. Do the operations "take derivative with respect to t" and "integrate from 0 to t" commute?

5. The wording of the question in Exercise 4 is unambiguous so long as we restrict ourselves to functions of a single variable. How would you reword the question if we now wanted to consider functions of two variables, say $f(x,t)$? Are there now any conditions that one can impose upon the form of $f(x,t)$ so that commutation will exist?

6. Complex numbers, $x + iy$, can be represented by matrices. Why can one not use 1×2 or 2×1 matrices for this representation, but must instead go to square 2×2 matrices? Show that the matrix representation

$$x + iy \equiv \begin{pmatrix} x & y \\ -y & x \end{pmatrix}$$

gives a consistent picture for the addition and multiplication of complex numbers. Work out the matrix that represents the reciprocal of $x + iy$.

7. The spin angular momentum matrices for a nucleus of spin quantum

number 1 are given by

$$\mathbf{I}_x = \frac{\hbar}{\sqrt{2}} \begin{pmatrix} 0 & 1 & 0 \\ 1 & 0 & 1 \\ 0 & 1 & 0 \end{pmatrix} \quad \mathbf{I}_y = \frac{\hbar}{\sqrt{2}} \begin{pmatrix} 0 & -i & 0 \\ i & 0 & -i \\ 0 & i & 0 \end{pmatrix} \quad \mathbf{I}_z = \hbar \begin{pmatrix} 1 & 0 & 0 \\ 0 & 0 & 0 \\ 0 & 0 & -1 \end{pmatrix}.$$

Work out the commutator $[\mathbf{I}_i, \mathbf{I}_j]$ for $i \neq j$; also, show that one has $\mathbf{I}^2 = \mathbf{I}_x{}^2 + \mathbf{I}_y{}^2 + \mathbf{I}_z{}^2 = 2\hbar^2 \mathbf{1}$.

8. Demonstrate whether a singular square matrix can ever satisfy the Cayley–Hamilton theorem.

9. Find rapidly $\mathbf{A}^{-3}$ if the matrix is

$$\begin{pmatrix} 2 & 3 \\ 3 & 4 \end{pmatrix}.$$

10. Determine whether the matrices $\mathbf{A}$ and $\mathbf{B}$ are similar or not:

$$\mathbf{A} = \begin{pmatrix} 8 & 6 \\ -3 & -1 \end{pmatrix} \quad \mathbf{B} = \begin{pmatrix} 6 & 2 \\ -2 & 1 \end{pmatrix}.$$

11. Show that for the matrix below one can solve the characteristic equation

$$\mathbf{A} = \begin{pmatrix} 2 & 1 \\ -1 & 4 \end{pmatrix}$$

easily enough, but that the matrix cannot be diagonalized, that is, *that one cannot find a nonsingular matrix* $\mathbf{C}$ *such that* $\mathbf{C}^{-1}\mathbf{A}\mathbf{C}$ *is in diagonal form.* Note the special wording here. The difficulty arises from the fact that the roots of the characteristic equation are not all distinct, and except in special cases (when $\mathbf{A}$ is real and symmetric) the matrix $\mathbf{C}$ needed for the similarity transformation will not exist.

12. The electron spin step-up and step-down operators are the combinations $\mathbf{S}_x + i\mathbf{S}_y$ and $\mathbf{S}_x - i\mathbf{S}_y$, respectively. Write these out as matrices. The two possible spin states of an electron may be represented by the matrix $\begin{pmatrix} 1 \\ 0 \end{pmatrix}$, in which the electron has spin angular momentum $+\frac{1}{2}\hbar$, and by $\begin{pmatrix} 0 \\ 1 \end{pmatrix}$, in which the electron has spin angular momentum $-\frac{1}{2}\hbar$. Allow the step-up and step-down operators to operate on both these functions so that you can see where the names step-up and step-down come from.

13. The operator $\hat{O} = -i\hbar(d/dx)$ is the quantum mechanical operator for the x component of linear momentum. Suppose that the set of functions ψ_i on which $\hat{O}$ can operate are defined for the interval $-L$ to $+L$. Show that $\hat{O}$ is an Hermitian operator if the ψ_i are periodic, that is, if $\psi_i(-L) = \psi_i(+L)$, and thus demonstrate that the Hermiticity of an

operator is not an inherent property of the operator but depends on the boundary conditions.

14. Suppose one has a column vector X_i and two operators (square matrices) A and B.

(a) Show that if X_i is to be simultaneously an eigenvector of A and of B, then the commutator $[A, B]$ must be the zero matrix.

(b) In quantum mechanics when two operators A and B *commute*, the meaning is that the observables which they represent can, in principle, be measured simultaneously with absolute precision. Is it possible to simultaneously measure the x and y components of electron spin with absolute precison? What about S^2 and S_z?

15. Find the 3×3 matrix operator that represents reflection through the xz plane. Is it an orthogonal matrix? Now work out the 3×3 matrix for inversion through the origin and discover what happens when reflection through the xz plane is followed by inversion by multiplying the two matrices above.

16. In connection with Example 54 (a) work out from the eigenvectors what the two normal modes of vibration for the linear AB_2 molecule will look like.

17. Although in Example 54 (b) only one eigenvector for the degenerate mode of vibration was examined, the mathematics says that there has to be another one. Find such an eigenvector by requiring it to be orthogonal to each of the other two, and then sketch what the vibrational mode would look like. Where else in chemistry have you encountered the phenomenon of degeneracy?

18. The following matrix is Hermitian, and so it should have real eigenvalues:

$$\begin{bmatrix} 1 & i & 4 \\ -i & -1 & 2i+3 \\ 4 & 3-2i & 2 \end{bmatrix}.$$

Convince yourself that all three eigenvalues actually are real. (Hint: recall Example 4.)

19. From Example 50 it is seen that the ijth element ($i = 1, j = 2$) of the y component of electron spin is $-\frac{1}{2} i \hbar$. Explain what this statement means, mathematically.

20.* By making use of the definition of the Cayley product of two square matrices, prove that the transpose of the product of two such matrices is equal to the product of the individual transposes taken in the reverse order. Then use this result to show that the product of a square matrix and its transpose is a symmetric matrix.

21.* Let the force constant k in Hooke's law take the form $4\pi^2 m_i \nu^2$. Then show that the solution to Newton's second law of motion is

$$X_i = A_i \sin(2\pi\nu t + \delta).$$

22.* Set up the eigenvalue–eigenvector problem for the vibrational spectrum of a square planar compound, AB_4 (A much heavier than B). Find the frequencies and sketch the normal modes of vibration. Estimate with the aid of Table 6.1 the frequencies for xenon tetrafluoride, and compare your results with the following data: $\nu_1 = 543$ cm^{-1}, $\nu_5 = 502$ cm^{-1}, and $\nu_6 = 586$ cm^{-1} [data taken from H. H. Claassen, C. L. Chernick, and J. G. Malm, *J. Am. Chem. Soc.*, **85**, 1927 (1963)].

VECTORS AND TENSORS

3 ADDITION, MULTIPLICATION, AND DIFFERENTIATION OF VECTORS

Some quantities in physical science possess only magnitude; examples are energy, volume, and temperature. Other quantities possess both magnitude and direction; these are called *vectors*. Examples of vectors are force, dipole moment, and angular momentum. It is principally to Oliver Heaviside and to the American scientist J. Willard Gibbs (1839–1903) that we owe the introduction of vector algebra as a conveneint mathematical tool in physical science. Gibbs' writing on the subject was originally in the form of a privately circulated pamphlet for students; it later became very widely known.[1]

Mathematically we represent a vector $\mathbf{A}$ in ordinary three-dimensional space by means of an expression of the form

$$\mathbf{A} = a_1\mathbf{i} + a_2\mathbf{j} + a_3\mathbf{k}$$

where $\mathbf{i}, \mathbf{j}$, and $\mathbf{k}$ are unit vectors parallel to the x, y, and z axes, respectively. The interpretation of the coefficients is that the length or magnitude of the vector is $(a_1^2 + a_2^2 + a_3^2)^{1/2}$, and the magnitudes of the projection of the vector onto the x, y, and z axes, respectively, are given by a_1, a_2, and a_3 (see Figure 6.6).

---

[1] See J. W. Gibbs, *Scientific Papers*, Vol. II, Dover, New York, 1961, pp. 17–90.

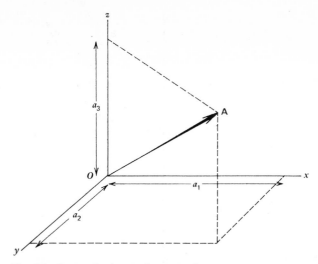

Fig. 6.6 Geometric picture of a vector **A**.

The tail of a vector need not be positioned at the origin of the coordinate system; that is, a vector may be translated without changing its length. In order to preserve the magnitudes of the projections, it is necessary that in the translation process motion be restricted to being parallel to that of the original direction. If the addition of two vectors **A** and **B** be defined algebraically according to

$$\mathbf{A} + \mathbf{B} = (a_1\mathbf{i} + a_2\mathbf{j} + a_3\mathbf{k}) + (b_1\mathbf{i} + b_2\mathbf{j} + b_3\mathbf{k})$$
$$= (a_1 + b_1)\mathbf{i} + (a_2 + b_2)\mathbf{j} + (a_3 + b_3)\mathbf{k},$$

then the above statements permit an easy geometric visualization of vector addition. Thus in Figure 6.7*a* the vector sum of **A** and **B** is seen to be the vector obtained by placing the tail of **B** at the head of **A** and drawing a new line from the tail of **A** to the head of **B**. Multiplication of a vector by a positive constant *C* (Figure 6.7*b*) gives a new vector pointing in the same direction as the original one and with magnitude *C* times that of the first.

Gibbs introduced two types of useful multiplication among vectors. The *direct product* (what we now call the *dot product* or *scalar product*) of two vectors is the scalar quantity obtained by multiplying the product of their magnitudes by the cosine of the angle θ made by their directions:

$$\mathbf{A} \cdot \mathbf{B} = |\mathbf{A}| \, |\mathbf{B}| \cos\theta.$$

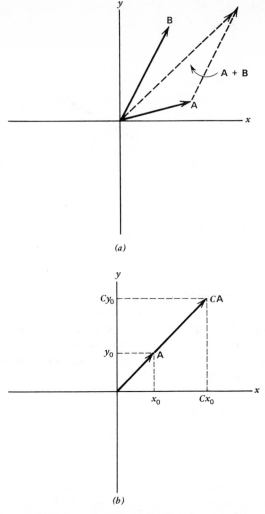

Fig. 6.7 (*a*) Addition of two vectors, and (*b*) multiplication of a vector by a constant.

It follows from this that since $\cos 0° = 1$ and $\cos 90° = 0$,

$$\mathbf{i} \cdot \mathbf{i} = \mathbf{j} \cdot \mathbf{j} = \mathbf{k} \cdot \mathbf{k} = 1$$

all other products $= 0$.

These give for two vectors **A** and **B** the following result:

$$\mathbf{A} \cdot \mathbf{B} = (a_1\mathbf{i} + a_2\mathbf{j} + a_3\mathbf{k})(b_1\mathbf{i} + b_2\mathbf{j} + b_3\mathbf{k})$$

$$= a_1 b_1 + a_2 b_2 + a_3 b_3.$$

The dot product has a readily visualizable extension. The dot product of two vectors can be written as the sum of the following products containing the unit quantity 1:

$$\mathbf{A} \cdot \mathbf{B} = \sum_i a_i b_i 1.$$

Now suppose that $\mathbf{A}$ and $\mathbf{B}$, instead of being discrete functions of a finite vector space, are continuous functions: $A = a(x)$ and $B = b(x)$. If a_i and b_i are now interpreted to mean the functions $a(x)$ and $b(x)$ evaluated at some arbitrary point lying in the interval $[x_i, x_{i+1}]$, then the definite integral of the product of A and B may be written as

$$\int_d^c AB\,dx = \lim_{\Delta x \to 0} \sum_i a_i b_i (x_{i+1} - x_i).$$

This expression is the continuous analogue of the dot product. Suppose the definite integral turns out to have a value of zero; then this is just what we mean when we say that two functions are orthogonal. Therefore, the concept of orthogonality of two functions is nothing more than a logical extension of the dot product of two vectors being zero.

The following physical significance may be attached to the dot product. Suppose we have two vectors $\mathbf{A}$ and $\mathbf{B}$ as shown in Figure 6.8. The magnitude of vector $\mathbf{A}$ projected onto vector $\mathbf{B}$ is OP or $|\mathbf{A}| \cos\theta$. If $\mathbf{B}$ were to have unit magnitude, then OP would be the dot product of $\mathbf{A}$ and $\mathbf{B}$.

The dot product $\mathbf{A} \cdot \mathbf{B}$ is the magnitude of $\mathbf{B}$ times the length of the projection of $\mathbf{A}$ onto $\mathbf{B}$, or equivalently, the magnitude of $\mathbf{A}$ times the projection of $\mathbf{B}$ onto $\mathbf{A}$.

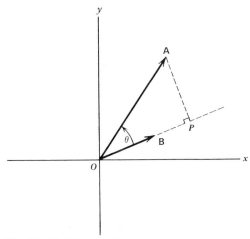

Fig. 6.8 Significance of the dot product.

This interpretation is particularly useful when one is dealing with such physical quantities as velocities, forces, or magnetic moments such as would be involved in an understanding of electron spin or nuclear magnetic resonance spectroscopy.

Finally, we ask if there is a connection between dot multiplication and matrix multiplication. If we let one vector, say **A**, be represented by a row matrix, $(a_1 \quad a_2 \quad a_3)$, and another vector, say **B**, be represented by a column matrix, then it is seen that matrix multiplication leads to a 1×1 matrix. If we agree to interpret here a 1×1 matrix as just a scalar quantity, then the result is identical to the dot product of **A** and **B**:

$$(a_1 \quad a_2 \quad a_3) \begin{bmatrix} b_1 \\ b_2 \\ b_3 \end{bmatrix} = a_1 b_1 + a_2 b_2 + a_3 b_3 = \mathbf{A} \cdot \mathbf{B}.$$

The *skew product* (Gibbs' terminology; today we call this the *cross product* or the *vector product*) of two vectors **A** and **B** is a vector function of **A** and **B**. Its magnitude is obtained by multiplying the product of the magnitudes of **A** and **B** by the sine of the angle made by their directions. Its direction is at right angles to **A** and **B** and may be defined as that in which an ordinary (right-handed) screw advances as it turns so as to carry **A** toward **B** (see Figure 6.9). This choice of direction is a purely arbitrary one but is used universally.

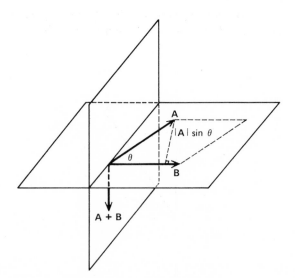

Fig. 6.9 The cross product $\mathbf{A} \times \mathbf{B}$ of two vectors.

It is easy to see that $\mathbf{B} \times \mathbf{A}$ has to be different from $\mathbf{A} \times \mathbf{B}$ for the vector corresponding to the first must point in a direction opposite to that for the second. Vector multiplication, like matrix multiplication, is not commutative, but vector multiplication is more than that; it is anticommutative like the Pauli spin matrices. This is a result of the presence of the factor $\sin\theta$ in the definition of the magnitude of $\mathbf{A} \times \mathbf{B}$, and of vector multiplication obeying the distributive law of multiplication over addition (see Section 1.1). Thus consider any vector; its cross product with itself is zero because $\sin 0° = 0$. Now consider

$$(\mathbf{A}+\mathbf{B}) \times (\mathbf{A}+\mathbf{B}) = (\mathbf{A} \times \mathbf{A}) + (\mathbf{A} \times \mathbf{B}) + (\mathbf{B} \times \mathbf{A}) + (\mathbf{B} \times \mathbf{B})$$

and note that the left side is therefore zero, and on the right side the first and fourth terms are also zero. We are left then with

$$0 = (\mathbf{A} \times \mathbf{B}) + (\mathbf{B} \times \mathbf{A})$$

or, equivalently, with

$$\mathbf{A} \times \mathbf{B} = -(\mathbf{B} \times \mathbf{A}).$$

The unit vectors clearly must satisfy the relations

$$\mathbf{i} \times \mathbf{i} = \mathbf{j} \times \mathbf{j} = \mathbf{k} \times \mathbf{k} = 0$$

$$\mathbf{i} \times \mathbf{j} = \mathbf{k} = -\mathbf{j} \times \mathbf{i}$$

$$\mathbf{j} \times \mathbf{k} = \mathbf{i}; \quad \mathbf{k} \times \mathbf{i} = \mathbf{j}.$$

Reference to Figure 6.9 supplies a geometric interpretation of the cross product.

The magnitude of the cross product $\boldsymbol{A} \times \boldsymbol{B}$ is the area of the parallelogram formed with sides $\boldsymbol{A}$ and $\boldsymbol{B}$.

The appearance of vector cross products in scientific expressions is very common.

It is useful to know what the cross product of two vectors is in terms of their components. By direct cross multiplication and utilization of the rules for handling $\mathbf{i}$, $\mathbf{j}$, and $\mathbf{k}$, we have

$$\mathbf{A} \times \mathbf{B} = (a_1\mathbf{i} + a_2\mathbf{j} + a_3\mathbf{k}) \times (b_1\mathbf{i} + b_2\mathbf{j} + b_3\mathbf{k})$$

$$= (a_1b_1\mathbf{i} \times \mathbf{i} + a_1b_2\mathbf{i} \times \mathbf{j} + a_1b_3\mathbf{i} \times \mathbf{k})$$

$$+ (a_2b_1\mathbf{j} \times \mathbf{i} + a_2b_2\mathbf{j} \times \mathbf{j} + a_2b_3\mathbf{j} \times \mathbf{k})$$

$$+ (a_3b_1\mathbf{k} \times \mathbf{i} + a_3b_2\mathbf{k} \times \mathbf{j} + a_3b_3\mathbf{k} \times \mathbf{k})$$

$$= (a_2b_3 - a_3b_2)\mathbf{i} + (a_3b_1 - a_1b_3)\mathbf{j} + (a_1b_2 - a_2b_1)\mathbf{k}.$$

Inspection shows that this result can be put in the form of a determinant in such a way that the results are easily remembered:

$$\mathbf{A} \times \mathbf{B} = \begin{vmatrix} \mathbf{i} & \mathbf{j} & \mathbf{k} \\ a_1 & a_2 & a_3 \\ b_1 & b_2 & b_3 \end{vmatrix}.$$

We now want to take up three applications of vectors to chemistry that involve successively the addition of vectors, the dot product of two vectors, and the cross product of two vectors. Let us consider first the vector model of the atom. In beginning courses one learns that the ground state of the lithium atom is $1s^2 2s$. Another way of representing this state makes use of what are called *Russell–Saunders symbols*.[2] These symbols detail information about the various types of angular momenta possessed by the electrons in the atom. A typical Russell–Saunders symbol has the form

$$^{2s+1}L_J$$

where the symbols have the following meaning:

S the resultant spin angular momentum (in units of $\hbar$) of all electrons in the atom; the spin angular momentum s of each electron is restricted to values $\pm \frac{1}{2}$; S is always given as the absolute value;

L the resultant orbital angular momentum (again, in units of $\hbar$, and always as the absolute value) of all electrons in the atom; since the orbital angular momentum l of an electron can be any non-negative integer, the resultant L can also be any non-negative integer; L is generally just represented by a letter according to the following scheme:

$$L = 0, 1, 2, 3, 4, 5, \ldots$$
$$S \ P \ D \ F \ G \ H$$

[2]After the astrophysicists H. N. Russell and F. A. Saunders who published an important paper on the subject in 1925 in the *Astrophysical Journal*.

J the resultant total angular momentum of all electrons in the atom, given as the absolute value.

Since angular momentum is a vector quantity, the resultant in each of the three cases above means the vector sum. The essence of Russell–Saunders (or LS) coupling, then, is that the spin angular momenta s of the electrons couple with each other to give S, and similarly for the orbital angular momenta l to give L; finally, L and S couple with each other. Other coupling schemes are conceivable, but the Russell–Saunders scheme seems to work best for light elements in accounting for their spectra and magnetic moments.

If we now look at a ground-state lithium atom, we have from Pauli's exclusion principle $s_1 = +\frac{1}{2}$, $s_2 = -\frac{1}{2}$, $s_3 = \pm\frac{1}{2}$, and therefore $S = \frac{1}{2}$. All three electrons are s electrons, so that $l_1 = l_2 = l_3 = 0$, and thus $L = 0$. Hence $J = L + S = \frac{1}{2}$. The term symbol, accordingly, is $^2S_{\frac{1}{2}}$. The quantity $2S + 1$ is called the *multiplicity* of the state; ground-state lithium is said to be in a doublet state since the multiplicity for it is 2.

It is not too hard to see that associated with a given electron configuration (distribution of electrons in orbitals) there may be several states arising from the different coupling of the momenta.

Example 56. An excited lithium atom contains the valence electron in a $3d$ orbital; what electronic states are possible and what are their Russell–Saunders symbols?

Answer. For this configuration S is still $\frac{1}{2}$. The orbital angular momenta, however, are

$$l_1 = l_2 = 0$$

$$l_3 = 2$$

and hence $L = 2$. The L vector and S vector can combine in either of two ways as shown in Figure 6.10a. This arises because quantum mechanics says that J is quantized, it being restricted to values $L + S, L + S - 1, \ldots, |L - S|$. The two states above thus have $J = 1\frac{1}{2}$ and $2\frac{1}{2}$, and the term symbols are $^2D_{1\frac{1}{2}}$ and $^2D_{2\frac{1}{2}}$. Both these states lie far above the ground state (by about 89.5 kcal mole^{-1}), but are themselves close together. From tables it is found that the $J = 2\frac{1}{2}$ state is about 0.04 cm^{-1} above the $J = 1\frac{1}{2}$ state; this amounts to about 0.11 cal mole^{-1} (see Figure 6.10b).

A magnetic dipole when placed in a magnetic field acquires a certain potential energy. To understand this we may look on a magnetic dipole as a

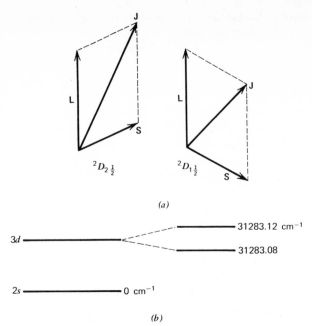

(a)

$$3d \quad \text{—————————} \quad <\begin{array}{l} \text{—————— 31283.12 cm}^{-1} \\ \text{—————— 31283.08} \end{array}$$

$$2s \quad \text{—————————} \quad 0 \text{ cm}^{-1}$$

(b)

Fig. 6.10 (a) Two Russell–Saunders states for an excited lithium atom, and (b) their separation on an energy-level diagram (scale exaggerated).

pair of monopoles of pole strengths $+p$ and $-p$ separated by a distance R and possessing a magnetic dipole moment of $\mu = pR$. This is a convenient fiction because although there are no such things as magnetic monopoles in Nature, this simple picture leads to results in accord with experiment. All magnetic moments are actually the result of closed circulations of various elementary particles according to present-day theory.

Now suppose such a dipole is placed in a homogeneous magnetic field (see Figure 6.11) of magnetic induction **B**. There will be no net force on the dipole, but there will be a torque exerted about an axis through O tending to align the dipole with the field. The magnitude of the torque at each end is given by

$$\text{torque} = \text{distance} \times \text{force}$$

$$= \tfrac{1}{2}R \times (pB \sin \theta)$$

and hence the total torque on the dipole is just twice this or $\mu B \sin \theta$. Work must be done by an external agent in order to alter the orientation of the dipole in the field, and this work is stored as potential energy E in the system. Any value of θ may be chosen as the zero of the potential energy; it

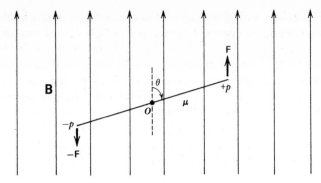

Fig. 6.11   A magnetic dipole in a magnetic field.

is customary to take $\theta = 90°$ for this purpose. Then we have

$$E = \int_{\pi/2}^{\theta} \mu B \sin \theta \, d\theta$$

$$= - \mu B \cos \theta$$

and now we see that this can be written more compactly as a dot product:

$$E = - \boldsymbol{\mu} \cdot \mathbf{B}.$$

Many nuclei by virtue of the circulation of their nucleons possess magnetic moments. These nuclei also possess spin angular momentum $\mathbf{I}$, and the two quantities are related through the expression

$$\boldsymbol{\mu} = g_N \left(\frac{e}{2Mc} \right) \mathbf{I}$$

where M is the mass of the proton and g_N is the nuclear g factor for the particular nucleus of interest. If we agree to always express $\mathbf{I}$ in units of $\hbar$, then we may rewrite this equation as $\boldsymbol{\mu} = g_N \beta_N \mathbf{I}$, where β_N is referred to as the *nuclear magneton* ($\beta_N = e\hbar/2Mc = 5.05 \times 10^{-24}$ erg G^{-1}). This equation shows that the $\boldsymbol{\mu}$ and $\mathbf{I}$ vectors lie either parallel or antiparallel depending on the sign of g_N.

Example 57.   In the nuclear magnetic resonance (nmr) experiment a sample containing nuclei that are magnetically active ($\mu \neq 0$) is immersed in a magnetic field and irradiated with electromagnetic radiation. One continuously alters the frequency of the radiation so as to discover those frequencies at which transitions occur among the various spin energy levels of the nuclei. Discuss briefly the energy levels of a bare deuterium nucleus in a magnetic field.

Answer.   By analogy with the properties of electron spin and orbital angular
momentum as discussed briefly in Example 56, nuclear spin angular momentum **I** is predicted by quantum mechanics to be quantized. Only certain orientations of **I** relative to **B** can be obtained
in a measurement; for deuterium it is found that these are those
orientations where the vector projection of **I** onto **B** has magnitude
$+1$, 0, or -1 units of $\hbar$ (Figure 6.12a) (deuterium, accordingly, is
said to have a spin of 1). There will therefore be only three energy
levels, whose separation depends on the magnitude of **B**. From the
dot product formula for E one has for the energy levels (Figure
6.12b)

$$E = -\boldsymbol{\mu} \cdot \mathbf{B}$$

$$= -g_N \beta_N \mathbf{I} \cdot \mathbf{B}$$

$$= -g_N \beta_N B, 0, + g_N \beta_N B.$$

For ^{2}H it is known that $g_N = 0.857$. In a magnetic field of magnetic
induction 10,000 G, the separation between adjacent levels works
out to be about 0.06 μcal mole^{-1}.

A nucleus with a magnetic moment behaves in a magnetic field similarly
to a spinning top in a gravitational field. In both cases the angular
momentum vector, when inclined at an angle θ to the direction of the field,
experiences a torque tending to align it parallel to the field. This torque

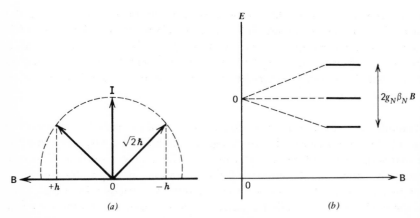

Fig. 6.12   Spin energy levels of deuterium in a magnetic field.

causes the tip of the angular momentum vector to precess about the field axis (see Figure 6.13).

Now from elementary mechanics the torque **L** (a vector quantity) is defined as the time rate of change of the angular momentum **l**, and from elementary electromagnetism the torque for a magnetic dipole in a magnetic field is the vector cross product $\boldsymbol{\mu} \times \mathbf{B}$. Hence one can write

$$\frac{d\mathbf{l}}{dt} = \boldsymbol{\mu} \times \mathbf{B},$$

but we also have seen that $\boldsymbol{\mu}$ and **l** (or **I** in the earlier notation) are directly related. Thus one has the important relation

$$\boxed{\frac{d\mathbf{I}}{dt} = g_N \left(\frac{e\hbar}{2Mc} \right) \mathbf{I} \times \mathbf{B}} \ .$$

This expression is useful in understanding the nature of the basic nmr experiment. It says that the spin angular momentum vector of a nucleus, say that of hydrogen ^{1}H, precesses about **B** with an angular frequency $2\pi\nu_0$ (ν_0 is the frequency and has units of cycles per second, or Hertz) defined by

$$\frac{d\mathbf{I}}{dt} = 2\pi\nu_0\mathbf{I},$$

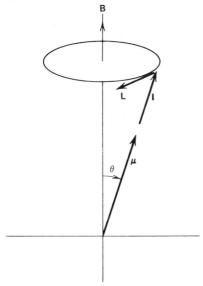

Fig. 6.13   Precession of a magnetic dipole.

and that the angular frequency therefore is given by the expression

$$2\pi\nu_0 = g_N \frac{eB}{2Mc} \, .$$

In other words the system can absorb circularly polarized electromagnetic radiation from an external source only if the radiation has angular frequency equal to or close to $2\pi\nu_0$ as given above. The frequency ν_0 here is called the *Larmor frequency*. When radiation at the Larmor frequency is beamed on the sample, resonance is said to take place and one records this as an absorption peak in a spectrum. If the static field **B** has a magnitude of 14,100 G (as on conventional ^{1}H nmr spectrometers), then the Larmor frequency for the bare proton ($g_N = 5.585$) works out to be about 60.0 MHz.

Finally, to conclude this section let us consider differentiation of vectors. No really new problems are introduced here. Thus a vector $\mathbf{A} = a(t)\mathbf{i} + b(t)\mathbf{j} + c(t)\mathbf{k}$ has a derivative with respect to t of

$$\frac{d\mathbf{A}}{dt} = \frac{da(t)}{dt}\mathbf{i} + \frac{db(t)}{dt}\mathbf{j} + \frac{dc(t)}{dt}\mathbf{k}$$

and a product $f(t)\mathbf{A}$ has a derivative

$$\frac{df(t)}{dt}\mathbf{A} + f(t)\frac{d\mathbf{A}}{dt} \, .$$

If **A** and **B** are vector functions of t, then the derivative of their dot product is given by the expression

$$\mathbf{A} \cdot \frac{d\mathbf{B}}{dt} + \frac{d\mathbf{A}}{dt} \cdot \mathbf{B}$$

and the derivative of their cross product $\mathbf{A} \times \mathbf{B}$ is given by

$$\mathbf{A} \times \frac{d\mathbf{B}}{dt} + \frac{d\mathbf{A}}{dt} \times \mathbf{B}.$$

The order of the terms in the cross multiplications is important, as usual.

As an interesting application of vector differentiation, let us think back again to angular momentum. The angular momentum $\mathbf{l}$ of a body rotating about some fixed axis (see Figure 6.14a) is given by the cross product $\mathbf{l} = \mathbf{r} \times \mathbf{p}$, where **p** is the linear momentum ($\mathbf{p} = m\mathbf{v}$) of the body. Differentiation of the cross product with respect to time gives the torque **L**:

$$\mathbf{L} = \frac{d\mathbf{l}}{dt} = \mathbf{r} \times \frac{d\mathbf{p}}{dt} + \frac{d\mathbf{r}}{dt} \times \mathbf{p}.$$

This can be simplified because it is not hard to see that $d\mathbf{r}/dt$ is parallel to **p**. Suppose in Figure 6.14b that $\mathbf{r}_1$ is the position of **r** at some initial time and $\mathbf{r}_2$

is its position Δt units later; the average velocity is $\Delta \mathbf{r}/\Delta t$ or $(\mathbf{r}_2 - \mathbf{r}_1)/\Delta t$. Now this vector is not quite perpendicular to $\mathbf{r}_1$, but in the limit as θ approaches $0°$ it will become so and $(\mathbf{r}_2 - \mathbf{r}_1)/\Delta t$ will approach $d\mathbf{r}/dt$. Since $d\mathbf{r}/dt$ and $\mathbf{p}$ will then be parallel, their cross product will be zero due to the sine term in the definition of the cross product. This is the mathematical way of looking at this question; the physical way is just as good. We simply note that $d\mathbf{r}/dt$ is the definition of velocity $\mathbf{v}$. Since the linear momentum $\mathbf{p}$ is defined to be the product of the scalar m times the velocity $\mathbf{v}$, it follows that $d\mathbf{r}/dt$ is parallel to $m\mathbf{v}$. In any case, one can write

$$\frac{d\mathbf{l}}{dt} = \mathbf{r} \times \frac{d\mathbf{p}}{dt}$$

$$= \mathbf{r} \times m\frac{d\mathbf{v}}{dt}$$

$$= \mathbf{r} \times \mathbf{F}$$

and thus we see that torque may also be thought of as the product of the length of a lever arm and a force (applied at its tip). Torque is seen to have the same set of fundamental units as work or energy, but is of course different from energy since torque is a vector and not a scalar quantity. The above expression for the torque was used directly in the earlier discussion of the potential energy of a magnetic dipole in a magnetic field.

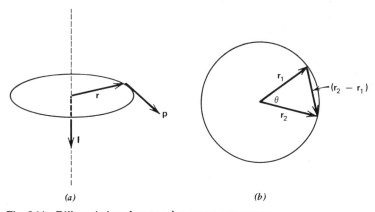

(a)   *(b)*

Fig. 6.14 Differentiation of an angular momentum vector.

4 GRADIENT, DIVERGENCE, CURL, AND LAPLACIAN

Vector quantities that contain differential operators arose out of the researches of Hamilton and have proved to be extremely useful in the writing of many equations in physical science. Equations in electricity and magnetism such as Maxwell's equations would be hard to imagine without the language of gradient, divergence, and curl.

The symbol ∇, that Hamilton introduced and termed "nabla" because it looks like an ancient Hebrew musical instrument of that name (Figure 6.15),[3] stands for the vector differential operator (in Cartesian coordinates)

$$\nabla = i \frac{\partial}{\partial x} + j \frac{\partial}{\partial y} + k \frac{\partial}{\partial z} .$$

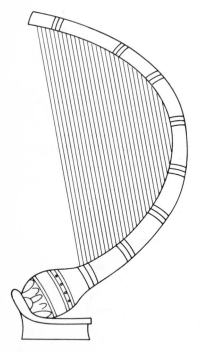

Fig. 6.15 A nabla.

[3]Few, if any, legitimate illustrations of ancient Hebrew musical craft exist because the ancient Hebrews obeyed implicitly the law of their race not to make any graven images or likenesses of any thing in the heaven above or in the earth beneath. Nevertheless, scholars have decided that use of the Hebrew instrument, the nevel, was probably acquired during the time of King Solomon from the Phoenicians, and that this same instrument is almost certainly what was later referred to by Greek and Latin writers as the nabla, nablium, or nablum. The nabla is classified as a harp (more precisely, a vertical angular harp), and its form is assumed to be like that known in ancient Egyptian and Phoenician times. It is said to have had 10–12 or even as many as 20 strings. In English editions of the Old Testament the term "psaltery" may in many places be the translation for the nabla. For readers with a musical bent see the works by J. Stainer, *The Music of the Bible*, 2nd ed., Novello, London, 1914, pp. 28–45; and by C. Sachs, *The History of Musical Instruments*, W. W. Norton, New York, 1940, pp. 114–117.

If we apply this to the vector function $\mathbf{f} = f_1\mathbf{i} + f_2\mathbf{j} + f_3\mathbf{k}$, where f_1, f_2, and f_3 are all functions of x, y, and z, and with the proviso that $\mathbf{i}^2 = \mathbf{j}^2 = \mathbf{k}^2 = -1$, $-\mathbf{ji} = \mathbf{ij} = \mathbf{k}$ and so on cyclically, we get the result

$$\nabla\mathbf{f} = -\left(\frac{\partial f_1}{\partial x} + \frac{\partial f_2}{\partial y} + \frac{\partial f_3}{\partial z}\right) + \left[\left(\frac{\partial f_3}{\partial y} - \frac{\partial f_2}{\partial z}\right)\mathbf{i} + \left(\frac{\partial f_1}{\partial z} - \frac{\partial f_3}{\partial x}\right)\mathbf{j} + \left(\frac{\partial f_2}{\partial x} - \frac{\partial f_1}{\partial y}\right)\mathbf{k}\right].$$

The quantity on the right, compounded of a scalar part and a three-dimensional vector, is a creation of Hamilton's; it is called a *quaternion*. The *ijk* relations above are the ones Hamilton used in his search for a consistent algebra for higher-dimensional complex numbers.

Now this result by itself is not important. Mathematicians were interested in quaternions for a while, but the scientists never were. It was Gibbs who saw that something more useful could be obtained by separating out the scalar part (which we today call the *divergence* of $\mathbf{f}$) from the vector part (which we today call the *curl* of $\mathbf{f}$) and adopting a different set of *ijk* rules for each. The result is that the divergence is defined as the dot product of ∇ and a vector function, and the curl is defined as the cross product of ∇ and a vector function.

$$\operatorname{div}\mathbf{f} = \nabla\cdot\mathbf{f} = \frac{\partial f_1}{\partial x} + \frac{\partial f_2}{\partial y} + \frac{\partial f_3}{\partial z}$$

$$\operatorname{curl}\mathbf{f} = \nabla\times\mathbf{f} = \left(\frac{\partial f_3}{\partial y} - \frac{\partial f_2}{\partial z}\right)\mathbf{i} + \left(\frac{\partial f_1}{\partial z} - \frac{\partial f_3}{\partial x}\right)\mathbf{j} + \left(\frac{\partial f_2}{\partial x} - \frac{\partial f_1}{\partial y}\right)\mathbf{k}$$

We emphasize again that the *ijk* rules for quaternions and vectors are different, and that within vectors the rules for dot multiplication are again different from those for cross multiplication. Edna Kramer in her historical survey of mathematics points out that P. G. Tait (1890) in his textbook on quaternions called the Gibbs vectors "hermaphrodite monsters compounded of the notations of Hamilton and Grassmann." The mathematicians and scientists in the old days could be quite colorful when they wanted to. The various multiplication rules are summarized in Table 6.2.

Table 6.2   Rules for Unit Vectors

Operations	Quaternions	Dot multiplication	Cross multiplication
$\mathbf{i}^2, \mathbf{j}^2, \mathbf{k}^2$	-1	$+1$	0
$\mathbf{ij}, \mathbf{jk}, \mathbf{ki}$	$\mathbf{k}, \mathbf{i}, \mathbf{j}$	0	$\mathbf{k}, \mathbf{i}, \mathbf{j}$
Is multiplication commutative?	No	Yes	No

Another conceivable operation that can be performed with the nabla operator is to operate on a scalar function. Thus if $f = f(x,y,z)$, operation on it by ∇ generates the *gradient* of f:

$$\operatorname{grad} f = \nabla f = \mathbf{i}\frac{\partial f}{\partial x} + \mathbf{j}\frac{\partial f}{\partial y} + \mathbf{k}\frac{\partial f}{\partial z}.$$

The gradient is a vector, but to see what it means physically we need to return to the concept of the directional derivative, that was introduced in Section 2.3. Suppose the function $f(x,y,z)$ is defined and is differentiable in some region of space, and let S_1 be a surface or collection of points for which $f(P)$ is some constant k. Let S_2 be another surface, very close to S_1, and for which $f(P') = k + \Delta k$. Then the directional derivative at point A and in the direction of the line from A to A' is

$$\lim_{\Delta s \to 0} \frac{f(A') - f(A)}{|\Delta s|} = \frac{df(P)}{ds}.$$

Now the change $f(A') - f(A)$ does not depend where on S_2 one is located, but the derivative does. It assumes its maximum value when $|\Delta s|$ is a minimum, and this occurs when Δs is coincident with AB, where B is that point on S_2 which is nearest to point A (see Figure 6.16). If $\mathbf{n}$ is a vector of unit length pointing from A to B, then $\mathbf{n}(df(P)/dn)$ is a vector that is in magnitude and direction the greatest space rate of increase in $f(P)$. We call this vector the gradient of $f(P)$ at point A. But how does this definition tie in with the differential definition given earlier?

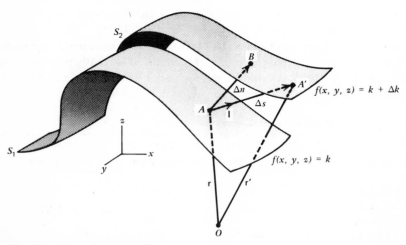

Fig. 6.16   Illustrating the gradient.

Return again to the directional derivative at A and pointing in a general direction AA'. Let $\mathbf{l} = \mathbf{i}(dx/ds) + \mathbf{j}(dy/ds) + \mathbf{k}(dz/ds)$ be a unit vector pointing in this direction. Such a vector does have unit length because the square of the line element, $(ds)^2$, is just $(dx)^2 + (dy)^2 + (dz)^2$. From the chain rule we can express the directional derivative as

$$\frac{df(P)}{ds} = \frac{\partial f(P)}{\partial x}\frac{dx}{ds} + \frac{\partial f(P)}{\partial y}\frac{dy}{ds} + \frac{\partial f(P)}{\partial z}\frac{dz}{ds}$$

or in terms of a dot product

$$\frac{df(P)}{ds} = \left[\mathbf{i}\frac{\partial f(P)}{\partial x} + \mathbf{j}\frac{\partial f(P)}{\partial y} + \mathbf{k}\frac{\partial f(P)}{\partial z} \right] \cdot \mathbf{l}$$

$$= \left\| \left[\mathbf{i}\frac{\partial f(P)}{\partial x} + \mathbf{j}\frac{\partial f(P)}{\partial y} + \mathbf{k}\frac{\partial f(P)}{\partial z} \right] \right\| \cos\theta.$$

If we now specialize this to the case where $\theta = 0^0$, then $df(P)/ds$ becomes $df(P)/dn$ which is the magnitude of the gradient by our definition above. Thus we see that the magnitude of the gradient can be expressed as

$$\left\| \left[\mathbf{i}\frac{\partial f(P)}{\partial x} + \mathbf{j}\frac{\partial f(P)}{\partial y} + \mathbf{k}\frac{\partial f(P)}{\partial z} \right] \right\|.$$

The gradient at any point is a vector whose magnitude evaluated at that point is the maximum value which the directional derivative can attain there.

Example 58. A point dipole with a dipole moment of $\boldsymbol{\mu}$ is centered at the origin. From electromagnetic theory it is known that the electric potential $\psi(\mathbf{r})$ at $\mathbf{r}$ due to this point dipole is given by

$$\psi(\mathbf{r}) = \frac{\boldsymbol{\mu} \cdot \mathbf{r}}{4\pi\varepsilon_0 r^3}.$$

Find the electric field at $\mathbf{r}$.

Answer. The electric field is negative the gradient of the electric potential.

$$\mathbf{E} = -\nabla\psi(\mathbf{r})$$

In terms of a Cartesian coordinate system we can write the

potential as

$$E = -\left(i\frac{\partial}{\partial x} + j\frac{\partial}{\partial y} + k\frac{\partial}{\partial z}\right)\left[\frac{x\mu_x + y\mu_y + z\mu_z}{4\pi\varepsilon_0\left(x^2 + y^2 + z^2\right)^{3/2}}\right].$$

The x component of E works out to be

$$\frac{-1}{4\pi\varepsilon_0}\left[\frac{r^2\mu_x - 3x(x\mu_x + y\mu_y + z\mu_z)}{r^5}\right]$$

and similarly for the y and z components. Combination of the three components produces

$$E = \frac{1}{4\pi\varepsilon_0}\left\{\frac{3r(\mu\cdot r)}{r^5} - \frac{\mu}{r^3}\right\}.$$

A sample calculation is illustrative. Suppose the dipole is a molecule of hydrogen chloride ($|\mu| = 1.084$ D) oriented along the z axis. For points along the x and y axes the potential is zero because μ and r are orthogonal and μ has a component only along the z axis. For a point P on the z axis located z units from the origin we have

$$E = E_z = \frac{1}{4\pi\varepsilon_0}\left\{\frac{3\mu z^2}{z^5} - \frac{\mu}{z^3}\right\}$$

$$= \frac{\mu}{2\pi\varepsilon_0 z^3}.$$

At a distance of 10 A^0, for example, this becomes

$$E = \frac{(1.084\times10^{-18}\mathrm{esu\,cm})(3.33\times10^{-10}\mathrm{C\,esu^{-1}})(10^{-2}\mathrm{m\,cm^{-1}})}{2\pi(8.854\times10^{-12}\mathrm{F\,m^{-1}})(10^{-9}\mathrm{m})^3}$$

$$= 0.065\times10^9\ \mathrm{C\ F^{-1}m^{-1}}$$

$$= \boxed{65\ \mathrm{MV\ m^{-1}}}.$$

Such a dipole would cause appreciable electrostriction in solution in its immediate vicinity, although not as much as would an ion placed at the same location.

The divergence of a vector **A** has already been defined as the scalar $\nabla \cdot \mathbf{A}$. The physical meaning of the divergence may be seen by considering the flow of anything (heat, charge, matter, etc.) through a volume element. The analysis is similar to that given in connection with Fick's second law of diffusion in Section 5.4. Consider a volume element $d\tau = dx\,dy\,dz$, with one corner located at the point (x_0, y_0, z_0), and let **J** represent the rate of flow per unit area across a face normal to **J**. The component of **J** along the x axis is shown in Figure 6.17. At the left face the rate of flow in the x direction is $J_x\,dy\,dz$. However at the right face the flow rate is slightly different because J_x is different there. It has changed by the amount dJ_x, so that the flow rate is now $(J_x + dJ_x)\,dy\,dz$. The net flow out, right face minus left face, is therefore

$$\left(\frac{\partial J_x}{\partial x}\right)_{x_0} dx\,dy\,dz.$$

The other two directions are analyzed in an analogous manner. The results in these cases can be combined with that above to give for the total loss rate from the volume element of

$$\left(\frac{\partial J_x}{\partial x} + \frac{\partial J_y}{\partial y} + \frac{\partial J_z}{\partial z}\right)_{(x_0, y_0, z_0)} d\tau.$$

The divergence $\nabla \cdot \mathbf{J}$ of a vector $\mathbf{J}$ is the net outward volume flow rate per unit volume.

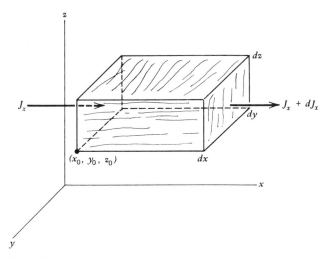

Fig. 6.17 Physical significance of the divergence of a vector.

If the density (not the flow density) of substance under consideration is $\rho(x,y,z,t)$, the loss rate per unit volume may also be expressed as $-(\partial\rho/\partial t)$. Therefore, one has the identity

$$\nabla\cdot\mathbf{J}+\frac{\partial\rho}{\partial t}=0.$$

This equation is known as the *continuity equation*. Mathematically it expresses a law of conservation (of energy, charge, matter, etc.). An incompressible fluid must flow out of a given volume element as fast as it flows in; such a flow field would therefore have zero divergence and is said to be *solenoidal*. The flow fields of liquids (but not of gases) are approximately solenoidal and for them one must have $\partial\rho/\partial t\cong0$. Or to take another example $\mathbf{J}$ might be the electric current density, that is, the flow per unit time across a unit surface of electric charges, and ρ would be the charge density in some region. The continuity equation then expresses the law of conservation of charge in this region. If the flow of charges is a stationary one the charge density does not change and one has

$$\operatorname{div}\mathbf{J}=0.$$

The curl of a vector, $\nabla\times\mathbf{A}$, is another vector. Since it is defined as a cross product, the mnemonic given in Section 6.3 can be used:

$$\operatorname{curl}\mathbf{A}=\begin{vmatrix} \mathbf{i} & \mathbf{j} & \mathbf{k} \\ \dfrac{\partial}{\partial x} & \dfrac{\partial}{\partial y} & \dfrac{\partial}{\partial z} \\ A_x & A_y & A_z \end{vmatrix}.$$

A physical interpretation of the curl of a vector can be given but is not as transparent as that for the divergence. In simple terms the name implies that a small hypothetical paddle wheel, when placed in a fluid (material or otherwise) described by a fluid flow field $\mathbf{A}$, would tend to rotate in regions where curl $\mathbf{A}\neq0$ and would remain stationary in regions where curl $\mathbf{A}=0$.

Our interest in the operations of divergence or of curl are in those situations in electromagnetism that impinge upon problems of chemical interest. Sooner or later in any treatment of the magnetic and electrical properties of substances (as in susceptibilities, magnetic resonance, and nuclear quadrupole spectroscopy) one is bound to come across the two electromagnetic potentials: ψ ($\mathbf{r}$), the electric potential, and $\mathbf{A}(r)$, the magnetic potential. Certain of the equations of electromagnetism are most conveniently written in terms of ψ and $\mathbf{A}$. We have already met the electric potential in Example 58. In a pure electric field it is defined by the relation $\mathbf{E}=-\operatorname{grad}\psi$. The magnetic potential is defined by the relation $\mathbf{B}=\operatorname{curl}\mathbf{A}$ where $\mathbf{B}$, of course, is the magnetic flux density (the magnetic field, less accurately). In experiments it is **B** and **E**, not **A** and ψ, that determine observable phenomena such as the force on an ion in solution or in a mass spectrometer, so it is relevant to ask to what extent **A** and ψ are determined by **B** and **E**. It is not hard to see that **A** and ψ are not uniquely defined by **B** and **E**. For example, suppose some magnetic potential **A** is replaced by a new potential **A**′ given by

$$\mathbf{A}' = \mathbf{A} - \nabla f$$

where f is any scalar function of position. We now ask what is curl **A**′? Obviously, the answer is given by

$$\nabla \times \mathbf{A}' = \nabla \times \mathbf{A} - \nabla \times (\nabla f)$$

but we do not yet know what is the curl of a gradient.

To help us in cases like this, where we need to know some particular vector identity, the following theorem may be useful. It contains a number of vector identities, all of which can be proved in a straightforward manner using the basic definitions of dot and cross multiplication.

Theorem 21. *If* f *and* g *are scalar functions, and* **A**, **B**, *and* **C** *are vector functions, then the following are true*:

1. $(\mathbf{A} \times \mathbf{B}) \cdot \mathbf{C} = (\mathbf{B} \times \mathbf{C}) \cdot \mathbf{A} = (\mathbf{C} \times \mathbf{A}) \cdot \mathbf{B}$
2. $\mathbf{A} \times (\mathbf{B} \times \mathbf{C}) = (\mathbf{A} \cdot \mathbf{C})\mathbf{B} - (\mathbf{A} \cdot \mathbf{B})\mathbf{C}$
3. $\text{curl} (\mathbf{A} \times \mathbf{B}) = (\text{div}\,\mathbf{B})\mathbf{A} - (\text{div}\,\mathbf{A})\mathbf{B} + (\mathbf{B} \cdot \text{grad})\mathbf{A} - (\mathbf{A} \cdot \text{grad})\mathbf{B}$
4. $\text{div}(\mathbf{A} \times \mathbf{B}) = \mathbf{B} \cdot \text{curl}\,\mathbf{A} - \mathbf{A} \cdot \text{curl}\,\mathbf{B}$
5. $\text{curl}\,\text{grad}\,f = \text{div}\,\text{curl}\,\mathbf{A} = 0$
6. $\text{grad}\,(fg) = f\,\text{grad}\,g + g\,\text{grad}\,f$
7. $\text{div}(f\mathbf{A}) = (\text{grad}\,f) \cdot \mathbf{A} + f\,\text{div}\,\mathbf{A}$
8. $\text{curl}\,(f\mathbf{A}) = (\text{grad}\,f) \times \mathbf{A} + f\,\text{curl}\,\mathbf{A}$

The first part of number 5, for example, can be worked out using the mnemonic for cross multiplication:

$$\nabla \times (\nabla f) = \begin{vmatrix} \mathbf{i} & \mathbf{j} & \mathbf{k} \\ \dfrac{\partial}{\partial x} & \dfrac{\partial}{\partial y} & \dfrac{\partial}{\partial z} \\ \dfrac{\partial f}{\partial x} & \dfrac{\partial f}{\partial y} & \dfrac{\partial f}{\partial z} \end{vmatrix}$$

$$= \mathbf{i}\left(\frac{\partial^2 f}{\partial y\,\partial z} - \frac{\partial^2 f}{\partial z\,\partial y} \right) + \mathbf{j}\left(\frac{\partial^2 f}{\partial z\,\partial x} - \frac{\partial^2 f}{\partial x\,\partial z} \right) + \mathbf{k}\left(\frac{\partial^2 f}{\partial x\,\partial y} - \frac{\partial^2 f}{\partial y\,\partial x} \right)$$

$$= 0.$$

Therefore, returning to our problem we find

$$\mathbf{B}' = \text{curl}\,\mathbf{A}' = \text{curl}\,\mathbf{A} = \mathbf{B}$$

and thus the magnetic field is unaltered by the transformation of the potential. Such a transformation is called a *gauge transformation*; it plays an important role in molecular orbital theories of molecules in magnetic fields.

Since the curl is a differential operator, it is not mathematically valid to say

$$\nabla \times \mathbf{A} = -\mathbf{A} \times \nabla$$

as one could do with any pair of ordinary vectors $\mathbf{A}$ and $\mathbf{B}$. Expressions of a form like that on the right side of the above equation occur in the quantum mechanical treatment of angular momentum. You will recall we said that in classical mechanics the angular momentum of a particle in motion about some axis is given by the cross product

$$\mathbf{l} = \mathbf{r} \times \mathbf{p}.$$

In making the transition from classical to quantum mechanics the rule is that x_j components of linear momentum are to be substituted mathematically by the operators $-i\hbar(\partial/\partial x_j)$. This means, then, that angular momentum at the atomic level is defined by the vector expression

$$\hat{\mathbf{l}} = -i\hbar(\mathbf{r} \times \nabla)$$

and this equation shows how angular momentum is treated as an operator in quantum mechanics. Angular momentum as a quantity with a magnitude and a direction does not emerge until the operator above has operated on some suitable wave function.

Example 59. Work out the $x, y,$ and z components of the angular momentum operator.

Answer. Even though $\hat{\mathbf{l}}$ is an operator, it is still defined as a cross product and we may (with care) use the mnemonic to work out the components:

$$\hat{\mathbf{l}} = -i\hbar \begin{vmatrix} \mathbf{i} & \mathbf{j} & \mathbf{k} \\ x & y & z \\ \dfrac{\partial}{\partial x} & \dfrac{\partial}{\partial y} & \dfrac{\partial}{\partial z} \end{vmatrix}.$$

Note that this time the partial derivatives appear on the bottom row. The x component consists of those terms that contain the unit vector $\mathbf{i}$:

$$\mathbf{i}\hat{l}_x = -i\hbar\mathbf{i}\left(y\frac{\partial}{\partial z} - z\frac{\partial}{\partial y} \right).$$

The other components follow similarly:

$$\mathbf{j}\hat{l}_y = -i\hbar\mathbf{j}\left(z\frac{\partial}{\partial x} - x\frac{\partial}{\partial z} \right)$$

$$\mathbf{k}\hat{l}_z = -i\hbar\mathbf{k}\left(x\frac{\partial}{\partial y} - y\frac{\partial}{\partial x} \right).$$

An important and frequently occurring differential operator arises when the nabla operator is allowed to operate twice on some scalar function as shown:

$$\nabla^2 f = \nabla \cdot (\nabla f).$$

This can be rewritten as

$$\nabla^2 f = \left(\mathbf{i}\frac{\partial}{\partial x} + \mathbf{j}\frac{\partial}{\partial y} + \mathbf{k}\frac{\partial}{\partial z} \right) \cdot \left(\mathbf{i}\frac{\partial f}{\partial x} + \mathbf{j}\frac{\partial f}{\partial y} + \mathbf{k}\frac{\partial f}{\partial z} \right)$$

$$= \frac{\partial^2 f}{\partial x^2} + \frac{\partial^2 f}{\partial y^2} + \frac{\partial^2 f}{\partial z^2}.$$

The differential operator $\nabla \cdot \nabla$ is thus the familiar Laplacian operator that has been mentioned before in this text (see Exercise 35* at the end of Chapter 5). The Laplacian in fact may also operate on vector functions, but this is not as common as operation on scalar functions. Places of common occurrence of the Laplacian are in many second-order differential equations describing natural phenomean such as the equations mentioned in Section 5.4.

For example, one of Maxwell's equations is

$$\nabla \cdot \mathbf{E} = \frac{\rho}{\varepsilon_0}.$$

This says that the divergence or the net outward flow per unit volume of an electric field into a volume element must be accounted for by the presence of free charges at a density ρ in that volume. As we have seen, an electric field may be alternatively expressed in terms of a potential, $\mathbf{E} = -\nabla\psi$. Therefore, Maxwell's equation may be rewritten using the Laplacian operator:

$$\nabla^2\psi = -\frac{\rho}{\varepsilon_0}.$$

This equation is called Poisson's equation (recall Exercise 37* at the end of Chapter 2). It is important in any sort of treatment of solutions of electrolytes where there are free ions present. The electric potential at any point in such a solution must be of a form mathematically that satisfies Poisson's equation. If no free ions but only neutral molecules are present, then $\rho = 0$ and the electric potential at any point in solution must satisfy Laplace's equation:

$$\nabla^2\psi = 0.$$

5* ORTHOGONAL COORDINATE SYSTEMS

On several occasions you have been exposed to problems involving coordinate systems other than a rectangular Cartesian coordinate system. The use of such systems is sometimes nothing more than a mathematical artifice to simplify an abstract problem but more commonly it is an exploitation of obvious symmetry in a physical situation. For example if you are studying some electrochemical process where ions or molecules move toward an electrode shaped in the form of a slender rod and positioned in the center of the cell, this situation is begging to be described by a coordinate system in which the radial distance from an axis is one of the variables. Cylindrical polar coordinates would probably be useful here. On the other hand, if the electrode is a rectangular strip or wafer positioned roughly parallel to two sides of the cell, then Cartesian coordinates would be more suitable.

In principle, there is no limit to the number of different coordinate systems that are possible. Roughly a dozen are in common usage, and of these perhaps four or five are very common. This section focuses on coordinate systems in such a way as to show that manipulations with them are all basically similar. In doing this we draw on some ideas from our study of vectors.

Any coordinate system (q_1, q_2, q_3) in three-dimensional space can be looked upon geometrically as three families of concentric surfaces. These surfaces might be planes, spheres, cones, ellipsoids, or whatever, and each results from setting one of the three independent variables equal to a constant and graphing the result. For example, in rectangular Cartesian coordinates if one sets $q_3 \equiv z = 3$, then the result is a plane (a surface) parallel to the xy plane and 3 units above it. The rectangular Cartesian coordinate system (see Figure 6.18) consists of three families of intersecting planes, and a point in space is located by selecting one plane from each family and finding where the three mutually intersect. With each family of surfaces, $q_i = $ constant, one can associate a unit vector $\mathbf{a}_i$ normal to the surface and pointing in the direction of increasing q_i. The increment of distance between any two points in space described by a coordinate system is then

$$d\mathbf{r} = \mathbf{a}_1 h_1 \, dq_1 + \mathbf{a}_2 h_2 \, dq_2 + \mathbf{a}_3 h_3 \, dq_3$$

and therefore the square of the distance between two neighboring points is given by the dot product summation

$$(dr)^2 = \sum_{j=1}^{3} \sum_{i=1}^{3} (\mathbf{a}_i \cdot \mathbf{a}_j) h_i h_j \, dq_i \, dq_j.$$

Of particular interest are those coordinate systems where the unit vectors at a point in space are always mutually perpendicular. For such *orthogonal coordinate systems* one has

$$\mathbf{a}_i \cdot \mathbf{a}_j = \delta_{ij}$$

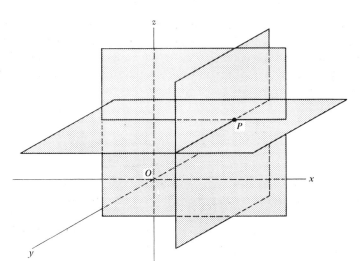

Fig. 6.18 The rectangular Cartesian coordinate system.

and therefore the square of the increment of distance is just

$$(dr)^2 = h_1^2(dq_1)^2 + h_2^2(dq_2)^2 + h_3^2(dq_3)^2.$$

The set of quantities $\{h_i\}$ specifies the nature of the (q_1, q_2, q_3) system; these coefficients are called the *metric*. Usually one is interested in transforming from the (x, y, z) coordinate system to the (q_1, q_2, q_3) system. For the (x, y, z) system $(dr)^2 = (dx)^2 + (dy)^2 + (dz)^2$, and since the variables q_1, q_2, and q_3 are independent, it follows from the above that

$$h_i^2 = \left(\frac{\partial x}{\partial q_i}\right)^2 + \left(\frac{\partial y}{\partial q_i}\right)^2 + \left(\frac{\partial z}{\partial q_i}\right)^2.$$

In order to use this relation one needs only to know the transformation laws connecting the two coordinate systems.

The three coordinates q_1, q_2, and q_3 need not in general be lengths, and the metric coefficients may depend on one or more of the q_i, but the product $h_i dq_i$ must have units of length. The corresponding area and volume elements are given by

$$dA_{ij} = |h_i h_j| dq_i dq_j$$

$$dV = |h_1 h_2 h_3| dq_1 dq_2 dq_3.$$

We now inquire how one would express the gradient, divergence, curl, and Laplacian in a general orthogonal coordinate system. The component of the gradient in the direction normal to the surface $q_i = $ constant will be the distance rate of change of the function in that direction. The increment of distance in this direction is $h_i dq_i$; it follows that the gradient is

$$\boxed{\nabla f(q_1, q_2, q_3) = \frac{\mathbf{a}_1}{h_1} \frac{\partial f}{\partial q_1} + \frac{\mathbf{a}_2}{h_2} \frac{\partial f}{\partial q_2} + \frac{\mathbf{a}_3}{h_3} \frac{\partial f}{\partial q_3}.}$$

The divergence requires more work to deduce its form. Let us return to the physical picture that was presented in the last section. In Figure 6.19 is sketched a differential volume element for a curvilinear orthogonal coordinate system. Point P has coordinates (q_1, q_2, q_3). The rate of flow into face A_{12} is given by the product of the flow vector $\mathbf{J}$ along the direction normal to A_{12} times the area of the face:

$$\text{rate of flow in} = J_3 dA_{12}$$

$$= J_3 h_1 h_2 dq_1 dq_2.$$

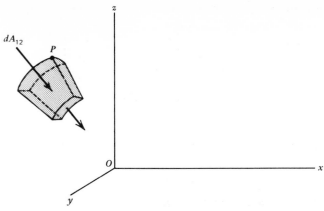

Fig. 6.19 A volume element in a curvilinear coordinate system.

A similar expression applies for the rate of flow out the oppeste face, but it must be remembered that the value of J_3 will have changed slightly and also that the metric coefficients h_1 and h_2 that are dependent in general on the coordinates, will have changed slightly. Accordingly, we write

$$\text{rate of flow out} = J_3\, dA_{12} + \left[\frac{\partial}{\partial q_3}(J_3 h_1 h_2)\, dq_3 \right] dq_1\, dq_2$$

$$= \left[J_3 h_1 h_2 + \frac{\partial (J_3 h_1 h_2)}{\partial q_3}\, dq_3 \right] dq_1\, dq_2$$

and hence the net outward flow rate along the q_3 direction is just

$$\frac{\partial (J_3 h_1 h_2)}{\partial q_3}\, dq_1\, dq_2\, dq_3.$$

Similar expressions apply to flow along the q_1 and q_2 directions. If we combine these and divide by the volume $dV = h_1 h_2 h_3\, dq_1\, dq_2\, dq_3$ to get the net outward flow rate per unit volume, we arrive at

$$\boxed{\nabla \cdot \mathbf{J} = \frac{1}{h_1 h_2 h_3} \left\{ \frac{\partial}{\partial q_1}(J_1 h_2 h_3) + \frac{\partial}{\partial q_2}(J_2 h_1 h_3) + \frac{\partial}{\partial q_3}(J_3 h_1 h_2) \right\}.}$$

Since we did not present a physical picture earlier of the curl of a vector, we give here just the result for a general coordinate system. As before, it is most convenient to express the curl in the form of a determinant:

$$
\nabla \times \mathbf{A} = \frac{1}{h_1 h_2 h_3}
\begin{vmatrix}
\mathbf{a}_1 h_1 & \mathbf{a}_2 h_2 & \mathbf{a}_3 h_s \\
\dfrac{\partial}{\partial q_1} & \dfrac{\partial}{\partial q_2} & \dfrac{\partial}{\partial q_3} \\
h_1 A_1 & h_2 A_2 & h_3 A_3
\end{vmatrix}.
$$

Finally, to obtain the Laplacian we use the formula for the divergence, $\nabla \cdot \mathbf{J}$, writing $\nabla f(q_1, q_2, q_3)$ for the vector $\mathbf{J}$:

$$
\nabla^2 f(q_1, q_2, q_3) = \frac{1}{h_1 h_2 h_3} \left[\frac{\partial}{\partial q_1} \left(\frac{1}{h_1} \frac{\partial f}{\partial q_1} h_2 h_3 \right) \right.
$$

$$
\left. + \frac{\partial}{\partial q_2} \left(\frac{1}{h_2} \frac{\partial f}{\partial q_2} h_1 h_3 \right) + \frac{\partial}{\partial q_3} \left(\frac{1}{h_3} \frac{\partial f}{\partial q_3} h_1 h_2 \right) \right]
$$

$$
= \boxed{
\begin{aligned}
& \frac{1}{h_1{}^2} \frac{\partial^2 f}{\partial q_1{}^2} + \frac{1}{h_2{}^2} \frac{\partial^2 f}{\partial q_2{}^2} + \frac{1}{h_3{}^2} \frac{\partial^2 f}{\partial q_3{}^2} \\
& + \frac{1}{h_1 h_2 h_3} \left[\frac{\partial f}{\partial q_1} \frac{\partial}{\partial q_1} \left(\frac{h_2 h_3}{h_1} \right) + \frac{\partial f}{\partial q_2} \frac{\partial}{\partial q_2} \left(\frac{h_1 h_3}{h_2} \right) + \frac{\partial f}{\partial q_3} \frac{\partial}{\partial q_3} \left(\frac{h_1 h_2}{h_3} \right) \right]
\end{aligned}
}.
$$

The rectangular Cartesian coordinate system, which is the simplest of all coordinate systems, is characterized by $h_1 = h_x = 1$, $h_2 = h_y = 1$, and $h_3 = h_z = 1$. This system is unique in that all of its h_i's are constant, and all of its unit vectors $\mathbf{a}_i$ have fixed directions in space.

In the cylindrical polar coordinate system the transformation equations are

$$
x = r \cos \phi
$$

$$
y = r \sin \phi
$$

$$
z = z
$$

and from the defining relation for the h_i's,

$$
h_i{}^2 = \left(\frac{\partial x}{\partial q_i} \right)^2 + \left(\frac{\partial y}{\partial q_i} \right)^2 + \left(\frac{\partial z}{\partial q_i} \right)^2,
$$

it follows that $h_1 = h_r = 1$, $h_2 = h_\phi = r$, and $h_3 = h_z = 1$. The gradient, divergence, curl, and Laplacian work out to be

$$\nabla f(r,\phi,z) = \mathbf{a}_r \frac{\partial f}{\partial r} + \frac{\mathbf{a}_\phi}{r} \frac{\partial f}{\partial \phi} + \mathbf{a}_z \frac{\partial f}{\partial z}$$

$$\nabla \cdot \mathbf{J}(r,\phi,z) = \frac{\partial J_r}{\partial r} + \frac{J_r}{r} + \frac{1}{r} \frac{\partial J_\phi}{\partial \phi} + \frac{\partial J_z}{\partial z}$$

$$\nabla \times \mathbf{A}(r,\phi,z) = \frac{1}{r} \begin{vmatrix} \mathbf{a}_r & r\mathbf{a}_\phi & \mathbf{a}_z \\ \frac{\partial}{\partial r} & \frac{\partial}{\partial \phi} & \frac{\partial}{\partial z} \\ A_r & rA_\phi & A_z \end{vmatrix}$$

$$\nabla^2 f(r,\phi,z) = \frac{\partial^2 f}{\partial r^2} + \frac{1}{r^2} \frac{\partial^2 f}{\partial \phi^2} + \frac{\partial^2 f}{\partial z^2} + \frac{1}{r} \frac{\partial f}{\partial r}.$$

The unit vectors in this coordinate system may be related to unit vectors in the (x,y,z) system by the equations

$$\mathbf{a}_i = \frac{1}{h_i} \frac{\partial \mathbf{r}}{\partial q_i}.$$

Thus for $\mathbf{a}_r$

$$\mathbf{a}_r = \mathbf{i} \frac{dx}{dr} + \mathbf{j} \frac{dy}{dr} + \mathbf{k} \frac{dz}{dr}$$

$$= \mathbf{i} \cos\phi + \mathbf{j} \sin\phi$$

$$= (\mathbf{i}x + \mathbf{j}y) / \sqrt{x^2 + y^2} .$$

Similarly,

$$\mathbf{a}_\phi = \frac{-\mathbf{i}}{r}(r\sin\phi) + \frac{\mathbf{j}}{r}(r\cos\phi)$$

$$= (-\mathbf{i}y + \mathbf{j}x) / \sqrt{x^2 + y^2}$$

$$\mathbf{a}_z = \mathbf{k}.$$

These equations show clearly how the cylindrical polar unit vectors change direction with a change in position in space.

Occasionally one wishes to express partial derivatives in the (x,y,z) system in terms of partial derivatives in another system (such as the cylindrical polar coordinate system). One way (the brute force way) to do this is to write $\partial f/\partial r$, $\partial f/\partial \phi$, $\partial f/\partial z$ using the chain rule

$$\frac{\partial f}{\partial r} = \frac{\partial f}{\partial x}\frac{\partial x}{\partial r} + \frac{\partial f}{\partial y}\frac{\partial y}{\partial r} + \frac{\partial f}{\partial z}\frac{\partial z}{\partial r}$$

$$\frac{\partial f}{\partial \phi} = \frac{\partial f}{\partial x}\frac{\partial x}{\partial \phi} + \frac{\partial f}{\partial y}\frac{\partial y}{\partial \phi} + \frac{\partial f}{\partial z}\frac{\partial z}{\partial \phi}$$

$$\frac{\partial f}{\partial z} = \frac{\partial f}{\partial x}\frac{\partial x}{\partial z} + \frac{\partial f}{\partial y}\frac{\partial y}{\partial z} + \frac{\partial f}{\partial z}\frac{\partial z}{\partial z}$$

and then to use Cramer's rule (see Chapter 1) to solve for the desired quantity:

$$\frac{\partial f}{\partial x} = \frac{\begin{vmatrix} \dfrac{\partial f}{\partial r} & \dfrac{\partial y}{\partial r} & \dfrac{\partial z}{\partial r} \\[2mm] \dfrac{\partial f}{\partial \phi} & \dfrac{\partial y}{\partial \phi} & \dfrac{\partial z}{\partial \phi} \\[2mm] \dfrac{\partial f}{\partial z} & \dfrac{\partial y}{\partial z} & \dfrac{\partial z}{\partial z} \end{vmatrix}}{\begin{vmatrix} \dfrac{\partial x}{\partial r} & \dfrac{\partial y}{\partial r} & \dfrac{\partial z}{\partial r} \\[2mm] \dfrac{\partial x}{\partial \phi} & \dfrac{\partial y}{\partial \phi} & \dfrac{\partial z}{\partial \phi} \\[2mm] \dfrac{\partial x}{\partial z} & \dfrac{\partial y}{\partial z} & \dfrac{\partial z}{\partial z} \end{vmatrix}} = \frac{\begin{vmatrix} \dfrac{\partial f}{\partial r} & \sin\phi & 0 \\[2mm] \dfrac{\partial f}{\partial \phi} & r\cos\phi & 0 \\[2mm] \dfrac{\partial f}{\partial z} & 0 & 1 \end{vmatrix}}{\begin{vmatrix} \cos\phi & \sin\phi & 0 \\[2mm] -r\sin\phi & r\cos\phi & 0 \\[2mm] 0 & 0 & 1 \end{vmatrix}}$$

$$= \frac{r\cos\phi\,\dfrac{\partial f}{\partial r} - \sin\phi\,\dfrac{\partial f}{\partial \phi}}{r\cos^2\phi + r\sin^2\phi}.$$

$$\therefore \frac{\partial}{\partial x} = \cos\phi\,\frac{\partial}{\partial r} - \frac{\sin\phi}{r}\,\frac{\partial}{\partial \phi}.$$

The elegant way is to equate the gradient $\nabla f(x,y,z)$ with the gradient $\nabla f(r,\phi,z)$, making use of the cylindrical polar unit vectors worked out previously:

$$\mathbf{i}\frac{\partial f}{\partial x} + \mathbf{j}\frac{\partial f}{\partial y} + \mathbf{k}\frac{\partial f}{\partial z} = \left(\mathbf{i}\cos\phi\,\frac{\partial f}{\partial r} + \mathbf{j}\sin\phi\,\frac{\partial f}{\partial r}\right)$$

$$+ \left(\frac{-\mathbf{i}\sin\phi}{r}\,\frac{\partial f}{\partial \phi} + \frac{\mathbf{j}\cos\phi}{r}\,\frac{\partial f}{\partial \phi}\right) + \mathbf{k}\frac{\partial f}{\partial z}.$$

If one equates the coefficients of **i** on both sides, then the same result as above is obtained.

Example 60. Show how Bessel's differential equation can arise in a study of Fick's second law of diffusion for an electrochemical cell shaped like that described in Exercise 34* at the end of Chapter 5.

Answer. Fick's second law in a Cartesian coordinate system is

$$\frac{\partial C}{\partial t} = D\left(\frac{\partial^2 C}{\partial x^2} + \frac{\partial^2 C}{\partial y^2} + \frac{\partial^2 C}{\partial z^2}\right).$$

It may be assumed that the electrode of interest is oriented along the z direction, and that the concentration gradient extends outward in the xy plane; C therefore has no dependency on z. The operator $(\partial^2/\partial x^2) + (\partial^2/\partial y^2)$ can be written in the cylindrical polar system either by allowing $\partial/\partial x$ to operate on itself, and likewise for $\partial/\partial y$, or by simply using the form for the Laplacian given earlier minus the $\partial^2 f/\partial z^2$ term:

$$\frac{\partial C}{\partial t} = D\left(\frac{\partial^2 C}{\partial r^2} + \frac{1}{r^2}\frac{\partial^2 C}{\partial \phi^2} + \frac{1}{r}\frac{\partial C}{\partial r}\right).$$

Now assume $C = T(t)R(r)\Phi(\phi)$ and insert this into the differential equation:

$$R(r)\Phi(\phi)\frac{dT}{dt} = D\left[T(t)\Phi(\phi)\frac{d^2R}{dr^2}\right.$$

$$\left. + \frac{1}{r^2}T(t)R(r)\frac{d^2\Phi}{d\phi^2} + \frac{1}{r}T(t)\Phi(\phi)\frac{dR}{dr}\right].$$

If both sides are divided by C, it is seen that the t dependency can be separated off.

$$-\kappa = \frac{1}{T}\frac{dT}{dt} = D\left[\frac{1}{R}\frac{d^2R}{dr^2} + \frac{1}{r^2}\frac{1}{\Phi}\frac{d^2\Phi}{d\phi^2} + \frac{1}{r}\frac{1}{R}\frac{dR}{dr}\right].$$

The ϕ dependency can further be separated off by multiplying both sides by r^2.

$$\frac{-1}{\Phi}\frac{d^2\Phi}{d\phi^2} = \alpha^2 = \frac{r^2}{R}\frac{d^2R}{dr^2} + \frac{r}{R}\frac{dR}{dr} + \frac{r^2\kappa}{D}$$

or

$$r^2\frac{d^2R}{dr^2} + r\frac{dR}{dr} + R\left(\frac{r^2\kappa}{D} - \alpha^2\right) = 0.$$

Finally if the substitution $r^2\kappa/D = s^2$ is made, then the equation

$$s^2\frac{d^2R}{ds^2} + s\frac{dR}{ds} + R(s^2 - \alpha^2) = 0$$

results, which is Bessel's equation of order α (see Table 5.5).

The spherical polar coordinate system is defined by the transformation equations

$$x = r\sin\theta\cos\phi$$

$$y = r\sin\theta\sin\phi$$

$$z = r\cos\theta$$

and for this coordinate system one has $h_1 = h_r = 1$, $h_2 = h_\theta = r$, and $h_3 = h_\phi = r\sin\theta$. Whereas the families of coordinate surfaces in the cylindrical polar system consist of sets of right circular cylinders ($r = $ constant), sets of half-planes through the z axis ($\phi = $ constant), and sets of planes parallel to the xy plane ($z = $ constant), the families of coordinate surfaces in the spherical polar coordinate system consist of sets of concentric spheres ($r = $ constant), sets of right circular cones ($\theta = $ constant), and sets of half-planes through the z axis ($\phi = $ constant). The previous formulas can be used to work out the gradient, divergence, curl, and Laplacian in this important system; the gradient, for example, is given by

$$\nabla f(r,\theta,\phi) = \mathbf{a}_r\frac{\partial f}{\partial r} + \mathbf{a}_\theta\frac{1}{r}\frac{\partial f}{\partial\theta} + \mathbf{a}_\phi\frac{1}{r\sin\theta}\frac{\partial f}{\partial\phi}.$$

The unit vectors are easily worked out in this system:

$$\mathbf{a}_r = \mathbf{i}\sin\theta\cos\phi + \mathbf{j}\sin\theta\sin\phi + \mathbf{k}\cos\theta$$

$$= \frac{\mathbf{i}x + \mathbf{j}y + \mathbf{k}z}{\sqrt{x^2 + y^2 + z^2}}$$

$$\mathbf{a}_\theta = \mathbf{i}\cos\theta\cos\phi + \mathbf{j}\cos\theta\sin\phi - \mathbf{k}\sin\theta$$

$$= \frac{\mathbf{i}xz + \mathbf{j}yz - \mathbf{k}(x^2 + y^2)}{r\sqrt{x^2 + y^2}}$$

$$\mathbf{a}_\phi = -\mathbf{i}\sin\phi + \mathbf{j}\cos\phi$$

$$= \frac{-\mathbf{i}y + \mathbf{j}x}{\sqrt{x^2 + y^2}}.$$

Once again these expressions show how unit vectors (such as $\mathbf{a}_\theta$ above) in coordinate systems other than the rectangular Cartesian coordinate system change direction with a change in spatial position (see Figure 6.20).

The Laplacian written in spherical polar coordinates is rather complex. It has already been given in Exercise 35* at the end of the last chapter; you should take the trouble to verify its form.

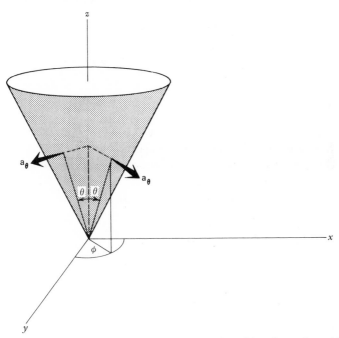

Fig. 6.20   Illustration of how $\mathbf{a}_\theta$ changes direction with a change in position.

Example 61.   Show that the hydrogen wave functions are eigenfunctions of the operator for the z component of the electron orbital angular momentum.

Answer.   From Example 59 we have that the z component of the operator $\hat{l}$ is given in Cartesian coordinates by

$$\hat{l}_z = -i\hbar\left(x\frac{\partial}{\partial y} - y\frac{\partial}{\partial x}\right).$$

Since the hydrogen wave functions are usually formulated in spherical polar coordinates we convert the operator to its equivalent in this coordinate system. The partial derivatives may be found in the same way as was described in connection with the cylindrical polar coordinate sysem: the results are given in Exercise 22. Therefore, we have

$$\hat{l}_z = -i\hbar \Big[r\sin^2\theta \sin\phi \cos\phi (\partial/\partial r)$$

$$+ \sin\theta \cos\theta \sin\phi \cos\phi (\partial/\partial\theta) + \cos^2\phi (\partial/\partial\phi)$$

$$- \big\{ r\sin^2\theta \sin\phi \cos\phi (\partial/\partial r)$$

$$+ \sin\theta \cos\theta \sin\phi \cos\phi (\partial/\partial\theta) - \sin^2\phi (\partial/\partial\phi) \big\} \Big]$$

$$= -i\hbar \frac{\partial}{\partial\phi}.$$

The wave functions have the form $\psi(r,\theta,\phi) = R(r)\Theta(\theta)\Phi(\phi)$; the $R(r)$ and $\Theta(\theta)$ functions are special functions and are described in the next chapter. The $\Phi(\phi)$ function, however, is simple:

$$\Phi(\phi) = \frac{1}{\sqrt{2\pi}} \exp(im_L\phi).$$

Operation of $\hat{l}_z$ on $\psi(r,\theta,\phi)$ thus gives

$$\hat{l}_z\psi = -i\hbar(im_L)\psi \frac{\partial\phi}{\partial\phi}$$

$$= \boxed{m_L\hbar\psi}.$$

A measurement of the angular momentum along the z axis of a hydrogen atom in a state characterized by the magnetic quantum number m_L will thus yield a value of $m_L\hbar$.

The confocal elliptical coordinate system was mentioned in Section 3.1 and exploited in Exercise 20 of Chapter 3:

$$x = R\sqrt{\zeta^2 - 1}\,\sqrt{1 - \eta^2}\,\cos\phi$$

$$y = R\sqrt{\zeta^2 - 1}\,\sqrt{1 - \eta^2}\,\sin\phi$$

$$z = R\zeta\eta.$$

Actually, in this form the system is hard to visualize. Let us define $\zeta = \cosh u$

and $\eta = \cos v$. Then the transformation equations become

$$x = R \sinh u \sin v \cos \phi \quad 0 \leqslant u < \infty$$
$$y = R \sinh u \sin v \sin \phi \quad 0 \leqslant v \leqslant \pi$$
$$z = R \cosh u \cos v \quad 0 \leqslant \phi \leqslant 2\pi$$

and in this form the coordinate system is often referred to as the *prolate spheroidal coordinate system*. It is useful in evaluating "two-center" integrals such as arise in the quantum chemistry of systems like H_2^+.

The metric coefficients work out to be

$$h_1 = h_u = R\sqrt{\cosh^2 u - \cos^2 v} = R\sqrt{\sinh^2 u + \sin^2 v}$$

$$h_2 = h_v = R\sqrt{\sinh^2 u + \sin^2 v}$$

$$h_3 = h_\phi = R \sinh u \sin v.$$

To see what the families of surfaces look like we let u, v, and ϕ, successively, be constant. For constant u one can express the three equations in the combined form

$$\frac{x^2}{a^2} + \frac{u^2}{a^2} + \frac{z^2}{b^2} = 1. \quad (b > a)$$

This is the equation of a prolate spheroid (see Figure 6.21a). Cross sections down the z axis are ellipses. For constant v one has

$$\frac{z^2}{d^2} - \frac{x^2}{c^2} - \frac{y^2}{c^2} = 1$$

and this is the equation of a hyperboloid of two sheets (see Figure 6.21b). Cross sections here down the z axis are hyperbolas. Finally for constant ϕ one has the equation

$$\phi = \text{constant} = \tan^{-1}\left(\frac{y}{x}\right)$$

and this graphs as half-planes through the z axis.

As examples of transformations with the confocal elliptical coordinate system, we work out the volume differential element and the Laplacian. The volume element is given by $d\tau = |h_1 h_2 h_3| \, dq_1 \, dq_2 \, dq_3$, which becomes in this

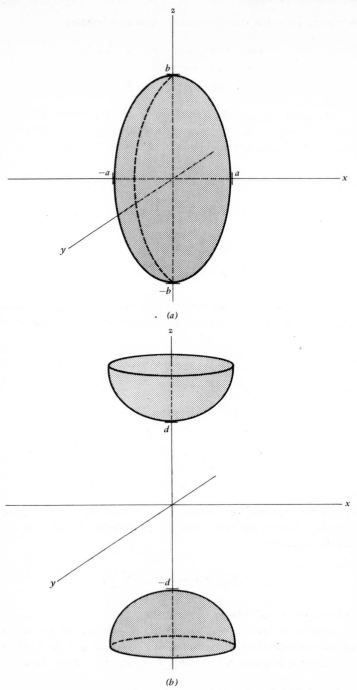

Fig. 6.21 Graph of (*a*) a prolate spheroid, and (*b*) an hyperboloid of two sheets.

system

$$d\tau = \left| R^3 \sinh u \sin v \sqrt{\cosh^2 u - \cos^2 v} \ \sqrt{\sinh^2 u + \sin^2 v} \ \right| du \, dv \, d\phi$$

$$= \left| R^3 \sinh u \sin v \sqrt{\cosh^4 u - 2\cosh^2 u \cos^2 v + \cos^4 v} \ \right| du \, dv \, d\phi$$

$$= \left| R^3 \sinh u \sin v \left(\cosh^2 u - \cos^2 v \right) \right| du \, dv \, d\phi,$$

or in the previous notation,

$$d\tau = \left| R^3 \sqrt{(\zeta^2 - 1)(1 - \eta^2)} \ (\zeta^2 - \eta^2) \frac{d\zeta}{\sqrt{\zeta^2 - 1}} \left(\frac{-d\eta}{\sqrt{1 - \eta^2}} \right) d\phi \right|$$

$$= R^3 (\zeta^2 - \eta^2) \, d\zeta \, d\eta \, d\phi.$$

This is the same result as would be obtained by the application of Theorem 7.

The Laplacian operating on a function $f(u,v,\phi)$ gives the following:

$$\nabla^2 f(u,v,\phi) = \left[\frac{1}{R^2(\sinh^2 u + \sin^2 v)} \left(\frac{\partial^2 f}{\partial u^2} + \frac{\partial^2 f}{\partial v^2} \right) + \frac{1}{R^2 \sinh^2 u \sin^2 v} \frac{\partial^2 f}{\partial \phi^2} \right]$$

$$+ \frac{1}{R^3 \sinh u \sin v (\sinh^2 u + \sin^2 v)} \left[R \cosh u \sin v \frac{\partial f}{\partial u} + R \sinh u \cos v \frac{\partial f}{\partial v} \right]$$

$$= \frac{1 + \coth u}{R^2(\sinh^2 u + \sin^2 v)} \left(\frac{\partial^2 f}{\partial u^2} + \frac{\partial f}{\partial u} \right) + \frac{1 + \cot v}{R^2(\sinh^2 u + \sin^2 v)} \left(\frac{\partial^2 f}{\partial v^2} + \frac{\partial f}{\partial v} \right)$$

$$+ \frac{1}{R^2 \sinh^2 u \sin^2 v} \frac{\partial^2 f}{\partial \phi^2}.$$

The expression is certainly messy, but there is the saving grace that it is obtained with much less labor this way than through the brute force method of determining the derivatives $\partial/\partial x$, $\partial/\partial y$, and $\partial/\partial z$ from Cramer's rule and then allowing them to operate on themselves to give the Laplacian operator.

6 CARTESIAN TENSORS

In Section 6.3 we pointed out that some quantities (called *scalars*) require only a magnitude to specify them completely, whereas other quantities (called vectors) require both a magnitude and a direction for complete specification. Still other quantities are even more complex; they require a magnitude and two or more directions. For quantities of this type that require two directions, one direction can be conceived of as that along which some physical action takes place and the other as that along which some measurement or observation is made. The *set* of magnitudes which comprise all the possible combinations of direction of action and direction of measurement makes up a *tensor*, and its parts are the components of the tensor.

A common example of tensorial character is shown by transparent crystals that are said to be *doubly refracting* or *birefringent*. Anyone who has ever looked at a word in newsprint through a crystal of calcite knows that one sees the word in double. The molecular constitution within the crystal is such that at the atomic level perpendicular directions present different environments to a traversing plane-polarized light beam; the crystal is said to be *anisotropic*. Consequently, a plane-polarized beam will be refracted at one angle as it enters along the *x* axis, say, and at a different angle as it enters along the *z* axis. Or equivalently, a beam of unpolarized light entering along one of the axes will be split into two disturbances (Figure 6.22) because the vertical vibrations in the beam will interact with the medium differently from the horizontal vibrations. The emerging disturbances will be traveling with different speeds and an observer will see double. The tensor involved here is the index of refraction tensor. The index of refraction is different for different directions through the crystal. Some substances such as salt are so symmetric that their bulk properties are independent of direction (*isotropic*). However by a suitable application of a tensile stress the relative positions of

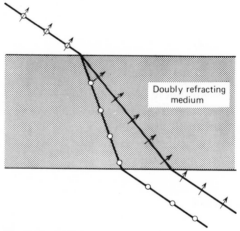

Fig. 6.22   Birefringence.

the atoms, ions, or molecules in a substance can be changed so that quantities such as the index of refraction or the electric polarizability will be tensors instead of scalars.

Before we pursue further some physical examples of tensors we need to go back and sharpen up some earlier material on vectors. Let P be a point in a rectangular Cartesian coordinate system and have coordinates (x_1, x_2, x_3) (Figure 6.23). Now let the coordinate system be rotated about some axis through the origin to a new position, and designate the coordinates of the point P (that has remained stationary) in the new system as (x_1', x_2', x_3'). Let the symbol λ_{ij} stand for the cosine of the angle between the x_i' axis in the primed coordinate system and the x_j axis in the unprimed coordinate system. The x_1' coordinate of P is the sum of the vector projections of the various components of P in the unprimed system onto the x_1' axis:

$$x_1' = \lambda_{11} x_1 + \lambda_{12} x_2 + \lambda_{13} x_3.$$

Similar statements apply to x_2' and x_3', or in general,

$$x_i' = \sum_{j=1}^{3} \lambda_{ij} x_j.$$

Conversely, if point P has coordinates (x_1', x_2', x_3') in the primed coordinate system, then to find its x_1 coordinate in the unprimed system one must sum

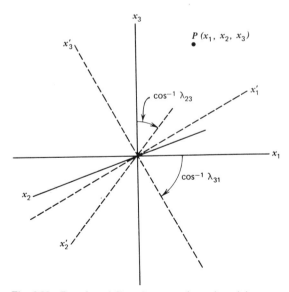

Fig. 6.23 Rotation of Cartesian axes about the origin.

the vector projections of the various components of P in the primed system onto the x_1 axis,

$$x_1 = \lambda_{11}x_1' + \lambda_{21}x_2' + \lambda_{31}x_3'$$

or more generally,

$$x_i = \sum_{j=1}^{3} \lambda_{ji}x_j'.$$

Either summation above implies the other, and each is determined exclusively by the fact that the two coordinate systems are rectangular Cartesian coordinate systems.

Now suppose that one has a quantity $\mathbf{A}$ that one suspects of being a vector. Initially all one knows is that $\mathbf{A}$ consists (in three-dimensional space) of the set of three quantities (A_1, A_2, A_3). Each of these three quantities is some given function of x_1, x_2, and x_3:

$$A_i = A_i(x_1, x_2, x_3).$$

If on rotation of the coordinate system the components of $\mathbf{A}$ transform in exactly the same way as do the coordinates of a point (like P above)

$$A_i' = \sum_{j=1}^{3} \lambda_{ij}A_j,$$

with these λ_{ij} coefficients being the same ones as discussed above, then $\mathbf{A}$ is said to be a vector. What this says physically is that the *form* of the vector $\mathbf{A}$ is left unchanged or is invariant upon a rotation of axes, and thus any physical law involving $\mathbf{A}$ will be expressed the same in the two coordinate systems.

To illustrate, suppose $\mathbf{A}$ is a quantity in the plane with the form $\mathbf{A} = (x_2, -x_1)$. Let the coordinate axes now be rotated an angle θ counterclockwise to give a new (primed) coordinate system. In this coordinate system we write $\mathbf{A}' = (x_2', -x_1')$. We want to investigate the relation between $\mathbf{A}$ and $\mathbf{A}'$. From material given in Section 6.2 we can rewrite $\mathbf{A}'$ as

$$\mathbf{A}' = \{ x_2 \cos\theta - x_1 \sin\theta, -x_2 \sin\theta - x_1 \cos\theta \}$$

but examination of this shows that

$$A_1' = A_1 \cos\theta + A_2 \sin\theta$$
$$= \lambda_{11}A_1 + \lambda_{12}A_2$$

and

$$A'_2 = A_1(-\sin\theta) + A_2\cos\theta$$
$$= \lambda_{21}A_1 + \lambda_{22}A_2,$$

or more compactly,

$$A'_i = \sum_{j=1}^{3} \lambda_{ij}A_j.$$

This is just the relation given earlier for the definition of a vector. Hence $\mathbf{A} = x_2\mathbf{i} - x_1\mathbf{j}$ is a vector quantity, but the quantity $\mathbf{B} = x_2\mathbf{i} + x_1\mathbf{j}$, for example, can be shown not to be a vector.

The defining relation for a vector can be put into the form of a matrix equation:

$$\begin{pmatrix} A'_1 \\ A'_2 \end{pmatrix} = \begin{pmatrix} \lambda_{11} & \lambda_{12} \\ \lambda_{21} & \lambda_{22} \end{pmatrix} \begin{pmatrix} A_1 \\ A_2 \end{pmatrix}$$

or

$$\mathbf{A}' = \lambda\mathbf{A}.$$

As a natural extension of this it is logical to ask about the transformation properties of a matrix product of two vectors. Thus let $\mathbf{A}$ and $\mathbf{B}$ be two vectors in an unprimed coordinate system. Their matrix product is

$$\begin{bmatrix} A_1 \\ A_2 \\ A_3 \end{bmatrix} (B_1 \quad B_2 \quad B_3) = \begin{bmatrix} A_1B_1 & A_1B_2 & A_1B_3 \\ A_2B_1 & A_2B_2 & A_2B_3 \\ A_3B_1 & A_3B_2 & A_3B_3 \end{bmatrix}$$

and in a primed rectangular Cartesian coordinate system obtained by rotating the first system about some axis through the origin their matrix product is

$$\begin{bmatrix} A'_1B'_1 & A'_1B'_2 & A'_1B'_3 \\ A'_2B'_1 & A'_2B'_2 & A'_2B'_3 \\ A'_3B'_1 & A'_3B'_2 & A'_3B'_3 \end{bmatrix}.$$

Since $\mathbf{A}$ and $\mathbf{B}$ must obey the transformation equations of vectors we can write

$$A_i'B_j' = \sum_{l=1}^{3} \lambda_{il}A_l \left[\sum_{k=1}^{3} \lambda_{jk}B_k \right]$$

$$= \sum_{l=1}^{3} \sum_{k=1}^{3} (\lambda_{il}\lambda_{jk})(A_lB_k).$$

This says that each element in the $A'B'$ matrix can be expressed in terms of the nine elements in the AB matrix, with the coefficients depending *only* on the rotation matrix relating the two coordinate systems. A similar statement can be made for each element in the AB matrix in relation to the nine elements in the $A'B'$ matrix. It is convenient to define A_lB_k to be the doubly-subscripted quantity T_{lk}.

$$T_{ij}' = \sum_{l=1}^{3} \sum_{k=1}^{3} \lambda_{il}\lambda_{jk}T_{lk}$$

Any quantity which transforms under rotation of a rectangular Cartesian coordinate system in the same manner as the elements T_{lk} *above is known as a Cartesian tensor of the second rank.*

The tensor in question is the *set* of nine elements T_{lk}. It is conveniently represented by a matrix, but it is important to see that not all 3×3 matrices are second-rank tensors since the important criterion is the transformation law. The *rank* of a tensor is the number of subscripts required on each element. A third-rank tensor, for example, would obey the transformation law

$$T_{abc}' = \sum_{i=1}^{3} \sum_{j=1}^{3} \sum_{k=1}^{3} \lambda_{ai}\lambda_{bj}\lambda_{ck}T_{ijk}.$$

A first-rank tensor is clearly what we have previously called a vector.

In this section we will consider only Cartesian tensors, that is, tensors relating to transformations between two rectangular Cartesian coordinate systems. In more general situations such as in general relativity, tensors relating to transformations between two curvilinear coordinate systems are important. The transformation laws in such cases are more complex than those for Cartesian tensors. The subject of tensor calculus for curvilinear tensors had been developed by the Italian mathematician Levi-Civita[4] (1873–1941), but remained almost completely unknown to the scientific world until Einstein was forced to master it shortly after the turn of the century and then use it in his early papers on general relativity. Properties of quantities that transform in the manner of Cartesian tensors of arbitrary rank were first discussed by C. Niven in 1874; the use of the name "tensor" for such quantities is apparently due to Gibbs.

The following further points regarding Cartesian tensors may be noted. First, the set of components relative to any one system of Cartesian axes is fully and completely descriptive of the tensor; the tensor itself is an entity independent of any particular system of axes. Second, once the components of a tensor relative to one system of Cartesian axes are known the components relative to any other system of Cartesian axes are also known. Third, it usually turns out that in the physical world any situation in which two vectors depend linearly on each other but in general point in different directions is tensorial in nature.

Think back to our earlier discussion of birefringence. A beam of polarized light entering a calcite crystal will be refracted. While passing through the crystal the radiation not only will propagate at a speed c_M different from that in a vacuum (ideally taken to be the external environment of the crystal), but its direction will be different (recall Figure 6.22). Now the index of refraction η is the ratio of the two speeds

$$\eta = \frac{c_{vac}}{c_M}$$

for an isotropic substance, but for an anisotropic material the equation has to show that not only the magnitude of c is changed, but also its direction, and that the size of these changes depends on which direction the electromagnetic radiation originally enters. The relation $c_{vac} = \eta c_M$ is no longer adequate; the c's must be replaced by vector quantities and the η by a tensor:

$$\mathbf{c}_{vac} = \tilde{\eta} \cdot \mathbf{c}_M.$$

This equation hints at another way in which second-rank tensors can be

---

[4]Tullio Levi-Civita, born in Padua, was one of Italy's greatest mathematicians. In 1900 Levi-Civita and his teacher Gregorio Ricci-Curbastro published a joint paper which presented the theory of the absolute differential calculus (i.e., tensor calculus) in the form that was used by Einstein a decade or so later. Levi-Civita continued to work for many years on development of the tensor calculus as well as on a variety of other mathematical subjects until 1938 when, under the yoke of Fascism, he was relieved of his professorship and dismissed from all Italian academies.

represented. In addition to being representable by means of matrices, tensors can be expressed in vector rotation. The quantity **ii**, whose meaning hitherto would be inexplicable, is called a *dyad*, and its meaning is given implicitly by the following relations:

$$\mathbf{i} \cdot \mathbf{ii} = \mathbf{ii} \cdot \mathbf{i} = \mathbf{i}$$

$$\mathbf{j} \cdot \mathbf{ii} = \mathbf{ii} \cdot \mathbf{j} = 0$$

$$\mathbf{i} \cdot \mathbf{ii} \cdot \mathbf{i} = 1.$$

The nine components of a second-rank tensor in three-dimensional space

$$\tilde{\mathbf{T}} = \begin{bmatrix} T_{11} & T_{12} & T_{13} \\ T_{21} & T_{22} & T_{23} \\ T_{31} & T_{32} & T_{33} \end{bmatrix}$$

can be written as the following sum of dyads:

$$\tilde{\mathbf{T}} = (T_{11}\mathbf{ii} + T_{12}\mathbf{ij} + T_{13}\mathbf{ik}) + (T_{21}\mathbf{ji} + T_{22}\mathbf{jj} + T_{23}\mathbf{jk})$$
$$+ (T_{31}\mathbf{ki} + T_{32}\mathbf{kj} + T_{33}\mathbf{kk}).$$

Let us now look at two second-rank tensors of chemical importance: the electric polarizability tensor and the nuclear magnetic shielding tensor. If a molecule is placed in an electric field, the nuclei present and the electron cloud will be subjected to a force causing minute displacements of their centers of gravity. This results in an induced electric dipole moment, and if the molecule is in fast rotation and the field is not too strong the size of the induced moment is accurately given by $\mu_{ind} = \alpha E$. The scalar α here is the electric polarizability. But suppose we could hold the molecule stationary when the field is applied. Then since the molecule would not in general be of spherical symmetry, the size and direction of the induced dipole moment would depend on the relative orientation of the molecule and the direction of the field. Along some directions the molecule would be differently susceptible to polarization than others owing to differing arrangements of the chemical bonds as presented to the entering electric vector. A diatomic molecule, for example, is usually more easily polarized (larger α) along the bond axis than perpendicular to it (Figure 6.24).

What all of this says is that μ_{ind} and E have to be treated as vectors and α as a tensor.

$$\mu_{ind} = \tilde{\alpha} \cdot \mathbf{E}$$

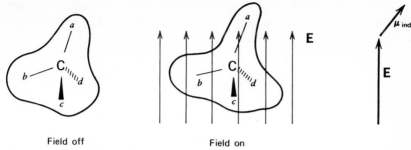

Field off   Field on

Fig. 6.24 Polarization of a molecule.

We can represent the polarizability by a 3×3 matrix:

$$\tilde{\alpha} = \begin{bmatrix} \alpha_{11} & \alpha_{12} & \alpha_{13} \\ \alpha_{21} & \alpha_{22} & \alpha_{23} \\ \alpha_{31} & \alpha_{32} & \alpha_{33} \end{bmatrix}.$$

Suppose we adopt the convention that the column index refers to the direction of the induced dipole moment. Then the element α_{12}, for example, means that if an electric field is applied to a molecule at some arbitrary angle, then the y component of that field will cause a polarization of the molecule in such a way that the x component of the induced dipole moment will have the magnitude.

$$\mu_x = \alpha_{12} E_y,$$

and so on, similarly.

A simple argument can be used to show that the $\tilde{\alpha}$ tensor must be symmetric; tensors need not be symmetric, but many tensors representing physical properties have this characteristic. We return to our molecule that is positioned in some electric field (as it would be if it were part of a crystal) and inquire about the energy needed to polarize the crystal. This should be given by the integral

$$\Delta U = \int_0^{\mu} \mathbf{E} \cdot d\mathbf{\mu}$$

but since $d\mathbf{\mu} = \tilde{\alpha} \cdot d\mathbf{E}$ the integral becomes

$$\Delta U = \int_0^{\varepsilon} \mathbf{E} \cdot \tilde{\alpha} \cdot d\mathbf{E} = \tfrac{1}{2} \sum_{ij} \alpha_{ij} E_i E_j.$$

Let us now turn on the field in the x direction; from the formula the energy change is seen to be just $\frac{1}{2}\alpha_{11}E_x^2$. Next, we turn on a field in the y direction. The energy change involved here is $\frac{1}{2}\alpha_{12}E_xE_y + \frac{1}{2}\alpha_{22}E_y^2$. The total energy of polarization is thus

$$\Delta U = \frac{1}{2}\left(\alpha_{11}E_x^2 + \alpha_{12}E_xE_y + \alpha_{22}E_y^2\right).$$

Now we do something clever that is analogous to the sort of *Gedanken* experiment one reads about in connection with Hess' law in thermodynamics in a freshman chemistry course: we repeat the experiment by polarizing the molecule along a different path. This time let us turn on the field in the y direction first; the polarization energy is $\frac{1}{2}\alpha_{22}E_y^2$. Next we turn on the field in the x direction; the polarization energy is $\frac{1}{2}\alpha_{21}E_yE_x + \frac{1}{2}\alpha_{11}E_x^2$. The total energy of polarization is thus

$$\Delta U = \frac{1}{2}\left(\alpha_{11}E_x^2 + \alpha_{21}E_xE_y + \alpha_{22}E_y^2\right).$$

Our molecule has a short memory. After the experiment has gotten underway, it has forgotten what the experimenter actually did; it only knows that it is now being subjected to electric fields from both the x and y directions. The two energies of polarization above should therefore be identical, and this requires that $\alpha_{12} = \alpha_{21}$. Similar statements can be made about α_{13} versus α_{31} and α_{23} versus α_{32}. The $\tilde{\alpha}$ tensor is therefore real and symmetric, or in other words, it is Hermitian.

This Hermiticity has an important consequence; since any Hermitian matrix can be diagonalized, it means that by a suitable rotation of the axes a new coordinate system can always be found in which all the off-diagonal elements are zero. Therefore, in such a system all information about the polarizability tensor is specified by just the three components α_{11}, α_{22}, and α_{33}. We'll return to this point shortly, but first let's get a feel for polarizability by looking at some data. Table 6.3 gives some polarizabilities (obtained from refractive index measurements) for some small molecules. The numbers in column 5 are the averages of numbers in columns 2–4.

Two interesting things emerge from these data. Columns 2–4 for the diatomic molecules show that it is easier to distort the electron cloud when one pushes along the bond axis than when one pushes perpendicular to the axis. Diatomic hydrogen is anomalous in this regard; perhaps this is because of its small size. First members of any sequence are often out of line. The numbers in column 5 generally show an increase in the polarizability as the total number of electrons in the molecule increases. Substances such as HI have large, mushy, easily deformable electron clouds.

Table 6.3 Some Polarizability Data

Molecule	α_{11}	α_{22}	α_{33}	$\langle \alpha \rangle$	Remarks[a,b]
HBr	42.3	33.2	33.2	36.2	α_{11} sym. axis
HI	65.8	48.9	48.9	54.5	α_{11} sym. axis
H_2	6.8	8.9	8.9	8.2	α_{11} sym. axis
H_2S	40.4	34.4	40.1	38.3	$\alpha_{22} \perp$ plane; α_{33} sym. axis
CH_3OCH_3	62.6	45.4	48.8	52.3	$\alpha_{22} \perp$ C—O—C plane; α_{33} sym. axis
N_2	24.3	14.3	14.3	17.6	α_{11} sym. axis

[a] Data taken from K. G. Denbigh, *Trans. Faraday Soc.*, **36**, 936 (1940).
[b] Columns 2–5 are in units of $10^{-25} cm^3$.

The importance of polarizability also shows up in Fajans' rules concerning coordination complexes. According to K. Fajans a given anionic or neutral ligand is more polarized, the larger the cation charge-to-radius ratio. This makes sense because such a cation is the source of a larger electric field. Also, the greater the polarization of the ligand the more covalent is the bond to the central metal; the covalent character increases with an increase in anion size or anion charge (greater number of electrons). Fajans also showed how the concept of polarizability could be used to explain the appearance of color in some cases. Other things being equal, the presence of a more polarizable ligand means a greater ease of transfer of electron density from anion to cation to produce an excited state of the complex. The resulting charge-transfer band, which may lie in the visible part of the electromagnetic spectrum, is in evidence in AgI (which is yellow), whereas AgCl is white, and in As_2S_3 (which exists in red and yellow forms), whereas As_2O_3 is colorless.

Another important tensor arises in the theory of nuclear magnetic resonance (nmr) spectroscopy. A bare nucleus when subjected to an external magnetic field B_0 feels the full effect of this field at its surface. If the nucleus is part of an atom or molecule, however, it is shielded by several electrons. The magnetic field affects the motion of the electrons causing them to produce a small induced magnetic field B_{ind}, whose direction is not necessarily parallel to that of B_0. To a good approximation, the size of this induced field is found experimentally to depend on the magnitude of B_0. The constant of proportionality is called the *nuclear shielding parameter*, σ. For molecules it is really a tensor and one should write

$$B_{ind} = \tilde{\sigma} \cdot B_0.$$

The composite effects of $\mathbf{B}_0$ and $\mathbf{B}_{ind}$ must now be included in order to determine the Larmor frequency for the nucleus of interest. From material given in Section 6.3 we can express this frequency as

$$\nu_0 = g_N \frac{e|(\tilde{1} - \tilde{\sigma}) \cdot \mathbf{B}_0|}{4\pi Mc}.$$

The tensor $\tilde{\sigma}$ is a complicated function of the electronic structure of the atom or molecule (as is also the polarizability tensor).

Earlier in this chapter we saw that Hermitian matrices can be diagonalized to give real eigenvalues. An argument similar to that used with the polarizability tensor can be invoked to show that $\tilde{\sigma}$ should be Hermitian. Therefore it should always be possible to find a rotated coordinate system in which the off-diagonal elements of the nuclear magnetic shielding tensor are zero.

$$\tilde{\sigma} = \begin{bmatrix} \sigma_{11} & 0 & 0 \\ 0 & \sigma_{22} & 0 \\ 0 & 0 & \sigma_{33} \end{bmatrix}$$

Example 62. Investigate if the real, symmetric matrix $\mathbf{A}$ can be diagonalized.

$$\mathbf{A} = \begin{pmatrix} 2 & 6 \\ 6 & -3 \end{pmatrix}$$

Answer. We know how to find the characteristic values of this matrix, but these are not eigenvalues unless the matrix can be diagonalized. We seek an angle θ such that a similarity transformation with the rotation matrix, $\mathbf{R}$, gives a diagonal matrix,

$$\mathbf{R}^{-1}\mathbf{A}\mathbf{R} = \mathbf{D}$$

or

$$\begin{pmatrix} \cos\theta & -\sin\theta \\ \sin\theta & \cos\theta \end{pmatrix} \begin{pmatrix} 2 & 6 \\ 6 & -3 \end{pmatrix} \begin{pmatrix} \cos\theta & \sin\theta \\ -\sin\theta & \cos\theta \end{pmatrix} = \begin{pmatrix} A_{11} & 0 \\ 0 & A_{22} \end{pmatrix}.$$

Multiplication of the matrices on the left gives

$$\begin{bmatrix} \begin{bmatrix} 2\cos^2\theta - 6\cos\theta\sin\theta - \\ 6\cos\theta\sin\theta - 3\sin^2\theta \end{bmatrix} & \begin{bmatrix} 2\cos\theta\sin\theta + 6\cos^2\theta - \\ 6\sin^2\theta + 3\cos\theta\sin\theta \end{bmatrix} \\ \begin{bmatrix} 2\cos\theta\sin\theta - 6\sin^2\theta + \\ 6\cos^2\theta + 3\cos\theta\sin\theta \end{bmatrix} & \begin{bmatrix} 2\sin^2\theta + 6\cos\theta\sin\theta + \\ 6\cos\theta\sin\theta - 3\cos^2\theta \end{bmatrix} \end{bmatrix}$$

and if the off-diagonal elements are to be zero, this implies

$$5\cos\theta\sin\theta - 6\sin^2\theta + 6\cos^2\theta = 0$$

or

$$(3\cos\theta - 2\sin\theta)(2\cos\theta + 3\sin\theta) = 0$$

$$\cos\theta = \tfrac{2}{3}\sin\theta, \quad -\tfrac{3}{2}\sin\theta.$$

From the relation $\cos^2\theta + \sin^2\theta = 1$, this yields for the values of the cosine and sine

$$\cos\theta = \pm\frac{2}{\sqrt{13}} \qquad \sin\theta = \pm\frac{3}{\sqrt{13}}$$

$$\cos\theta = \pm\frac{3}{\sqrt{13}} \qquad \sin\theta = \mp\frac{2}{\sqrt{13}}.$$

Either of these combinations yields for the diagonal elements 6 and -7. Therefore, we see that if **A** were a tensor, then in a coordinate system obtained by rotating the first system roughly 56° counter-clockwise, the tensor **A** would have the form

$$\boxed{\mathbf{A} = \begin{pmatrix} -7 & 0 \\ 0 & 6 \end{pmatrix}}.$$

The theorem associated with the above example has an interesting history. It was stated in its simplest form by Fermat[5] and by Descartes[6] as follows: a quadratic form $ax^2 + 2bxy + cy^2$ can always be transformed by a rotation of the plane into the normal form $\alpha x^2 + \beta y^2$, where the principal axes of the normal form coincide with the new coordinate axes. The term "principal axes" here means the major and minor axes of the ellipse in the graph of the equation $\alpha x^2 + \beta y^2 = $ constant; the term was introduced by Euler in 1765 in his study of the mechanics of rotating bodies. Lagrange in 1759 discussed a generalization of the principal axes theorem: any symmetric quadratic form $\sum_{ij}\alpha_{ij}x_ix_j$ in n-dimensional Euclidean space can be rewritten by means of an orthogonal transformation T in the form $\sum_i\lambda_ix_i^2$. Arthur Cayley and J. J. Sylvester in the nineteenth century used matrices to systematize the algebraic description of n-dimensional space. We have already seen that Sylvester (in 1852) showed that the λ_i are the roots of the characteristic

[5]After the French-born "prince of amateurs" Pierre de Fermat, 1601–1665, who helped found analytic geometry, probability theory, and also did important work in number theory.
[6]After the French-born mathematician René Descartes, 1596–1650, whose famous work *Discours de la Méthode* laid the foundations for analytic geometry (1637); Descartes has also come down to us as a prominent philosopher.

equation

$$\det(\mathbf{A} - \lambda \mathbf{I}) = 0.$$

Let us now formally state (without proof) what is called the *principal axes theorem* in the form that is the most relevant as far as second-rank Cartesian tensors are concerned.

Theorem 22. (Principal Axes Theorem). *Every symmetric, real matrix* **A** *is orthogonally equivalent to a diagonal matrix* **D**, *or for some orthogonal matrix* **T** *one has* **D** = **T**$^{-1}$**AT** *and* **D** *is in diagonal form.*

If we return now to Example 62, an important point to notice is that the sum of the diagonal elements (what we called the trace or spur back in Section 6.1) of the **A** matrix as originally written and in the diagonal form is the same. This is a general result for similar matrices. It follows, then, that in our earlier shielding tensor $\tilde{\sigma}$ the sum $\sigma_{11} + \sigma_{22} + \sigma_{33}$ must be an invariant quantity. For a molecule that is tumbling fast in solution, the tensor as such will not be observable. Only a time-averaged scalar value of $\tilde{\sigma}$ will be presented to the experimenter, this scalar value being just

$$\langle \tilde{\sigma} \rangle = \tfrac{1}{3}(\sigma_{11} + \sigma_{22} + \sigma_{33}).$$

Typical values of $\langle \tilde{\sigma} \rangle$ are $(10 - 1000) \times 10^{-6}$. Recall that these values are still relative to the bare nucleus, for which $\sigma = 0$ by definition. Since experiments with naked nuclei of hydrogen, carbon, and fluorine, for example, are impractical, it is more convenient to measure shielding parameters relative to that for some suitable standard molecule. One convention for doing this is to keep the nmr machine at a constant frequency ν_0 for both the standard and the sample, and to vary the static magnetic field slightly until the Larmor equation is satisfied:

$$\nu_0 = \frac{g_N e}{4\pi M c} B_{\text{sample}}\left(1 - \sigma_{\text{sample}}\right)$$

$$\nu_0 = \frac{g_N e}{4\pi M c} B_{\text{stand}}\left(1 - \sigma_{\text{stand}}\right).$$

Now define the quantity δ by the relation

$$\delta = \frac{B_{\text{stand}} - B_{\text{sample}}}{B_{\text{stand}}} \times 10^6$$

$$= \frac{\sigma_{\text{stand}} - \sigma_{\text{sample}}}{1 - \sigma_{\text{stand}}} \times 10^6$$

$$\cong (\sigma_{\text{stand}} - \sigma_{\text{sample}}) \times 10^6.$$

Values of δ obtained in this way are the familiar *chemical shifts* known to practicing chemists everywhere. They are dimensionless numbers and from the definition are quoted in parts per million. If the frequency is maintained constant, then the horizontal axis of the nmr spectrum may be regarded as either the magnetic field or the chemical shift, but it is seen from the above that increasing chemical shifts mean lower fields and vice versa. The definition also shows mathematically that the chemical shifts are the difference between two time-averaged second-rank tensors. In proton nmr spectroscopy the usual standard is tetramethylsilane $((CH_3)_4Si)$; in C-13 nmr spectroscopy a common standard has been carbon disulfide (CS_2), and in F-19 nmr spectroscopy a common standard has been hexafluorobenzene (C_6F_6). Some typical values of chemical shifts are collected in Table 6.4.

Table 6.4 Some Chemical Shifts

Compound ^1H nmr spectroscopy[a]	δ (ppm)
$(CH_3)_4Si$	0.00
$(CH_3)_2CO$	2.08
CH_2Cl_2	5.33
C_6H_6	7.27
C_6H_5CH*O	10.05
^{13}C nmr spectroscopy[b]	
$(CH_3)_2C*O$	-12
CS_2	0
C_6H_6	65
CCl_4	97
$C*H_3CN$	197
^{19}F nmr spectroscopy[b]	
HF	-82
BF_3	-12
C_6F_6	0
CF_3COOH	36
$C(CF_3)_4$	49
F_2	543

[a]Data from K. W. Bentley and G. W. Kirby (eds.), *Techniques of Chemistry*, Vol. IV, 2nd ed., Part I, Wiley-Interscience, New York, 1972, p. 230.
[b]Data from A. Carrington and A. D. McLachlan, *Introduction to Magnetic Resonance*, Harper & Row, New York, 1967, p. 62.

These data show that carbon and fluorine chemical shifts cover a much wider range than do proton chemical shifts. Much information about the shielding in the molecules is lost, however, by working only with the scalar averages. The diagonal components of the shielding tensor can be obtained from analyses of the spectra of substances dissolved in liquid crystals; this is presently an active area of research.

EXERCISES

1. Perform the indicated operations:
   (a) $2(3\mathbf{i} - 4\mathbf{j} + \mathbf{k}) - (\mathbf{j} + 2\mathbf{i} - 3\mathbf{k})$
   (b) $(\mathbf{i} + \mathbf{j}) \cdot (2\mathbf{i} - 2\mathbf{j})$
   (c) $2(3\mathbf{i} - 4\mathbf{j} + \mathbf{k}) \times (\mathbf{j} + 2\mathbf{i} - 3\mathbf{k})$
   (d) $\mathrm{grad}[xy(y^3 + z^3)]$
   (e) $\mathrm{div}(y\mathbf{i} - x\mathbf{j})$
   (f) $\nabla^2\left(\dfrac{1}{r}\right)$

2. Which of the following hold for scalar (dot) multiplication of vectors:
   (a) commutativity of multiplication;
   (b) distributive law of multiplication over addition;
   (c) associative law for multiplication;
   (d) the law of cancellation (i.e., if $\mathbf{a} \cdot \mathbf{b} = \mathbf{a} \cdot \mathbf{c}$, then $\mathbf{b} = \mathbf{c}$)?

3. To a fair approximation individual chemical bonds may be assigned *bond dipole moments*. Thus the values shown in Table 6.5 represent "best" values to be used in estimating molecular dipole moments as the vector sums of the individual bond dipole moments (bonds are drawn in the direction $- \rightarrow +$).

Table 6.5   Some Bond Dipole Moments

Bond	D	Bond	D
H—C	0.40	Cl—C	1.56
Br—C	1.48	F—C	1.51
O—H	1.53	O=C	2.40
N—H	1.31	O—C	0.86
N≡C	3.6	I—C	1.29

Estimate $|\boldsymbol{\mu}|$ for methylene bromide and compare with the gas phase value of 1.43 D [datum from R. C. Weast (ed.), *Handbook of Chemistry and Physics*, 53rd ed., Chemical Rubber Co., Cleveland, 1972, p. E-52].

4. When does the expression A/B ever have any meaning, mathematically?

5. The interaction between two dipoles separated by a distance $\mathbf{r}$ and having dipole moments $\boldsymbol{\mu}_1$ and $\boldsymbol{\mu}_2$ (Figure 6.25) is given by

$$E = \frac{3(\boldsymbol{\mu}_1 \cdot \mathbf{r})(\boldsymbol{\mu}_2 \cdot \mathbf{r})}{r^5} - \frac{\boldsymbol{\mu}_1 \cdot \boldsymbol{\mu}_2}{r^3}$$

$$= \frac{\mu_1 \mu_2}{r^3}(2\cos\theta_1 \cos\theta_2 - \cos\phi \sin\theta_1 \sin\theta_2)$$

where the angle ϕ is the angle between the $\boldsymbol{\mu}_1 - \mathbf{r}$ plane and the $\boldsymbol{\mu}_2 - \mathbf{r}$ plane. Show the eigenvalence of these two expressions.

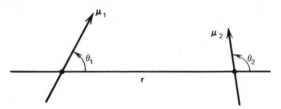

Fig. 6.25   Interaction of two dipoles.

6. The two unit vectors $\mathbf{a}$ and $\mathbf{b}$ lie in the xy plane and are inclined at angles θ and ϕ, respectively, from the x axis.

$$\mathbf{a} = \mathbf{i}\cos\theta + \mathbf{j}\sin\theta \qquad \mathbf{b} = \mathbf{i}\cos\phi + \mathbf{j}\sin\phi$$

From the physical significance of the dot product and of the cross product as given in the text, show easily how one may write

$$\mathbf{a} \cdot \mathbf{b} = \cos(\phi - \theta) \qquad \mathbf{a} \times \mathbf{b} = \mathbf{k}\sin(\phi - \theta)$$

and then use these relations to go on and derive the trigonometric expressions (first given in Chapter 1) for $\cos(\phi - \theta)$ and $\sin(\phi - \theta)$.

7. We already know that directed line segments can be regarded as vectors; discuss how surface areas could also be looked upon as vector quantities.

8. In a beaker of water that is being warmed over a Bunsen burner, the temperature of the water, in general, is higher at a point near the

bottom of the beaker than at a point near the top of the beaker. There is clearly a direction of increase in temperature from top to bottom. Does this mean that temperature is to be regarded as a vector instead of a scalar?

9. The Russell–Saunders coupling of two electrons is shown in the vector diagram in Figure 6.26. The meaning of this diagram is as follows: for the two individual electrons their spin angular momenta (s_1 and s_2) couple (i.e., vectorially add) to give S. The projections of s_1 and s_2 upon S are fixed, but otherwise s_1 and s_2 are free to precess about S. This is a fancy way of saying that we have experimental knowledge only of the lengths of s_1 and s_2 and not of their orientations in space. The same statements apply to the orbital angular momenta l_1 and l_2. Finally, the vector sum of S and L gives J; S and L have fixed projections upon J, but are otherwise free to precess. If a two-electron system consists of two nonequivalent p electrons (i.e., they have different principal quantum numbers), show that the states possible are ^3P, ^1D, ^1S, ^3D, ^1P, and ^3S, whereas if the two p electrons are equivalent, only the first three states are possible. Draw roughly the LS diagram for the states $^3P_1$, $^1D_2$, and $^1S_0$.

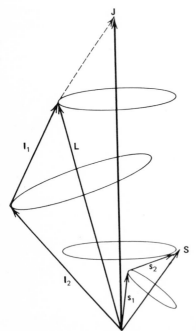

Fig. 6.26 LS coupling of two electrons.

10. Work out the term symbols for the ground states of the following elements: nitrogen, oxygen, magnesium, and titanium. For titanium draw the LS vector diagram. To work out the term symbols you will need to know Hund's rules (after the German scientist Friedrich Hund, 1896–): (a) from a given electron configuration the state with the largest multiplicity $(2S+1)$ is most stable; (b) of the terms with the same value of S, that with the largest L is most stable; and (c) for given S and L, the minimum J is most stable if there is a single, open subshell that is less than one-half full, and the maximum J is most stable if the subshell is more than one-half full. Most important of all, these statements are always to be applied in a manner consistent with the Pauli principle, which says that no two electrons may have the same set of values for the four quantum numbers n, l, m_L, s (m_L can have any integral value from $+l$ to $-l$).

11. A typical magnetic field strength in electron spin resonance (esr) spectrometers is 3000 G. For what approximate wavelength of the applied circularly polarized radiation will the frequency match the Larmor frequency of an "essentially free" electron? How much energy in cal mole^{-1} will separate the "spin-up" and the "spin-down" states of the electron?

12. A particle moving arbitrarily in space may always be considered *for an infinitesimal amount of time* to be moving in a plane, circular path about some particular axis (Figure 6.27). If the radius vector of the point changes from $\mathbf{r}$ to $\mathbf{r} + \delta\mathbf{r}$, then the situation can be expressed by the vector equation

$$\delta\mathbf{r} = \delta\boldsymbol{\theta} \times \mathbf{r}.$$

Let this change take place in a time δt. Then

$$\frac{\delta\mathbf{r}}{\delta t} = \frac{\delta\boldsymbol{\theta}}{\delta t} \times \mathbf{r}$$

and in the limit as $\delta t \to 0$,

$$\mathbf{v} = \frac{d\boldsymbol{\theta}}{dt} \times \mathbf{r}$$

$$= \boldsymbol{\omega} \times \mathbf{r}.$$

The quantity $\boldsymbol{\omega}$, which is the rate of change of the angular position, is the *angular velocity* (units of radians per second). The velocity $\mathbf{v}$ is that measured by an observer in a fixed frame of reference. But now suppose that the coordinate system moves with the particle. Then to

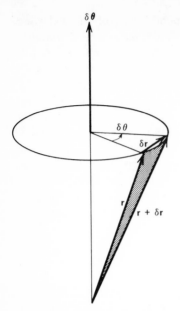

Fig. 6.27   Circular motion of a point.

our observer in a second but fixed coordinate system the velocity will be the sum of the velocity of the particle in the moving coordinate system plus the velocity of the moving coordinate system relative to the stationary system.

$$\frac{d\mathbf{r}}{dt} = \frac{\partial \mathbf{r}}{\partial t} + \boldsymbol{\omega} \times \mathbf{r}$$
$$\text{fixed} \quad \text{moving}$$

It is as if an observer on a riverbank (fixed system) is watching a person move about in a boat which is itself in motion (moving system) in the water.

Reflection will show that the above relation is generally valid for any other vector besides $\mathbf{r}$, so long as $\boldsymbol{\omega}$ is the angular velocity of the moving coordinate system relative to the fixed one. With this background in mind, think back to the material on nuclear magnetic resonance surrounding Example 57.

(*a*) Show for a nucleus with spin angular momentum $\mathbf{I}$ and immersed in a static magnetic field $\mathbf{B}$ that the effect of going to a description using a rotating coordinate system is to change the effective magnetic field by the term $(2Mc/g_N e\hbar)\boldsymbol{\omega}$.

(*b*) In the nmr experiment the constant field $\mathbf{B}$ may be taken to be along the z axis. A perturbing field $\mathbf{B}_1$ rotating with angular velocity

$-\omega$ is applied along the x axis. Show that in the rotating coordinate system the magnitude of the effective field is

$$|\mathbf{B}_{\text{eff}}| = \sqrt{\left(B - \frac{2Mc}{g_N e\hbar}\right)^2 + B_1^{\,2}} \ .$$

13. In what four possible ways can the nabla operate twice on a vector $\mathbf{A}$? What results in each of these four cases?

14. Refer once again to Figure 6.16. Let $d\mathbf{s}$ be a vector at point A of length ds and pointing in a general direction. Then from the definition of the gradient we have

$$d\mathbf{s} \cdot \nabla f(P) = d\mathbf{s} \cdot \mathbf{n} \frac{df(P)}{dn}$$

$$= \cos\theta \, ds \frac{df(P)}{dn}$$

and thus from this we conclude that

$$df(P) = d\mathbf{s} \cdot \nabla f(P).$$

How does this follow? Now replace the single function f by the product fg, and use the result above to show that the gradient of a product is given by

$$\nabla(fg) = f\nabla g + g\nabla f.$$

15. One of Maxwell's equations states $\operatorname{div} \mathbf{B} = 0$. Physically, what does this say in words?

16. For *uniform* magnetic fields one sometimes writes for the magnetic potential the cross product $\mathbf{A} = \frac{1}{2}\mathbf{B} \times \mathbf{r}$. Show that this is a valid potential.

17. In the text you were given expressions for the unit vectors in the spherical polar coordinate system. Work out the relations for the cross products and the dot products of these vectors.

18. You were also given the expression in the text for the gradient in the spherical polar coordinate system. Since angular momentum as an operator is defined in quantum mechanics as $\tilde{\mathbf{l}} = -i\hbar r \mathbf{a}_r \times \nabla$, show that this becomes

$$\hat{\mathbf{l}} = -i\hbar \left[\mathbf{a}_\phi \frac{\partial}{\partial\theta} - \mathbf{a}_\theta \frac{1}{\sin\theta} \frac{\partial}{\partial\phi} \right].$$

19. For the purposes of quantum mechanics, the square of the angular momentum operator working on a function $f(r,\theta,\phi)$ can be formulated as

$$\hat{\mathbf{l}} \cdot (\hat{\mathbf{l}} f).$$

Using the results of Exercises 17 and 18, show that this becomes

$$\hat{\mathbf{l}} \cdot (\hat{\mathbf{l}} f) = -\hbar^2 \left[\frac{1}{\sin^2\theta} \frac{\partial^2 f}{\partial\phi^2} + \frac{1}{\sin\theta} \frac{\partial}{\partial\theta} \left(\sin\theta \frac{\partial f}{\partial\theta} \right) \right]$$

Don't forget when doing this to differentiate the unit vectors themselves whenever necessary.

20. In Example 56 we added and subtracted spin and orbital angular momentum vectors. Now quantum mechanics distinguishes between the length of an orbital angular momentum vector and the magntiude that one would actually measure in an experiment. If a hydrogen atom is placed in a magnetic field (the field establishes a unique direction in space which we may take to be the z axis), then what one measures is the component of l along the z axis. This is expressed mathematically by writing the eigenvalue–eigenvector equation

$$\hat{l}_z \psi = m_L \hbar \psi.$$

The actual length of the l vector is given by $\hbar\sqrt{l(l+1)}$, and this corresponds to the eigenvalue–eigenvector equation

$$\hat{\mathbf{l}} \cdot \hat{\mathbf{l}} \psi = l(l+1)\hbar^2 \psi.$$

Take this equation and the expression given in the previous exercise and obtain (after assuming a separation of variables as was outlined at the end of the last chapter) as the Θ equation

$$\frac{1}{\sin\theta} \frac{d}{d\theta} \left(\sin\theta \frac{d\Theta}{d\theta} \right) - \frac{m^2}{\sin^2\theta} \Theta + l(l+1)\Theta = 0.$$

Here, $-m^2$ is the separation constant.

21. Finally, make the change of variables $u = \cos\theta$, $F(u) = \Theta(\theta)$, and show that the equation of the last exercise transforms into the associated Legendre equation given in Table 5.5. This is our end result of Exercises 17–21; it shows how a particular second-order differential equation arises as a result of a mathematical eigenvalue–eigenvector

description of some aspect of the physical world. Equations such as the associated Legendre equation have to be solved in order to obtain the familiar atomic orbitals used by chemists everywhere.

22. Show that the partial derivative operators $\partial/\partial x$, $\partial/\partial y$, and $\partial/\partial z$ become in spherical polar coordinates

$$\frac{\partial}{\partial x} = \sin\theta\cos\phi\frac{\partial}{\partial r} + \frac{\cos\theta\cos\phi}{r}\frac{\partial}{\partial\theta} - \frac{\sin\phi}{r\sin\theta}\frac{\partial}{\partial\phi}$$

$$\frac{\partial}{\partial y} = \sin\theta\sin\phi\frac{\partial}{\partial r} + \frac{\cos\theta\sin\phi}{r}\frac{\partial}{\partial\theta} + \frac{\cos\phi}{r\sin\theta}\frac{\partial}{\partial\phi}$$

$$\frac{\partial}{\partial z} = \cos\theta\frac{\partial}{\partial r} - \frac{\sin\theta}{r}\frac{\partial}{\partial\theta}.$$

23. After referring back to Example 59, show that the angular momentum differential operators satisfy the equation

$$\hat{l}_x\hat{l}_y - \hat{l}_y\hat{l}_x = i\hbar\hat{l}_z.$$

Compare this with your results in Exercise 3 of the first part of this chapter.

24. Is the quantity $x_1\mathbf{i} - x_2\mathbf{j}$ a vector? In the text it was stated that $x_2\mathbf{i} + x_1\mathbf{j}$ is not a vector; show this.

25. In the context of the more general concept of a tensor, give a definition of a scalar.

26. Some tensors $\tilde{\mathbf{T}}$, such as the electromagnetic field tensor, are *antisymmetric*; in such tensors one has $T_{ij} = -T_{ji}$. What can you say about the determinant of such tensors?

27. Can a third-rank tensor be represented by a matrix? How about a second-rank tensor in four-dimensional space?

28. Are the following matrices second-rank tensors?

$$\begin{pmatrix} y^2 & -xy \\ -xy & x^2 \end{pmatrix} \qquad \begin{pmatrix} xy & x^2 \\ -y^2 & -xy \end{pmatrix}$$

What about the matrices

$$\begin{pmatrix} y^2 & xy \\ xy & x^2 \end{pmatrix} \quad \text{and} \quad \begin{pmatrix} xy & y^2 \\ x^2 & -xy \end{pmatrix}?$$

29. In a free radical trapped in the solid state the magnetic moments of the electron and a neighboring proton are coupled through a term in the Hamiltonian of the form $\mathbf{S} \cdot \widetilde{\mathbf{T}} \cdot \mathbf{I}$. The classic study is by McConnell ($J.$ $Am.$ $Chem.$ $Soc.$, **82**, 766 (1960)) on $\cdot CH(COOH)_2$. Referred to crystal axes $\widetilde{\mathbf{T}}$ had the form shown; what are its principal values?

$$\begin{bmatrix} -53 & -7 & -17 \\ -7 & -82 & -15 \\ -17 & -15 & -41 \end{bmatrix}$$

30.* The orbital angular momentum step-up and step-down operators are defined in the same way as the electron spin step-up and step-down operators (recall Exercise 12 at the end of Part 1 of this chapter). From material given in the text and from Exercise 22 show that in spherical polar coordinates one has

$$\hat{l}_x + i\hat{l}_y = e^{i\phi}\left(\frac{\partial}{\partial\theta} + i\cot\theta \frac{\partial}{\partial\phi} \right)$$

$$\hat{l}_x - i\hat{l}_y = -e^{-i\phi}\left(\frac{\partial}{\partial\theta} - i\cot\theta \frac{\partial}{\partial\phi} \right).$$

31.* The gradient of a function has been written as a vector in the text, but the true test of a vector is whether or not it obeys the correct transformation law. Show that $\operatorname{grad} f(x_1,x_2,x_3)$ is indeed a vector.

32.* The *overlap integral* for an atomic orbital ϕ_1 centered on nucleus 1 and an atomic orbital ϕ_2 centered on nucleus 2 is given by the integral

$$S = \int \phi_1\phi_2 \, d\tau.$$

Redo Exercise 20 of Chapter 3, and then work out an expression for the overlap integral of two hydrogen $1s$ orbitals separated by a distance R in the hydrogen molecule–ion. Evaluate this overlap integral for the case where R is 1.10 Å.

33.* A charge q revolving about some axis possesses both a magnetic moment μ and angular momentum l. The simplicity of the situation suggests that the two should be related, and elementary considerations show that one has

$$\mu = \frac{q}{2mc} l.$$

Now an electron in an atom has both orbital and spin angular momentum, and one might expect the above relation to become

$$|\boldsymbol{\mu}_J| = \frac{-e\hbar}{2mc}\sqrt{J(J+1)} \ .$$

However, this magnetic moment turns out to be too small by a constant factor which depends on the state of the atom. The orbital contribution $|\boldsymbol{\mu}_L|$ to the atom's moment is given by

$$|\boldsymbol{\mu}_L| = \frac{-e\hbar}{2mc}\sqrt{L(L+1)} \ ,$$

and the spin contribution $|\boldsymbol{\mu}_S|$ is given by

$$|\boldsymbol{\mu}_S| = \frac{-e\hbar}{mc}\sqrt{S(S+1)} \ .$$

This is a relativistic result that is not explainable by classical mechanics. As a result, the vector diagram in Figure 6.28 obtains.
(a) In an experiment, one measures the projection of the true $\boldsymbol{\mu}$ onto $\mathbf{J}$, that is, the vector $\boldsymbol{\mu}_J(OA)$. If we represent this moment by the expression

$$|\boldsymbol{\mu}_J| = g\left(\frac{-e\hbar}{2mc}\right)\sqrt{J(J+1)} \ ,$$

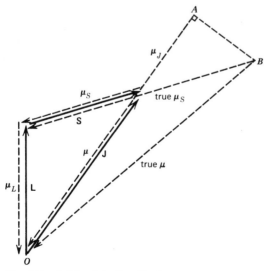

Fig. 6.28   Origin of the Landé g factor.

show that the *Landé* g *factor* is given by

$$g = 1 + \frac{J(J+1) + S(S+1) - L(L+1)}{2J(J+1)}.$$

(*b*) Compute the g factor for nitrogen in the electron configuration $1s^2 2s^2 2p^2 3p$ and with term symbol $^4P_{3/2}$. The observed value is 1.737 (datum taken from C. E. Moore, *Atomic Energy Levels*, Vol. I, National Bureau of Standards, Washington, D.C., 1971, p. 32). The g values for various states are obtained by analysis of the observed Zeeman splitting of spectral lines.

34.** In a vacuum two of Maxwell's equations are

$$\nabla \times \mathbf{B} = \varepsilon_0 \mu_0 \frac{\partial \mathbf{E}}{\partial t}$$

$$\nabla \times \mathbf{E} = -\frac{\partial \mathbf{B}}{\partial t}$$

where ε_0 and μ_0 are the electric and magnetic permittivities. Suppose one has a resonant cavity (an enclosed region where electromagnetic radiation can oscillate) such as is used in a conventional esr spectrometer. If the magnetic field is assumed to have a complex exponential time dependence $e^{-i\omega t}$, show that in the cavity the magnetic vector must obey a *Helmholtz equation* ($\nabla^2 \psi + \alpha^2 \psi = 0$).

35.** An electron in an electric field $\mathbf{E}_0$ has a potential energy of $-e\mathbf{r} \cdot \mathbf{E}_0$. Because of this the energy levels of atoms or molecules should be shifted when they are placed in an electric field, an effect known as`the *Stark effect*. For hydrogen the Schrödinger equation becomes (electric field oriented along the z axis)

$$\frac{-\hbar^2}{2m} \nabla^2 \psi - \frac{e^2}{r} \psi - eE_0 z\psi = E\psi.$$

Show that this is not separable in spherical polar coordinates, but is separable in parabolic coordinates, defined as

$$
\begin{aligned}
x &= \zeta\eta\cos\phi & 0 \leqslant \zeta < \infty \\
y &= \zeta\eta\sin\phi & 0 \leqslant \eta < \infty \\
z &= \tfrac{1}{2}(\zeta^2 - \eta^2) & 0 \leqslant \phi \leqslant 2\pi.
\end{aligned}
$$

SEVEN

Special Functions

1 THE ERROR, GAMMA, AND BETA FUNCTIONS

Among the out-of-the-way functions that crop up frequently in chemical and physical problems are such things as gamma functions, Hermite polynomials, Bessel functions, Chebychev polynomials, Legendre functions, the Dirac delta function and other generalized functions, and many other special functions. The list of "special functions" devised by man is almost endless, and any sort of comprehensive treatment is out of the question and beyond the scope of this book. In this chapter we focus on just a few of the more common special functions that arise in applications, while concentrating mainly on the mathematical properties of these functions. It should be realized that it is difficult (and pointless) to decide what kind of a function should be called a "special function." These functions do not involve any new or magical operations, but rather just the ordinary, well-known functions such as sine, exponential, or the logarithm. Rather, the adjective "special" is retained from earlier times when the functions in question were discussed in connection with particular problems in science or mathematics. For example, today one hardly remembers that Bessel functions were once discussed in relation to problems in celestial mechanics. As far as we are concerned, Bessel functions are simply abstract mathematical entities having certain properties that may be of use to us in certain problems.

It will be recalled that in Chapter 3 mention was made of some special integrals, of which the error function was one. As the name suggests, this function arose historically in connection with problems in chance. The error curve is sometimes called the Gaussian curve (after Karl Friedrich Gauss) or the law of Laplace (after Pierre Simon Laplace), but the person who really showed the connection between the curve and basic ideas in probability theory was Abraham de Moivre about one century earlier.[1] Consider the simple problem of the distribution of heads if 20 coins are flipped. If the coins are unbiased, then a plot of frequency f (or probability) versus the deviation x from 10 in the number of heads turned up is given by the stick diagram in Figure 7.1. The lines in this diagram are obtained using the formula for combinations given in Chapter 1. The line at zero deviation above, for example, is given by the frequency expression

$$f = \frac{20!/(10!\ 10!)}{\displaystyle\sum_{k=0}^{20} \frac{20!}{(20-k)!k!}}$$

$$\cong 0.18.$$

The sum of the frequencies for all 21 lines is, of course, unity. What de Moivre showed was that as the size of the sample increases indefinitely, the frequency plot approaches a smooth curve that is, in fact, the so-called Gaussian curve or normal probability curve. The equation of this curve (see Figure 3.6) in standard form is

$$f = \frac{1}{\sqrt{2\pi}} \exp\left(-\tfrac{1}{2}x^2\right)$$

where the factor $1/\sqrt{2\pi}$ ensures that the area under the entire curve (analogous to the sum of the frequencies in Figure 7.1) is unity.

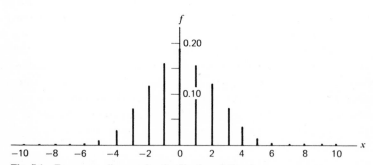

Fig. 7.1 Frequency diagram for the flipping of 20 coins.

[1]See Chapter 14 and other parts of the book by E. E. Kramer, *The Nature and Growth of Modern Mathematics*, Hawthorn, New York, 1970.

A more rigorous justification for the exponential form of the error curve can be given. Such a theory supposes that measurements to determine the magnitude of a certain quantity can be made independently of each other and can be given equal weight. Further, it is assumed that on the average the positive errors and the negative errors are evenly balanced. Then, using the principle that the chance that several independent events will take place is the product of the chances for each separate event, the exponential dependence on the square of the error can be deduced. We must note that because the Gaussian probability curve is a continuous function rather than a discrete one, we cannot ask for the probability that a particular measurement will have a deviation or error of *exactly* x, for this would be zero (this same idea is implicit in the wording of Exercise 6 of Chapter 2 and of Exercise 40* of Chapter 3). Rather we must ask for the error to fall in some range, say, x to x + dx, and this is given by the area under that small segment of the curve.

Several related integrals are often tabulated in different sources. What is usually referred to as the error function was defined in Chapter 3 as

$$\text{erf}(x) = \frac{2}{\sqrt{\pi}} \int_0^x \exp(-t^2)\,dt.$$

It is the area from $t = 0$ to $t = +x$ under the curve $y = (2/\sqrt{\pi})\exp(-t^2)$; as x approaches infinity $\text{erf}(x)$ approaches 1. Some tables also tabulate the complementary error function, $\text{erfc}(x) = 1 - \text{erf}(x)$. From the definition above this is easily seen to be just

$$\text{erfc}(x) = \frac{2}{\sqrt{\pi}} \int_x^\infty \exp(-t^2)\,dt.$$

Integrals similar to the error function occur in quantum chemistry, for example, where the integrands are sometimes used as alternatives to the normal hydrogenic wave functions; such wave functions when centered on particular nuclei are referred to as *Gaussian orbitals*, and when allowed to move off from the nucleus (or "float") are referred to as *floating Gaussian orbitals*. The usefulness of Gaussian orbitals is that multicenter integrals involving them are easier to handle than the same integrals employing hydrogenic wave functions.

Example 63. What is the overlap integral for two Gaussian orbitals centered on nuclei R units apart?

Answer. Let one Gaussian be centered at the origin (Figure 7.2) and have the form

$$\exp\left[-a\left(x^2+y^2+z^2\right)\right]$$

while the other Gaussian is centered at the point $(R,0,0)$ and has the form

$$\exp\left\{-b\left[(x-R)^2+y^2+z^2\right]\right\}.$$

The overlap integral is the product of these integrated over all space:

$$S = \iiint_{-\infty}^{\infty} \exp\left[-(a+b)(y^2+z^2)\right]$$

$$\times \exp(-ax^2)\exp\left[-b(x-R)^2\right]dx\,dy\,dz.$$

The point to see is that the product of two Gaussians can be expressed as a third Gaussian centered at a new point. To find this point above we attempt to rewrite the product $\exp(-ax^2)\times\exp[-b(x-R)^2]$ in the form $\exp[-(a+b)(x-C)^2+k]$, where C and k are constants to be determined. Simple algebra gives $C = bR(a+b)^{-1}$ and $k = [b^2R^2/(a+b)] - bR^2$. The overlap integral is therefore

$$S = \iiint_{-\infty}^{\infty} exp\left[bR^2\left(\frac{b}{a+b}-1\right)\right]$$

$$\times \exp\left\{-(a+b)\left[\left(x-\frac{bR}{a+b}\right)^2+y^2+z^2\right]\right\}dx\,dy\,dz.$$

The triple integral can be written as the cube of a single integral because the $x, y,$ and z dependences are separated and are identical

$$S = 8\exp\left[bR^2\left(\frac{b}{a+b}-1\right)\right]\left\{\int_0^{\infty}\exp\left[-(a+b)u^2\right]du\right\}^3$$

$$= \boxed{\left(\frac{\pi}{a+b}\right)^{3/2}\exp\left[bR^2\left(\frac{b}{a+b}-1\right)\right]}.$$

Before leaving the error function we first develop two useful power series representations.

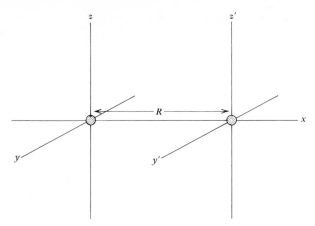

Fig. 7.2 Coordinate system for a two-center integral.

Example 64. Find power series representations for erf(x) when x is large and x is small.

Answer. For small x expand e^{-t^2} in a Maclaurin series.

$$e^{-t^2} = 1 - t^2 + \tfrac{1}{2}t^4 - \tfrac{1}{6}t^6 + \cdots -$$

Term-by-term integration from 0 to x gives

$$\text{erf}(x) = \frac{2}{\sqrt{\pi}}\left(x - \tfrac{1}{3}x^3 + \tfrac{1}{10}x^5 - \cdots +\right).$$

For large x we work with erfc(x) since for $x > 3$, say, erf(x) is negligibly different from unity. Successive integrations by parts give for erfc(x)

$$\text{erfc}(x) = \frac{2}{\sqrt{\pi}}\left[-\frac{1}{2t}\exp(-t^2)\Big|_x^\infty - \frac{1}{2}\int_x^\infty \frac{1}{t^2}\exp(-t^2)\,dt \right]$$

$$= \frac{1}{\sqrt{\pi}}\left[\frac{1}{x}\exp(-x^2) - \int_x^\infty \left(\frac{1}{t^3}\right)t\exp(-t^2)\,dt \right]$$

$$= \frac{1}{\sqrt{\pi}}\left[\frac{1}{x}\exp(-x^2) - \left\{ -\frac{1}{2t^3}\exp(-t^2)\Big|_x^\infty - \frac{3}{2}\int_x^\infty \frac{1}{t^4}\exp(-t^2)\,dt \right\} \right]$$

$$= \frac{\exp(-x^2)}{x\sqrt{\pi}}\left[1 - \frac{1}{2x^2} + \frac{3}{4x^4} - \cdots + \right].$$

Therefore, for large x we have

$$\operatorname{erf}(x) = 1 - \frac{\exp(-x^2)}{x\sqrt{\pi}}\left[1 - \frac{1}{2x^2} + \frac{1\cdot 3}{4x^4} - \cdots + \right]$$

$$\cong 1 - \frac{\exp(-x^2)}{x\sqrt{\pi}}\left[1 + \sum_{n=1}^{m}(-1)^n \frac{(2n-1)!}{(n-1)!}\frac{x^{-2n}}{2^{2n-1}}\right].$$

The last series above is interesting because it is a divergent series (when $m = \infty$) for all positive x. However we are not interested in using the entire series, but only the first few terms. The first m terms provide a good approximation to within an error of the order of magnitude of the $(m+1)$st term. Recall that in a footnote back in Chapter 4 we said that this is a property which characterizes many asymptotic series. Now the series above is actually an asymptotic series. To see this one has to revise the definition that was given earlier because now we are dealing with a series of reciprocal powers. A series $\sum_n a_n x^{-n}$ is an asymptotic expansion for $f(x)$ if for each fixed n the following limit holds:

$$\lim_{x\to\infty} x^n[f(x) - S_n(x)] = 0.$$

In our case above the difference between $f(x)$ and the nth partial sum, $S_n(x)$, is the integral left after the previous integration by parts. From this and the aid of Theorems 3 and 6 the asymptotic behavior of the series for $\operatorname{erf}(x)$ can be demonstrated.

So although we have here a series that is divergent (use Theorems 10 and 12 to investigate this), it is also asymptotic and computational accuracy may be good up to a certain number of terms. For example, in the series for $\operatorname{erf}(x)$ the absolute magnitude of the terms begins to increase after the fourth and eighth terms when $x = 2$ and $x = 3$, respectively. But the point is that the first few terms decay rapidly enough to give a suitable approximation even if the remaining terms (which are not used) diverge.[2] Early mathematicians often tried to ignore asymptotic series or to sweep them under the rug until about 1890 when Henri Poincaré (1854–1912) and T. J. Stieltjes put them on a firm basis. The interested reader is urged to consult the works by Bromwich, Hardy, and others that are listed in the Annotated Bibliography.

---

[2]Laplace in his book *Théorie Analytique des Probabilités* (1812) obtained the expansion for $\operatorname{erfc}(x)$ which we have derived above. He remarked that the series is divergent, but useful for obtaining values of $\operatorname{erfc}(x)$ for large x. This is just one example in sympathy with the witticism of Heaviside: "Aha! The series is divergent; therefore, we may be able to do something with it."

The error function bears a close relationship to another important integral that is commonly met. Consider the general integral

$$\int_0^\infty e^{-t^a} dt = I(a)$$

and make the change of variable $t^a = u$ (as you should have done in Exercise $1(h)$ of Chapter 3). Then $I(a)$ becomes

$$I(a) = \frac{1}{a} \int_0^\infty e^{-u} u^{(1/a)-1} du.$$

This integral arose in the research of Euler and others in trying to give mathematical meaning to a factorial $n!$ when n is nonintegral. It was noticed that the integral above can be evaluated by parts when $1/a$ is a positive integer n to give

$$\int_0^\infty e^{-u} u^{n-1} du = (n-1)!.$$

In the general case when n is any positive number the integral is referred to as the *gamma function*, $\Gamma(n)$. Obviously one has $\text{erf}(\infty) = (1/\sqrt{\pi})\Gamma(\frac{1}{2})$. The gamma function occurs often in various physical problems such as in the kinetic theory of gases.

A generalization of the gamma function in which the lower limit is variable is called the *incomplete gamma function*, and is defined as

$$\Gamma(n,x) = \int_x^\infty e^{-u} u^{n-1} du.$$

It is encountered only rarely, but a special case, namely, $\Gamma(0,x)$ does occur. This is the so-called *exponential integral* that was mentioned in Chapter 3.

$$Ei(x) = \int_x^\infty \frac{e^{-u}}{u} du.$$

An equivalent form of the gamma function sometimes occurs in which the substitution $u = \ln(1/t)$ has been made. The integral then becomes

$$\Gamma(n) = \int_0^1 \left(\ln \frac{1}{t} \right)^{n-1} dt$$

and either this form or the original form allows us to get a very useful identity. Replace n by $n+1$ and integrate by parts:

$$\Gamma(n+1) = \int_0^1 \left(\ln\frac{1}{t}\right)^n dt$$

$$= t\left(\ln\frac{1}{t}\right)^n\bigg|_0^1 + \int_0^1 n\left(\ln\frac{1}{t}\right)^{n-1} dt$$

$$= n\Gamma(n).$$

Tables often stop at $n=2$. According to this formula Γ (2.84), for example, equals $1.84\Gamma(1.84) = 1.84(0.943) = 1.73$.

Example 65. A mole of helium atoms is confined in a vessel at a temperature of $100°C$. What is the average value of the square of the speed of the atoms?

Answer. Assume the substance obeys the Maxwell distribution law of speeds given in Exercise 6 of Chapter 2. The average value of the square of the speed can then be expressed as

$$\langle v^2 \rangle = \frac{\int_0^\infty v^2 n(v)\,dv}{\int_0^\infty n(v)\,dv}$$

$$= \frac{\int_0^\infty 4\pi N_0 \left(\frac{m}{2\pi kT}\right)^{3/2} \exp(-mv^2/2kT)v^4\,dv}{N_0}.$$

To simplify this make the substitution $mv^2/2kT = u$. The average value of v^2 becomes

$$\langle v^2 \rangle = \frac{4kT}{m\sqrt{\pi}} \int_0^\infty e^{-u} u^{\frac{5}{2}-1}\,du$$

$$= \frac{4kT}{m\sqrt{\pi}} \Gamma(\tfrac{5}{2}).$$

The gamma function can be related to $\Gamma(\tfrac{3}{2})$ through the identity $\Gamma(\tfrac{5}{2}) = \tfrac{3}{2}\Gamma(\tfrac{3}{2})$, and $\Gamma(\tfrac{3}{2})$ can be related to $\Gamma(\tfrac{1}{2})$ through the identity

$\Gamma(\frac{3}{2}) = \frac{1}{2}\Gamma(\frac{1}{2})$. Hence we arrive finally at

$$\langle v^2 \rangle = \frac{3kT}{2m}$$

$$= \frac{3(1.38 \times 10^{-16} \mathrm{erg\,deg}^{-1})(373^\circ)}{2(4.00 \,\mathrm{g\,mole}^{-1})/(6.02 \times 10^{23} \,\mathrm{mole}^{-1})}$$

$$= \boxed{1.44 \times 10^{10} \mathrm{cm}^2 \mathrm{sec}^{-2}}.$$

Another useful function, called the beta function, is obtained by considering the product of two gamma functions:

$$\Gamma(n)\Gamma(m) = \int_0^\infty x^{n-1} e^{-x} dx \int_0^\infty y^{m-1} e^{-y} dy.$$

Now let $x = u^2$ and $y = v^2$ and write the product as a double integral:

$$\Gamma(n)\Gamma(m) = 4 \int_0^\infty \int_0^\infty u^{2n-1} v^{2m-1} e^{-(u^2+v^2)} du\, dv.$$

To simplify this we convert to polar coordinates in the uv plane (see Figure 7.3) and perform the integrations in just one quadrant. Recall from material

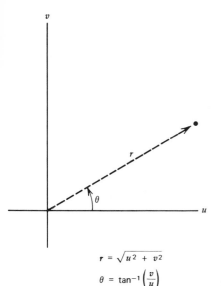

$r = \sqrt{u^2 + v^2}$

$\theta = \tan^{-1}\left(\frac{v}{u}\right)$

Fig. 7.3 Polar coordinates for integration.

given in Chapter 2 that the differential element $d\tau$ is

$$d\tau = dr \, d\theta \times \left| \frac{\partial (u,v)}{\partial (r,\theta)} \right|$$

$$= r \, dr \, d\theta.$$

This gives

$$\Gamma(n)\Gamma(m) = 4 \int_0^\infty r^{2n+2m-1} \exp(-r^2) \, dr \int_0^1 \sin^{2m-1}\theta \cos^{2n-1}\theta \, d\theta$$

and the trick now is to see that r and θ are just dummy variables. Let us define two new variables: $s = r^2$ and $t = \sin^2\theta$. Then

$$\Gamma(n)\Gamma(m) = 4 \int_0^\infty e^{-s} s^{n+m-\frac{1}{2}}\left(\tfrac{1}{2}s^{-\frac{1}{2}} \, ds\right) \int_0^1 t^{m-\frac{1}{2}}(1-t)^{n-\frac{1}{2}}\left(\tfrac{1}{2}\frac{dt}{t^{\frac{1}{2}}(1-t)^{\frac{1}{2}}}\right)$$

$$= \Gamma(n+m) \int_0^1 t^{m-1}(1-t)^{n-1} \, dt.$$

The integral on the right is designated as the *beta function*, $B(m,n)$, so that we have

$$\boxed{B(m,n) = \frac{\Gamma(m)\Gamma(n)}{\Gamma(m+n)}.}$$

By symmetry one must have $B(m,n) = B(n,m)$.

The utility of the beta function stems from its usefulness in the handling of integrals, and in providing useful relationships.

Example 66.   Derive a relationship between $\Gamma(n)$ and $\Gamma(1-n)$ for $0 < n < 1$.

Answer.   In the previous expression for $B(m,n)$ set $m = 1 - n$. Since $\Gamma(1) = 1$, then

$$\int_0^1 \frac{(1-t)^{n-1}}{t^n} \, dt = \Gamma(n)\Gamma(1-n).$$

The integral on the left is not easy to evaluate; it is best handled by contour integration in the complex plane (which we do not take up in this book), where it is shown to have the value $\pi/\sin n\pi$. For $n = \tfrac{1}{2}$, for example, this formula gives directly $\Gamma(\tfrac{1}{2}) = \sqrt{\pi}$.

Another useful relationship can be obtained by the following argument. In the definition of $B(n,n)$ let $t = \frac{1}{2}(1+z)$:

$$B(n,n) = \int_0^1 t^{n-1}(1-t)^{n-1}\,dt$$

$$= \int_{-1}^1 \left(\frac{1+z}{2}\right)^{n-1}\left(\frac{1-z}{2}\right)^{n-1}\frac{dz}{2}$$

$$= 2^{2-2n}\int_{-1}^1 (1-z^2)^{n-1}\,dz.$$

Now let $z^2 = u$; the integral can then be recast back into the form of another beta function.

$$B(n,n) = 2^{2-2n}\int_0^1 (1-u)^{n-1}\frac{du}{2\sqrt{u}}$$

$$= 2^{1-2n}\int_0^1 (1-u)^{n-1}u^{-\frac{1}{2}}\,du$$

$$= 2^{1-2n}B\left(\tfrac{1}{2},n\right).$$

But since $B(n,n) = [\Gamma(n)]^2/\Gamma(2n)$ and $B(\tfrac{1}{2},n) = \Gamma(\tfrac{1}{2})\Gamma(n)/\Gamma(n+\tfrac{1}{2})$ by definition, then

$$\frac{\Gamma(n)}{\Gamma(2n)} = 2^{1-2n}\frac{\sqrt{\pi}}{\Gamma(n+\tfrac{1}{2})}$$

or

$$\Gamma(2n) = \Gamma(n)\left\{\frac{2^{2n-1}\Gamma(n+\tfrac{1}{2})}{\sqrt{\pi}}\right\}.$$

This is one form of what is called *Legendre's duplication formula*. Another form is given by letting $n = m + \tfrac{1}{2}$:

$$(2m)! = m!\left\{\frac{(m-\tfrac{1}{2})!2^{2m}}{\sqrt{\pi}}\right\}.$$

Finally we present one example of the usefulness of the beta function in evaluating integrals.

Example 67.   Evaluate the definite integral $\int_0^{\pi/2}\cos^{\frac{1}{2}}\theta\,d\theta$.

Answer.   Let $\cos^{\frac{1}{2}}\theta = u^{\frac{1}{4}}$; by differentiation it follows that $d\theta = -\frac{1}{2}u^{-\frac{1}{2}}\times$
$(1-u)^{-\frac{1}{2}}\,du$. Then, these give

$$\int_0^{\pi/2}\cos^{\frac{1}{2}}\theta\,d\theta = -\frac{1}{2}\int_1^0 u^{-\frac{1}{4}}(1-u)^{-\frac{1}{2}}\,du$$

$$= \frac{1}{2}\int_0^1 u^{\frac{3}{4}-1}(1-u)^{\frac{1}{2}-1}\,du$$

$$= \frac{1}{2}B\left(\frac{3}{4},\frac{1}{2}\right)$$

$$= \frac{1}{2}\frac{\Gamma(\frac{3}{4})\Gamma(\frac{1}{2})}{\Gamma(\frac{5}{4})}.$$

In view of the preceding example, $\Gamma(\frac{3}{4})$ can be replaced by the quantity $\pi/(\Gamma(\frac{1}{4})\sin\frac{1}{4}\pi)$, and $\Gamma(\frac{1}{4})$ can be replaced by $4\Gamma(\frac{5}{4})$. The final result is

$$\int_0^{\pi/2}\cos^{\frac{1}{2}}\theta\,d\theta = \frac{(2\pi)^{3/2}}{16[\Gamma(\frac{5}{4})]^2}$$

$$= \boxed{1.20}.$$

2   LEGENDRE AND LAGUERRE POLYNOMIALS

The Legendre[3] differential equation has already been mentioned in Chapter 5 as an example of a second-order, ordinary, differential equation of the first degree. It arises very often in physical problems, for example, as a natural consequence of the mathematics involved in the solution of the Schrödinger equation for atomic hydrogen. The Legendre equation is

$$(1-x^2)\frac{d^2y}{dx^2} - 2x\frac{dy}{dx} + l(l+1)y = 0$$

and it is a special case of the so-called associated Legendre equation

$$(1-x^2)\frac{d^2y}{dx^2} - 2x\frac{dy}{dx} + \left[l(l+1) - \frac{m^2}{1-x^2}\right]y = 0$$

[3]After the French mathematician Adrien-Marie Legendre, 1752–1833.

where m and l are integers such that $|m| \leqslant |l|$. We solve the Legendre equation first.

Assume a series solution of the form $y = \sum_{n=0}^{\infty} a_n x^n$. Then substitution of this into the equation and simplification in the manner as was done in Chapter 5 leads to the recursion relationship (follow through on this yourself; don't take my word for it)

$$a_{n+2} = \left[\frac{n}{n+2} - \frac{l(l+1)}{(n+1)(n+2)} \right] a_n.$$

At this point the coefficients a_0 and a_1 are undetermined. For sufficiently large n one will eventually have $n > l$ so that from that point on all terms will be positive.

Now look at the subsequence of alternating terms. By Theorem 10 one has

$$\lim_{n \to \infty} \frac{a_{n+2} x^{n+2}}{a_n x^n} = \lim_{n \to \infty} x^2 \left[\frac{n}{n+2} - \frac{l(l+1)}{(n+1)(n+2)} \right]$$

$$= x^2.$$

The series will thus converge for $|x| < 1$ and diverge for $|x| > 1$. In some applications we would like the series to converge at $|x| = 1$ as well. To absolutely ensure this we chop off the series at some point as was done in the case of the Hermite differential equation (Section 5.3). This occurs when $n = l$; we then obtain a set of polynomials as our solutions, that are either even $(n = 2k)$ or odd $(n = 2k+1)$. These are the *Legendre polynomials*, $P_l(x)$.

For each polynomial a_0 or a_1 remains as yet undetermined. In many tables of Legendre polynomials it is conventional to assign values to a_0 or a_1 consistent with $P_l(1) = 1$. If this is done, then the first few polynomials become

$$P_0(x) = 1 \qquad P_1(x) = x$$
$$P_2(x) = \tfrac{1}{2}(3x^2 - 1) \qquad P_3(x) = \tfrac{1}{2}x(5x^2 - 3).$$

This set of polynomials agrees with those obtained from a generating function (recall Exercises 37* and 38* at the end of Chapter 4). This is actually an alternative way of defining the Legendre polynomials:

$$(1 - 2xt + t^2)^{-\frac{1}{2}} = \sum_{l=0}^{\infty} P_l(x) t^l.$$

To see how this works we expand the trinomial by means of the binomial theorem:

$$(1 - 2xt + t^2)^{-\frac{1}{2}} \equiv \left[1 - t(2x - t)\right]^{-\frac{1}{2}}$$

$$= \sum_{n=0}^{\infty} \frac{(2n)!}{n!\,2^n} \frac{1}{2^n n!} t^n (2x - t)^n.$$

The factor $(2n)!/(n!\,2^n)$ is the product of the first n odd integers. Next we expand $(2x - t)^n$ using the binomial theorem again. This, however, will not be an infinite series since n is a positive integer:

$$(2x - t)^n = \sum_{k=0}^{n} (-1)^k \frac{n!\,2^{n-k}}{(n-k)!\,k!} t^k x^{n-k}.$$

Combination of this with the previous series and reversal of the order of the summations give

$$(1 - 2xt + t^2)^{-\frac{1}{2}} = \sum_{n=0}^{\infty} \sum_{k=0}^{n} (-1)^k \frac{(2n)!}{2^{n+k} n!\,k!\,(n-k)!} t^{n+k} x^{n-k}.$$

Now in order to make this double series directly comparable to the defining series for $P_l(x)t^l$ we must make the exponent of t a single variable. Let $n + k = l$, so that the double series becomes

$$(1 - 2xt + t^2)^{-\frac{1}{2}} = \sum_{l=0}^{\infty} \sum_{k=0}^{\frac{1}{2}l} (-1)^k \frac{(2l - 2k)!}{2^l k!\,(l-k)!\,(l-2k)!} t^l x^{l-2k}.$$

The upper limit on the second summation sign is $\frac{1}{2}l$ because the exponent on x can never be negative; when l is an odd integer, then $\frac{1}{2}l$ should be replaced by $\frac{1}{2}(l - 1)$. Comparison of the double series above with the series for the $P_l(x)$ functions shows that

$$P_l(x) = \sum_{k=0}^{\frac{1}{2}l} (-1)^k \frac{(2l - 2k)!}{2^l k!\,(l-k)!\,(l-2k)!} x^{l-2k}.$$

When written in this form the Legendre polynomials are particularly susceptible to mathematical manipulations such as the deduction of recurrence relations.

One use of the series expression for $P_l(x)$ is in the derivation of what is called the *Rodrigues' formula*; this is still another shorthand way of getting the Legendre polynomials without recourse to solving the differential equation. Consider the multinomial $(x^2 - 1)^l$. Binomial expansion of this gives

$$(x^2 - 1)^l = \sum_{k=0}^{l} (-1)^k \frac{l!}{(l-k)!k!} x^{2l-2k}$$

and if this is differentiated l times,

$$\frac{d^l}{dx^l}(x^2 - 1)^l = \sum_{k=0}^{\frac{1}{2}l} (-1)^k \frac{l!}{(l-k)!k!} \frac{(2l-2k)!}{(l-2k)!} x^{l-2k}.$$

But now compare this expression with that for $P_l(x)$; we see that

$$\boxed{P_l(x) = \frac{1}{2^l l!} \frac{d^l}{dx^l}(x^2 - 1)^l}$$

For small l this formula can be used rapidly. Many of the important special functions used in science can be obtained alternatively from (a) a differential equation, (b) a generating function, or (c) a Rodrigues' formula.

At this point we might ask just why are the Legendre polynomials important mathematically. Reference to the discussion on the Sturm–Liouville equation (Section 5.3)

$$\frac{d}{dx}\left[f(x)\frac{dy}{dx} \right] + [g(x) + nh(x)]y = 0$$

reveals that the Legendre equation is a particular case of this equation with $f(x) = 1 - x^2$, $g(x) = 0$, $h(x) = 1$, and $n = l(l+1)$. Consequently the solutions of the Legendre equation will be orthogonal and can be normalized. Orthogonality is expressed by the integral (since $h(x) = 1$)

$$\int_{-1}^{1} P_l(x)P_m(x)\,dx = 0$$

if $l \neq m$; it is the continuum analogue of the fact that two vectors that are perpendicular to each other have zero as their dot product (Chapter 6). It is easy to see that orthogonality holds for cases where one of l and m is odd and the other is even. For then their product is an odd function and the indefinite integral becomes an even function; with limits of -1 and $+1$ this will vanish. When l and m are both odd or both even this argument cannot be employed.

Normalization is expressed by the integral

$$\int_{-1}^{1}\left[N_{l}P_{l}(x)\right]^{2}dx=1$$

where N_{l} is the normalization constant. If we take the $P_{l}(x)$ functions to be those that were tabulated previously, then it can be shown that the normalization constant is $\{(2l+1)/2\}^{\frac{1}{2}}$. The first few *normalized Legendre polynomials* are given in Table 7.1; these functions plus all the succeeding ones, then, constitute an orthonormal set. The first few normalized Legendre polynomials are graphed in Figure 7.4.

Table 7.1   Normalized Legendre Polynomials

$P_0(x)=\frac{1}{2}\sqrt{2}$	$P_1(x)=\frac{1}{2}x\sqrt{6}$
$P_2(x)=\frac{1}{4}\sqrt{10}\,(3x^2-1)$	$P_3(x)=\frac{1}{4}x\sqrt{7}\,(5x^2-3)$
$P_4(x)=\frac{3}{16}\sqrt{2}\,(35x^4-30x^2+3)$	$P_5(x)=\frac{1}{16}x\sqrt{22}\,(63x^4-70x^2+15)$

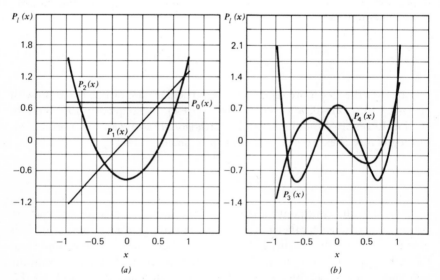

Fig. 7.4   Graphs of (a) $P_0(x)$, $P_1(x)$, and $P_2(x)$; and (b) $P_3(x)$ and $P_4(x)$.

What is more important, however, is that the set of all Legendre polynomials constitutes a *complete set*. You have already met one example of a complete set, namely, the set of all sines and cosines that comprise Fourier series. The idea behind a complete set can again be illustrated with an analogy from vectors. Any vector in the xy plane can be expressed as some combination of the unit $\mathbf{i}$ and $\mathbf{j}$ vectors. For example, a vector pointing from the origin to the point $(3,4)$ is simply the combination $3\mathbf{i} + 4\mathbf{j}$. The vector set $(\mathbf{i},\mathbf{j})$ is said to be a complete vector set for two-dimensional space. Now consider a vector in three-dimensional space; it cannot, in general, be represented by a combination of just $\mathbf{i}$ and $\mathbf{j}$ vectors. We can, in fact, find a vector that is orthogonal to all members of our previous set, namely, the vector $\mathbf{k}$ that is orthogonal to any vector in the xy plane. Now, the set $(\mathbf{i},\mathbf{j},\mathbf{k})$ is a complete set for three-dimensional vector space. The continuum analogue is that any function $f(x)$ defined on the interval $[-1,1]$ can be represented by some combination (it may be finite or infinite) of Legendre polynomials:

$$f(x) = \sum_{l=0}^{\infty} a_l P_l(x).$$

For example, any polynomial of degree n can be written as a linear combination of Legendre polynomials with $l \leqslant n$. Thus using the tabulated set of orthonormal Legendre polynomials, it is easy to see that

$$f(x) = 2x^2 - x + 1 = \tfrac{4}{15}\sqrt{10}\, P_2(x) - \tfrac{1}{3}\sqrt{6}\, P_1(x) + \tfrac{5}{3}\sqrt{2}\, P_0(x).$$

For more complex functions or for functions that are discontinuous at certain points in the interval it is necessary to proceed systematically. The procedure is the same as that used in constructing Fourier series (see Section 4.5), and the requirements on $f(x)$ are essentially the same: it must be single-valued, have only a finite number of discontinuities, and have a finite integral $\int_{-1}^{1} |f(x)|\, dx$. If these are satisfied, then the resulting *Legendre series* will converge to $f(x)$ at all points of continuity, and to the midpoint at discontinuities such as the point $x = 0$ of the step function

$$f(x) = \begin{cases} 2 & -1 < x < 0 \\ 0 & 0 < x < 1. \end{cases}$$

We mention briefly two important applications of Legendre polynomials. Legendre functions, or more exactly, associated Legendre functions, are a multiplicative part of the solutions to the Schrödinger equation for hydrogen. When the molecular orbitals for a many-electron system are considered, it is convenient to express them as linear combinations (in principle, infinite, but in practice, finite) of the hydrogenic orbitals. If the Legendre functions were not a complete set then the molecular orbitals that would be constructed could not be guaranteed to be accurate over the entire range.

Legendre functions are also useful in dealing with problems where there is a potential ψ, such as an electrostatic potential, that is associated with an inverse square force. Thus if an ion of charge $+e$ is located at some point A (Figure 7.5), the electrostatic potential (in mks units) at point B is given by

$$\psi = \frac{e}{4\pi\varepsilon_0} \frac{1}{|R - r_0|} .$$

This is inconvenient; we would like the potential to involve just powers of R, the distance from the origin, rather than r, the distance from the ion. From elementary trigonometry

$$\frac{1}{|R - r_0|} = \frac{1}{r} = \left[R^2 + r_0^2 - 2Rr_0\cos\theta\right]^{-\frac{1}{2}}$$

and if this is expanded by means of the binomial theorem,

$$\frac{1}{r} = \frac{1}{R} - \frac{1}{2}\frac{1}{R^3}\left(r_0^2 - 2r_0R\cos\theta\right)$$

$$+ \frac{3}{8}\frac{1}{R^5}\left(r_0^4 - 4r_0^3R\cos\theta + 4r_0^2R^2\cos^2\theta\right) - \cdots +$$

$$= \frac{1}{R}\cdot 1 + \frac{r_0}{R^2}(\cos\theta) + \frac{r_0^2}{R^3}\left(\tfrac{3}{2}\cos^2\theta - \tfrac{1}{2}\right) + \cdots +.$$

The coefficients in parentheses look like Legendre polynomials if we make the argument of these polynomials $\cos\theta$ instead of x. In terms of *unnormalized* Legendre functions, we can finally express the potential as the series

$$\psi = \frac{e}{4\pi\varepsilon_0 R}\sum_{l=0}^{\infty}\left(\frac{r_0}{R}\right)^l P_l(\cos\theta).$$

The usefulness of doing this becomes even more apparent if one is dealing with a collection of charges (as in some region in an electrolyte solution).

Sometimes one desires to be able to go rapidly from one (or two) Legendre polynomial to another. Useful recursion relationships for doing this are best created from the generating function. Suppose the generating function is

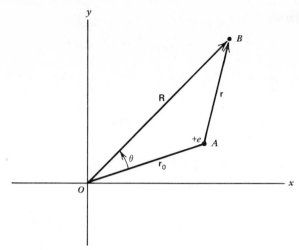

Fig. 7.5 Finding the electrostatic potential at a point near an ion.

differentiated with respect to t; this gives

$$\frac{x-t}{1-2xt+t^2}\sum_{l=0}^{\infty}P_l(x)t^l=\sum_{l=0}^{\infty}lP_l(x)t^{l-1}.$$

However, the series on the right cannot have the dummy index begin at 0 because t can never have a negative exponent. If we redefine the index there and rearrange terms, then the equation

$$(x-t)\sum_{l=0}^{\infty}P_l(x)t^l-\left[(1-2xt+t^2)\sum_{l=0}^{\infty}(l+1)P_{l+1}(x)t^l\right]=0$$

results. If this is to be valid for all t, we must require that the total coefficient of each power of t vanish separately. Thus if we consider a particular power l for t, then if we gather together all the terms that contain t^l we have

$$t^l[xP_l(x)-P_{l-1}(x)-(l+1)P_{l+1}(x)+2xlP_l(x)-(l-1)P_{l-1}(x)]=0$$

or finally,

$$\boxed{(2l+1)xP_l(x)=(l+1)P_{l+1}(x)+lP_{l-1}(x)}.$$

Differentiation of the generating function with respect to x gives the recursion relation

$$P'_{l+1}(x) + P'_{l-1}(x) = 2xP'_l(x) + P_l(x)$$

and if this is combined with the recursion relation above, there results the useful expression

$$\boxed{P'_{l+1}(x) - P'_{l-1}(x) = (2l+1)P_l(x)}.$$

Closely related to the Legendre differential equation is the *associated Legendre differential equation*:

$$(1-x^2)\frac{d^2y}{dx^2} - 2x\frac{dy}{dx} + \left[l(l+1) - \frac{m^2}{1-x^2}\right]y = 0.$$

Rather than try to solve this directly it is easier to derive it from the Legendre equation. If this latter equation is differentiated m times (see Theorem 2), there results

$$(1-x^2)\frac{d^{m+2}y}{dx^{m+2}} - 2x(m+1)\frac{d^{m+1}y}{dx^{m+1}} + [l(l+1) - m(m+1)]\frac{d^m y}{dx^m} = 0.$$

Now make the substitution above

$$z = (1-x^2)^{\frac{1}{2}m}\frac{d^m y}{dx^m}$$

and after much labor the differential equation transforms into

$$\frac{d^2z}{dx^2} - \frac{2x}{1-x^2}\frac{dz}{dx} + \frac{l(l+1)z}{1-x^2} - \frac{m^2 z}{(1-x^2)^2} = 0.$$

This is just the associated Legendre differential equation, and hence its solutions are polynomials that have the form

$$\boxed{P_l^m(x) = (1-x^2)^{\frac{1}{2}m}\frac{d^m P_l(x)}{dx^m}}.$$

Since $P_l(x)$ is a polynomial of the lth degree, it is clear that $m \leqslant l$. If $P_l(x)$ is expressed by the Rodrigues' formula, then mathematically one can have $m < 0$ even though differentiation a negative number of times has no meaning. Also, from the Rodrigues' formula it is seen that $m \geqslant -l$. You will recognize in the combined statement $|m| \leqslant l$ the restriction that you first learned in freshman chemistry for the magnetic quantum number in the description of the states of hydrogen.

The associated Legendre polynomials $P_l^m(x)$ can be normalized, are orthogonal, and form a complete set. The normalization constant is

$$\left\{ \frac{(2l+1)(l-m)!}{2(l+m)!} \right\}^{\frac{1}{2}}$$

and a few of the normalized functions are given in column 1 of Table 7.2. In the quantum mechanical solution of the hydrogen atom (recall Exercise 35* of Chapter 5) the associated Legendre differential equation is usually written in terms of the independent variable $\cos\theta$. If we make this change of argument above, then the resulting polynomials will be the normalized θ parts of the hydrogen wave functions. These are sampled in column 2 of Table 7.2. If $P_l^m(\cos\theta)$ is a normalized solution to the differential equation, then it can be shown that $-P_l^m(\cos\theta) = P_l^{-m}(\cos\theta)$ will be a solution also, and so many books do not make a distinction in sign between $P_1^1(\cos\theta)$ and $P_1^{-1}(\cos\theta)$, writing instead $P_1^{\pm 1}(\cos\theta) = \frac{1}{2}\sin\theta\sqrt{3}$.

Table 7.2 Some Normalized Associated Legendre Polynomials

$P_0^0(x) = \frac{1}{2}\sqrt{2}$	$1s$	$P_0^0(\cos\theta) = \frac{1}{2}\sqrt{2}$
$P_1^0(x) = \frac{1}{2}x\sqrt{6}$	$2p_z$	$P_1^0(\cos\theta) = \frac{1}{2}\sqrt{6}\cos\theta$
$P_1^1(x) = \frac{1}{2}\sqrt{3}\,(1-x^2)^{\frac{1}{2}}$	$2p_x$	$P_1^1(\cos\theta) = \frac{1}{2}\sqrt{3}\sin\theta$
$P_1^{-1}(x) = -\frac{1}{2}\sqrt{3}\,(1-x^2)^{\frac{1}{2}}$	$2p_y$	$P_1^{-1}(\cos\theta) = -\frac{1}{2}\sqrt{3}\sin\theta$

The higher associated Legendre polynomials are tedious to obtain. Starting with the Rodrigues' formula for $P_l(\cos\theta)$ we see that a total of $l+m$ differentiations are needed in order to get $P_l^m(\cos\theta)$. An alternative way of writing the normalized associated Legendre polynomials in $\cos\theta$ so that fewer differentiations are required is

$$P_l^m(\cos\theta) = (-1)^m \left\{ \frac{(2l+1)(l+m)!}{2(l-m)!} \right\}^{\frac{1}{2}} \frac{(\sin\theta)^{-m}}{2^l l!}$$

$$\times \frac{d^{l-m}}{(d\cos\theta)^{l-m}} \left[(\cos^2\theta - 1)^l \right].$$

Thus with very little labor we compute $P_3^2(\cos\theta)$ as

$$P_3^2(\cos\theta) = (-1)^2 \left\{ \frac{7\cdot5!}{2\cdot1!} \right\}^{\frac{1}{2}} \frac{(\sin\theta)^{-2}}{2^3 3!} \frac{d^1}{(d\cos\theta)^1} (\cos^2\theta - 1)^3$$

$$= \frac{\sqrt{420}}{48\sin^2\theta} 3(\cos^2\theta - 1)^2 (2\cos\theta)$$

$$= \tfrac{1}{4}\sqrt{105} \, \sin^2\theta \cos\theta.$$

This is the θ part of one of the hydrogen f orbitals.

In the separation of variables for the Schrödinger equation for hydrogen, the easiest equation to solve is the Φ equation:

$$\frac{1}{\Phi(\phi)} \frac{d^2\Phi(\phi)}{d\phi^2} = -m^2.$$

It has normalized solutions of $(2\pi)^{-\frac{1}{2}} e^{\pm i|m|\phi}$. The product of either of these times a normalized associated Legendre function of $\cos\theta$ gives rise to a *spherical harmonic*:

$$Y_l^m(\theta,\phi) = \frac{1}{\sqrt{2\pi}} e^{im\phi} P_l^m(\cos\theta).$$

These functions constitute the complete angular parts of the hydrogen wave functions. The spherical harmonics are a complete set of functions, and they are orthogonal to one another according to the relation

$$\int_0^{2\pi} \int_0^{\pi} Y_l^{m_1}(\theta,\phi)^* \, Y_l^{m_2}(\theta,\phi) \sin\theta \, d\theta \, d\phi$$

$$= \frac{1}{2\pi} \int_0^{2\pi} \int_0^{\pi} \exp(-im_1\phi) P_l^{m_1}(\cos\theta) \exp(im_2\phi) P_l^{m_2}(\cos\theta) \sin\theta \, d\theta \, d\phi$$

$$= 0.$$

Note that in this integral one of the spherical harmonics must be written as a complex conjugate. Let us recall once again the relations one learns for the quantum numbers in the description of hydrogen.

$$n = 1, 2, 3, 4, \ldots \quad \text{Principal quantum number}$$
$$0 \leqslant l \leqslant n - 1 \quad \text{Azimuthal quantum number}$$
$$-l \leqslant m \leqslant l \quad \text{Magnetic quantum number}$$

The function $Y_2^{-1}(\theta,\phi) = -\frac{1}{2}\sqrt{15/2\pi}\ e^{-i\phi}\cos\theta\sin\theta$ thus belongs to one of the $3d$ (or $4d$, $5d$, etc.) orbitals.

Except for the states with $m=0$, the hydrogen wave functions are seen to be complex. Now by Theorem 18 we know that any linear combination of the wave functions will also be a solution of the Schrödinger equation. Since $e^{\pm im\phi} = \cos m\phi \pm i\sin m\phi$, we could construct the following real functions:

$$"p_x" = \tfrac{1}{2}\sqrt{2}\ (p_x - p_y) = \tfrac{1}{2}\sqrt{2}\left[\tfrac{1}{2}\sqrt{\frac{3}{2\pi}}\ \sin\theta\,(\cos\phi + i\sin\phi)\right.$$

$$\left. + \tfrac{1}{2}\sqrt{\frac{3}{2\pi}}\ \sin\theta\,(\cos\phi - i\sin\phi)\right]$$

$$= \tfrac{1}{2}\sqrt{\frac{3}{\pi}}\ \sin\theta\cos\phi$$

$$"p_y" = \tfrac{1}{2}i\sqrt{2}\ (p_x + p_y) = \tfrac{1}{2}i\sqrt{2}\left[\tfrac{1}{2}\sqrt{\frac{3}{2\pi}}\ \sin\theta\,(\cos\phi + i\sin\phi)\right.$$

$$\left. - \tfrac{1}{2}\sqrt{\frac{3}{2\pi}}\ \sin\theta\,(\cos\phi - i\sin\phi)\right]$$

$$= -\tfrac{1}{2}\sqrt{\frac{3}{\pi}}\ \sin\theta\sin\phi.$$

These two p functions still satisfy Schrödinger's equation, are orthogonal, and lead to the same eigenvalue (orbital energy) as before. They are not, however, eigenvalues of $\hat{l}_z$, in contrast to the original p_x and p_y functions, implying that for a system described by such functions angular momentum along the z axis is not a constant of the motion.

You will notice that the "p_y" function contains a negative sign. This sign is a consequence of our definition of the spherical harmonics (some workers include a factor of $(-1)^m$ in the definition), but since it is the square of a wave function that has physical significance, the minus sign is irrelevant. The square of this wave function is

$$["p_y"]^2 = \frac{3}{4\pi}\sin^2\theta\sin^2\phi$$

and in the yz plane $\phi = 90°$ or $\sin^2\phi = 1$. A plot on polar axes of a cross

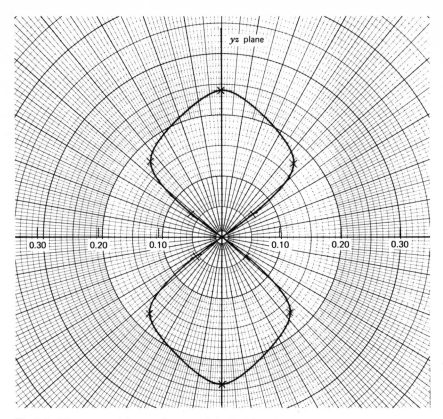

Fig. 7.6 The square of the angular part of the "p_y" function.

section of $[\text{"}p_y\text{"}]^2$ in the yz plane is shown in Figure 7.6. You will recognize in this the familiar qualitative shape of a p-orbital (this is not the complete story, however, behind working out the contour plot of an orbital).

We conclude this section with brief mention of another set of functions, which although they are not as commonly used as the Legendre polynomials, are encountered also in the quantum description of hydrogen. The associated Laguerre differential equation is

$$x\frac{d^2y}{dx^2} + (k+1-x)\frac{dy}{dx} + ny = 0$$

and when $k = 0$ this becomes the Laguerre differential equation.[4] The

---

[4]After the French mathematician Edmond Laguerre (1834–1886).

polynomial solutions to the Laguerre differential equation are the Laguerre polynomials, $L_n(x)$, some of which are given in Table 7.3. These polynomials do not form a complete, orthonormal set, but the functions $e^{-\frac{1}{2}x}L_n(x)$ do constitute such a set for the interval $0 \leqslant x < \infty$.

Table 7.3   Some Laguerre Polynomials

$L_0(x) = 1$ $L_2(x) = x^2 - 4x + 2$

$L_1(x) = -x + 1$ $L_3(x) = -x^3 + 9x^2 - 18x + 6$

$L_4(x) = x^4 - 16x^3 + 72x^2 - 96x + 24$

The associated Laguerre polynomials are related to the Laguerre polynomials in a manner similar to that of the associated Legendre polynomials to the Legendre polynomials.

$$L_{n+k}^k(x) = (-1)^k \frac{d^k}{dx^k}[L_{n+k}(x)]$$

The associated Laguerre differential equation can be put into Sturm–Liouville form by multiplying it by $e^{-x}x^k$; the orthonormality condition can then be shown to be

$$\int_0^\infty e^{-x}x^{k+1}L_{n+k}^k(x)L_{m+k}^k(x)dx = \frac{2(n+k+1)[(n+k)!]^3}{n!}\delta_{mn}.$$

The associated Laguerre polynomials occur in the solution to the radial part of the Schrödinger equation for hydrogen.

3 BESSEL FUNCTIONS

At this junction,
It is time to wrestle
With a well-known function,
Due to Herr Bessel.

Although special cases of the Bessel differential equation and of the Bessel functions had been encountered in researches as early as 1703, the first systematic study of them was made in 1824 by the German astronomer Friedrich Wilhelm Bessel (1784–1846) in a paper titled "Investigation of the

Part of Planetary Perturbation which Arises from the Motion of the Sun.'' The differential equation that bears Bessel's name is

$$x^2 \frac{d^2y}{dx^2} + x\frac{dy}{dx} + (x^2 - n^2)y = 0$$

and it certainly ranks on at least an equal footing with the Legendre equation in importance.

This may not seem credible to us because we are not so used in chemistry to hearing about Bessel functions as we are about Legendre functions. The apparent absence of Bessel functions is illusory, however, and this becomes clearer when we realize that both Bessel's and Legendre's equations arise in a natural sort of way when partial differential equations such as Laplace's equation or the wave equation (see Chapter 5) are separated in particular coordinate systems. For example, when the Helmholtz equation, $(\nabla^2\psi + k^2\psi = 0)$, or Laplace's equation $(k = 0)$, is separated in spherical polar, prolate spheroidal, or oblate spheroidal coordinates, the associated Legendre equation arises. When Laplace's equation, however, is separated in cylindrical polar coordinates or in parabolic coordinates, Bessel's equation arises.

We seek a solution to Bessel's differential equation as a power series of the form

$$y = \sum_{k=0}^{\infty} a_k x^{k+s},$$

where writing the independent variable as x^{k+s} simply gives us a more flexible form for y. If this is substituted into the differential equation and the coefficients of x^s examined (that is, $k = 0$), then one has the relation

$$a_0[s^2 - n^2] = 0.$$

This *indicial equation* has the two roots $s = \pm n$. From the coefficients of x^{s+1} one has

$$a_1\left[(s+1)^2 - n^2\right] = 0$$

or, $a_1 = 0$ in view of the value for s. The relation for general k is

$$a_k = \frac{-a_{k-2}}{(k+s)^2 - n^2}$$

and since $a_1 = 0$, this means that all odd a_k's are zero too.

We now have two possibilities: a set of a_k's when $s = +n$, and another set when $s = -n$. In the first case define $k = 2m(m = 1, 2, 3, \ldots)$; then the recursion relation becomes

$$a_{2m} = \frac{-a_{2m-2}}{4m(m+n)}.$$

The first few coefficients can be written easily in order to see the trend:

$$a_0 = a_0$$

$$a_2 = \frac{-a_0}{4(1+n)} \qquad m = 1$$

$$a_4 = \frac{a_0}{32(2+n)(1+n)} \qquad m = 2$$

$$a_6 = \frac{-a_0}{384(3+n)(2+n)(1+n)} \qquad m = 3.$$

It is not too hard to see that the general term can be expressed with the aid of the gamma function as

$$a_{2m} = a_0 \frac{(-1)^m \Gamma(n+1)}{m! 2^{2m} \Gamma(m+n+1)}.$$

The solution to the differential equation is, therefore,

$$y = \sum_{m=0}^{\infty} a_0 \frac{(-1)^m \Gamma(n+1)}{m! 2^{2m} \Gamma(m+n+1)} x^{2m+n}$$

and at this point a_0 is still undetermined. In order to bring y into the standard form, it is conventional to take $a_0 = 2^{-n}/\Gamma(n+1)$. Then changing y to $J_n(x)$ gives

$$\boxed{J_n(x) = \sum_{m=0}^{\infty} \frac{(-1)^m}{m! \Gamma(m+n+1)} \left(\frac{x}{2}\right)^{2m+n}}.$$

This expression is referred to as a *Bessel function of the first kind and of order n*. It is, as indicated, an infinite series in contrast to Hermite, Legendre, associated Legendre, and Laguerre functions because we did not use the recursion relation between a_{2m} and a_{2m-2} to chop off the series beyond some point. The above solution is valid for any non-negative n; in many instances the n will be a positive integer and the series will allow one to derive useful identities such as

$$\frac{dJ_0(x)}{dx} = -J_1(x).$$

Because Bessel functions are infinite series and not finite polynomials, we recognize that we must determine for which values of the argument the series converge. Absolute convergence can be examined by employing d'Alembert's ratio test (refer back to Theorem 10). The ratio of the absolute values of two consecutive terms is easily found to be

$$\frac{|(m+1)\text{st term}|}{|m\text{th term}|} = x^2 \left[\frac{1}{4(m+1)(m+n+1)} \right]$$

and the limit of this as m increases without bound is zero. Hence the Bessel function of the first kind and of order n is convergent absolutely for all real x.

At this point we might just pause and ask the very basic question, what do Bessel functions look like? To answer this let us return to the differential equation and make the substitution $y = z/\sqrt{x}$. This gives the transformed equation

$$\frac{d^2z}{dx^2} + \left(1 - \frac{n^2 - \frac{1}{4}}{x^2} \right) z = 0,$$

which somehow looks simpler and more susceptible to qualitative analysis. If n assumed a value of $\pm \frac{1}{2}$, then one would have the even simpler equation

$$\frac{d^2z}{dx^2} + z = 0,$$

which has solutions $z = A \sin x$ and $z = B \cos x$. Reverting back to the original dependent variable we would then have $y = Ax^{-\frac{1}{2}}\sin x$ and $y = Bx^{-\frac{1}{2}}\cos x$. These expressions are the expressions for damped sine and cosine waves. It is clear that even for larger values of n the same qualitative results will be obtained if x is very large. For very small x, say $x < 1$, we may approximate $J_n(x)$ by just the first term of the series. This term is $x^n/(2^n n!)$, so that $J_0(x)$ behaves roughly like $1, J_1(x)$ behaves like $\frac{1}{2}x, J_2(x)$ behaves like $x^2/8$, and so on. The first few Bessel functions are graphed in Figure 7.7.

A three-term recurrence relation would be of great use in handling Bessel functions, and it is not hard to discover one. First, we arrange expressions for

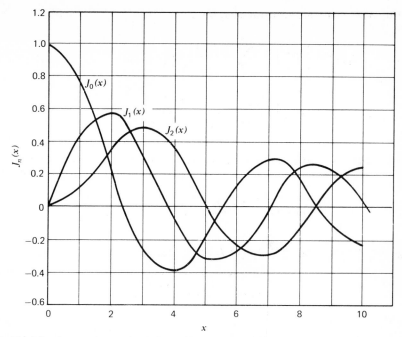

Fig. 7.7 Graphs of some Bessel functions of the first kind.

$J_{n-1}(x)$ and $J_{n+1}(x)$ so that they involve the same powers of $\frac{1}{2}x$:

$$J_{n-1}(x) = \sum_{m=0}^{\infty} \frac{(-1)^m}{m!(m+n-1)!} \left(\frac{x}{2}\right)^{2m+n-1}$$

$$= \frac{1}{(n-1)!} \left(\frac{x}{2}\right)^{n-1} + \sum_{k=0}^{\infty} \frac{(-1)^{k+1}}{(k+1)!(k+n)!} \left(\frac{x}{2}\right)^{2k+n+1}$$

$$J_{n+1}(x) = \sum_{k=0}^{\infty} \frac{(-1)^k}{k!(k+n+1)!} \left(\frac{x}{2}\right)^{2k+n+1}$$

Some elementary algebra gives for the sum of these two Bessel functions

$$J_{n-1}(x) + J_{n+1}(x) = \frac{1}{(n-1)!} \left(\frac{x}{2}\right)^{n-1} + n \sum_{k=0}^{\infty} \frac{(-1)^{k+1}}{(k+1)!(k+n+1)!} \left(\frac{x}{2}\right)^{2k+n+1}$$

Let us now write out an expression for $J_n(x)$:

$$J_n(x) = \frac{1}{n!}\left(\frac{x}{2}\right)^n + \sum_{m=1}^{\infty} \frac{(-1)^m}{m!(m+n)!}\left(\frac{x}{2}\right)^{2m+n}$$

$$= \frac{1}{n!}\left(\frac{x}{2}\right)^n + \sum_{k=0}^{\infty} \frac{(-1)^{k+1}}{(k+1)!(k+n+1)!}\left(\frac{x}{2}\right)^{2k+n+2}$$

Notice that if we now multiply this expression by $n(\frac{1}{2}x)^{-1}$, then we get

$$\frac{2n}{x}J_n(x) = \frac{n}{n!}\left(\frac{x}{2}\right)^{n-1} + n\sum_{k=0}^{\infty} \frac{(-1)^{k+1}}{(k+1)!(k+n+1)!}\left(\frac{x}{2}\right)^{2k+n+1}$$

and this is seen to be identical to $J_{n-1}(x) + J_{n+1}(x)$:

$$\boxed{J_{n-1}(x) + J_{n+1}(x) = \frac{2n}{x}J_n(x)}.$$

Thus, given $J_0(x)$ and $J_1(x)$, for example, one can numerically compute $J_2(x)$, and so on.

Another useful relation is a generating function for the $J_n(x)$, that can be derived from the preceding recurrence relation. Let us assume a generating function of the form

$$f(x,t) = \sum_{n=-\infty}^{\infty} J_n(x)t^n.$$

If we take the three-term recurrence relation, multiply it by t^n, and sum from $-\infty$ to $+\infty$, then comparison with the generating function shows that

$$tf(x,t) + \frac{1}{t}f(x,t) = \frac{2t}{x}\frac{\partial f(x,t)}{\partial t}.$$

This is a differential equation of the variables separable type,

$$dt\frac{x(t+t^{-1})}{2t} = \frac{d[f(x,t)]}{f(x,t)}$$

with the solution

$$\tfrac{1}{2}x(t-t^{-1}) = \ln f(x,t) + \ln G(x).$$

Notice that the constant of integration must be expressed more generally as a function of x rather than just a pure number. Taking antilogarithms gives the generating function as

$$f(x,t) = \frac{e^{\frac{1}{2}x(t-t^{-1})}}{G(x)}.$$

To find the specific form for the denominator, we now write out the numerator as the product of the Maclaurin series expansions for $e^{\frac{1}{2}xt}$ and $e^{-\frac{1}{2}xt^{-1}}$.

$$f(x,t) = \frac{\left[1+(xt/2)+(x^2t^2/8)+\cdots+\right]\left[1-(x/2t)+(x^2/8t^2)-\cdots+\right]}{G(x)}$$

From this we see that the coefficient of t^0 is given by the series

$$\frac{\left[1-\dfrac{x^2}{4}+\dfrac{x^4}{64}-\dfrac{x^6}{2304}+\cdots-\right]}{G(x)} = \frac{\displaystyle\sum_{m=0}^{\infty}\frac{(-1)^m}{m!\,m!}\left(\frac{x}{2}\right)^{2m}}{G(x)}$$

and if this coefficient is to be identical to $J_0(x)$ according to the generating function, one must have $G(x)\equiv 1$. The final result, then, is

$$\boxed{\exp\left[\tfrac{1}{2}x(t-t^{-1})\right]=\sum_{n=-\infty}^{\infty}J_n(x)t^n}.$$

We have not yet defined Bessel functions where the index n is negative even though we have included them in the generating function. This could be used as a definition of such functions when n is a negative integer; actually, if one returns to the indicial equation and works with the second root, $s=-n$, things become more complicated. Additional types of Bessel functions arise that are valid solutions of the differential equation. For nonintegral $-n$ one can write

$$J_{-n}(x) = \sum_{m=0}^{\infty}\frac{(-1)^m}{m!\,\Gamma(m-n+1)}\left(\frac{x}{2}\right)^{2m-n}$$

and this will be a series [independent of $J_n(x)$] with first term $(\tfrac{1}{2}x)^{-n}/\Gamma(1-n)$. If $-1<-n<0$, then there is no problem, but what if $-n<-1$? This means that we have to extend the notion of the gamma function to negative arguments. To do this we recall an important identity:

$$\Gamma(x) = \frac{\Gamma(x+1)}{x}.$$

Since $\Gamma(1) = 1$, this shows that $\Gamma(0)$ must blow up. Now for $0 < x < 1$ the gamma function is positive, but for $-1 < x < 0$ the denominator in the above fraction will be negative so that $\Gamma(x)$ in that region will also be negative. Hence for $x = 0$ the value of $\Gamma(x)$ depends on the direction from which $x = 0$ is approached:

$$\lim_{x \to 0^+} \Gamma(x) = +\infty$$

$$\lim_{x \to 0^-} \Gamma(x) = -\infty$$

This behavior is similar to that of $\tan\theta$ at $\theta = \frac{1}{2}\pi$. Continuing the analysis one sees that $\Gamma(x) = \pm\infty$ at all negative integers. A graph of the gamma function is shown in Figure 7.8; it is worth careful study.

The gist of this digression is that if $-n$ is a negative integer then the first few terms in $J_{-n}(x)$ will be zero because of the gamma function in the denominator. To see what the result will be we write out some of the terms in $J_3(x)$ and $J_{-3}(x)$:

$$J_3(x) = \frac{(-1)^0}{0!\,\Gamma(4)}\left(\frac{x}{2}\right)^3 + \frac{(-1)^1}{1!\,\Gamma(5)}\left(\frac{x}{2}\right)^5 + \frac{(-1)^2}{2!\,\Gamma(6)}\left(\frac{x}{2}\right)^7 + \cdots +$$

$$J_{-3}(x) = \frac{(-1)^0}{0!\,\Gamma(-2)}\left(\frac{x}{2}\right)^{-3} + \frac{(-1)^1}{1!\,\Gamma(-1)}\left(\frac{x}{2}\right)^{-1} + \frac{(-1)^2}{2!\,\Gamma(0)}\left(\frac{x}{2}\right)^1$$

$$+ \frac{(-1)^3}{3!\,\Gamma(1)}\left(\frac{x}{2}\right)^3 + \frac{(-1)^4}{4!\,\Gamma(2)}\left(\frac{x}{2}\right)^5 + \frac{(-1)^5}{5!\,\Gamma(3)}\left(\frac{x}{2}\right)^7 + \cdots +$$

$$= (-1)^3 \left[\frac{(-1)^0}{3!\,\Gamma(1)}\left(\frac{x}{2}\right)^3 + \frac{(-1)^1}{4!\,\Gamma(2)}\left(\frac{x}{2}\right)^5 + \frac{(-1)^2}{5!\,\Gamma(3)}\left(\frac{x}{2}\right)^7 + \cdots + \right].$$

Hence for integral $-n$, $J_{-n}(x) = (-1)^n J_n(x)$, and thus $J_{-n}(x)$ is not a solution independent of $J_n(x)$. Since the Bessel equation is a second-order equation, there have to be two independent solutions.

Early workers considered the expression

$$Y_s(x) = \frac{\cos s\pi\, J_s(x) - J_{-s}(x)}{\sin s\pi}.$$

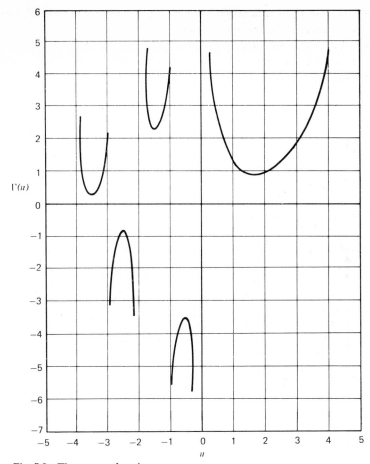

Fig. 7.8 The gamma function.

For nonintegral s the functions $J_s(x)$ and $J_{-s}(x)$ are distinct, and so $Y_s(x)$, which is a linear combination of them, will be a solution to the differential equation. When s is integral, the expression is of the $0/0$ indeterminate type. The limit of the expression as s approaches an integer n was found to exist, to satisfy the differential equation, and to have the same asymptotic form as does $J_n(x)$ for large x. Thus if we define $Y_n(x)$ to be $\lim_{s \to n} Y_s(x)$, then $Y_s(x)$ is a solution of Bessel's equation for *all* s, and for the general solution to the differential equation when n is integral, we must take

$$y = A J_n(x) + B Y_n(x).$$

We call $Y_n(x)$ *Weber's form of the Bessel function of the second kind and of order n.*

An investigation of its properties is outside the scope of this book. Figure 7.9 contains the graphs of a few more Bessel functions. We remark in conclusion that with the Bessel functions of the first and second kind one can expand an arbitrary function in terms of them for an arbitary interval (a, b). Details can be found in the more advanced literature.

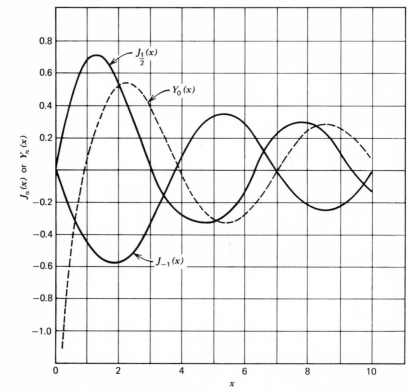

Fig. 7.9   Graphs of some Bessel functions.

THE DIRAC DELTA FUNCTION

The material in this concluding section of the book is intrinsically interesting. Although the mathematics is of rather recent vintage and has not yet filtered down to any extent into elementary first-year calculus texts, the origins of the mathematical ideas derive from simple physical concepts that have been around for a very long time. Entities such as a point mass, a point dipole, or an instantaneous force are idealistic but useful quantities in physical science. They do not exist, strictly, but may be said to approximate real situations when their effects are indistinguishable with given measuring equipment from the effects of physically realizable masses, dipoles, forces, etc. Thus suppose we are interested in a force that is ideally applied instantaneously at time $t=0$ in such a way that a unit impulse results. Then

$$F(t)=0 \qquad t\neq 0$$

$$\int_{-\infty}^{\infty} F(t)\,dt=1$$

and our problem is to determine what mathematical meaning can be attached to the symbol $F(t)$, even though we know that any normal function that is zero everywhere except at a single point (or even except at a countably infinite collection of points) must have a zero integral.

A clue as to how to set up the mathematics comes from the fact that the need to use such tricky functions as $F(t)$ above never arises except when the function is in combination with some other function, that is well-behaved and under an integral sign. Let us for the moment call $F(t)$ an example of a *generalized function*, without as yet defining it more specifically, and write it more generally as $g(t)$. We now look at the integral

$$\mathcal{F}(f) = \int_{-\infty}^{\infty} g(t) f(t)\,dt$$

where $f(t)$ is an ordinary, continuous, well-behaved function. This integral is what we called in Section 3.5 a functional; its domain of definition is not a set of numbers but a set of well-behaved functions $f(t)$. Suppose we choose as one possible functional the integral of $f(t)$ from x to ∞. Then

$$\mathcal{F}(f) = \int_{x}^{\infty} f(t)\,dt = \int_{-\infty}^{\infty} g(t) f(t)\,dt$$

and it is clear that in order for the two integrals to be equal one must have

$$g(t)=\begin{cases} 0 & -\infty < t < x \\ 1 & x < t < \infty. \end{cases}$$

This $g(t)$ is called the *Heaviside step function*, $H(t-x)$. It is basically similar to the signum function mentioned in Exercise 30[*] of Chapter 2 except for the size of the step. The Heaviside step function is a perfectly decent, ordinary function. Some authors define its value at $t=x$ (see Figure 7.10) to be $\frac{1}{2}$, but this is unnecessary since its value at that one point is immaterial in integrations. The step function has some interesting consequences that we

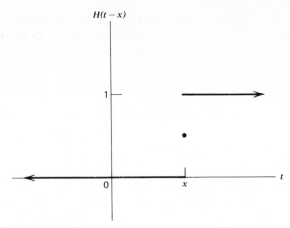

Fig. 7.10 The Heaviside step function (with a point at $t = x$ included).

mention quickly. It can be used to simplify integrals with variable limits of integration by shrinking the integrand to 0 outside the range of the limits. Thus a way of writing $\int_{-\infty}^{a} f(x)\,dx$ is as the integral $\int_{-\infty}^{\infty} f(x)H(a-x)\,dx$, since for $x > a$ one has $H(a-x) = 0$. The step function itself has an integral; it is called the *ramp function*, $R(x)$:

$$\int_{-\infty}^{x} H(u)\,du = R(x) = xH(x).$$

From this you should be able to see readily what $R(x)$ looks like. Note that in terms of the previous statement we can write $R(x)$ still another way,

$$R(x) = \int_{-\infty}^{x} H(u)\,du = \int_{-\infty}^{\infty} H(u)H(x-u)\,du$$

and thus $R(x)$ is a convolution integral of the step function with itself. More generally this suggests that convolution with $H(u)$ means identically integration:

$$\int_{-\infty}^{\infty} f(u)H(x-u)\,du = \int_{-\infty}^{x} f(u)\,du.$$

To return, as another functional $\mathcal{F}(f)$ let us choose $f(0)$, so that now

$$\mathcal{F}(f) = f(0) = \int_{-\infty}^{\infty} g(t)f(t)\,dt.$$

Although this might accidentally be true for some specific $f(t)$ in our domain, there is no ordinary function $g(t)$ for which this holds for all $f(t)$ in the domain. We understand $g(t)$ here, therefore, to be a generalized function; it occurs as the kernel of a functional. More loosely, a generalized function is defined by its action on $f(t)$ as spelled out by the functional $\mathcal{F}(f) = \int_{-\infty}^{\infty} g(t) f(t) dt$, in general, or by the functional $\mathcal{F}(f) = f(0)$ in particular. Generalized functions thus include normal functions [e.g., $H(t)$] and "oddball" functions. The particular "oddball" function just described is called the *Dirac delta function*,[5] $\delta(t)$. An important point to see is that since we have generalized the notion of function in order to discuss functionals such as $f(0)$, we must sacrifice the desirable feature of being able to talk about the "values" of the generalized function. Technically, we work only with $\delta(t)$ when it is combined with some other function under an integral sign.

The question now is: how can we obtain a mathematical representation for $\delta(t)$ that will permit us some physical feeling for this entity? We return to our original picture of the very concentrated force leading to a unit impulse, and we construct a sequence of functions $\delta_n(t)$ as pictured in Figure 7.11:

$$\delta_n(t) = \begin{cases} \frac{1}{2}n & -\frac{1}{n} < t < \frac{1}{n} \\ 0 & |t| > \frac{1}{n} . \end{cases}$$

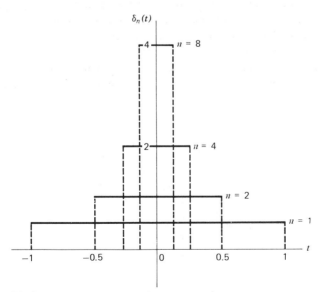

Fig. 7.11 A dirac delta function representation.

[5]After the British-born physicist Paul A. M. Dirac (1902–   ), winner of the 1933 Nobel Prize in physics.

As $n \to \infty$ the function $\delta_n(t)$ becomes more and more concentrated about $t = 0$; the area at all times, however, remains constant at unity. Now we compute the limit integral

$$\lim_{n \to \infty} \int_{-\infty}^{\infty} \delta_n(t) f(t) \, dt = \lim_{n \to \infty} \int_{-\frac{1}{n}}^{\frac{1}{n}} \left(\tfrac{1}{2}n\right) f(t) \, dt.$$

Even though we are not given $f(t)$ specifically we can use an elementary idea to simplify the integral. For some point $t = \zeta$ lying between $1/n$ and $-1/n$, the integral $\int_{-1/n}^{1/n} f(\zeta) \, dt = f(\zeta) \int_{-1/n}^{1/n} dt = \dfrac{2}{n} f(\zeta)$ can be made equal in value to $\int_{-1/n}^{1/n} f(t) \, dt$. This is the *mean value theorem for definite integrals*, and its plausibility is suggested by Figure 7.12. Hence we have finally

$$\lim_{n \to \infty} \int_{-\infty}^{\infty} \delta_n(t) f(t) \, dt = \lim_{n \to \infty} \left[\left(\tfrac{1}{2}n\right)\left(\frac{2}{n}\right) f(\zeta) \right] = f(0)$$

since as n increases without bound, ζ gets pinched in between two numbers that are both very close to zero. The sequence is said to be a *delta sequence*; even though the limit process is done outside the integral, we still say that the limit of the sequence of $\delta_n(t)$ functions is the Dirac delta function. From Figure 7.11 we see that at $t = 0$ the sequence diverges as $n \to \infty$. Pictorially, we might think of the $\delta(t)$ function as being an infinitely high spike at the origin, and zero everywhere else, but this is sloppy wording and we must remember that $\delta(t)$ is not a real function since the "value" infinity is not permitted to a function.

We will not attempt a more detailed mathematical treatment here and the reader is referred to the books by Lighthill and Erdélyi listed in the

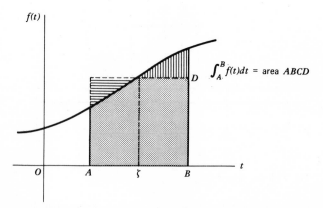

Fig. 7.12   The mean value theorem for definite integrals.

Annotated Bibliography for deeper discussions. There one works with other sequences of functions besides the rectangular pulse functions to represent the Dirac delta function and other generalized functions. In the development of the theory it turns out to be important to have the $g_n(t)$ functions possess derivatives of all orders and to have them together with their derivatives decay very rapidly as $t \to \infty$. By the statement $\int_{-\infty}^{\infty} g(t) f(t) dt$ $= f(0)$, then, we shall mean $\lim_{n \to \infty} \int_{-\infty}^{\infty} g_n(t) f(t) dt = f(0)$. More than one sequence of functions can be used to define a given generalized function, and in fact, the whole idea here is that the precise shape of the pulse is unimportant. The rectangular pulse is convenient because it is easy to work with under the integral sign, but for cases where smoothly continuous derivatives of the $g_n(t)$ functions are required, other sequences will be more useful. Some other δ sequences are shown in Figure 7.13.

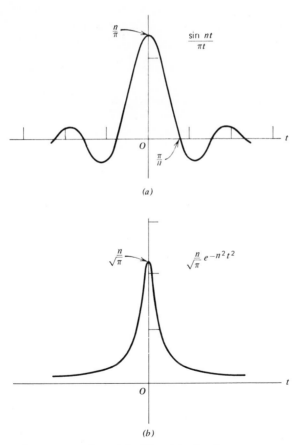

(a)

(b)

Fig. 7.13 Some other representations of the Dirac delta function.

Now that we have defined the delta function in terms of a particular limit operation we are in a position to see how the delta function can be said to have a Fourier transform or a Laplace transform.

Example 68.   Work out the Laplace transform of the Dirac delta function.

Answer.   To be general let us write the delta function as $\delta(x - x_0)$; this says that our infinitely high spike is located at $x = x_0$. The Laplace transform may then be written

$$\int_0^\infty e^{-sx}\delta(x - x_0)\,dx.$$

Since we would like the lower limit to be $-\infty$ in order to work with the delta function, we assume without much loss of generality that $x_0 > 0$ and then insert in the integrand the Heaviside step function. This allows us to write the transform as

$$F(s) = \int_{-\infty}^\infty e^{-sx}H(x)\delta(x - x_0)\,dx$$

and hence we have for this integral

$$F(s) = \exp(-sx_0)H(x_0)$$

$$\boxed{= \exp(-sx_0)}.$$

This result is consistent with entry no. 27 in Table 5.4.

Singular functions like the Dirac delta function commonly occur in chemistry in situations involving electron spin. Experiment shows that in addition to three coordinates a spin factor is needed in the description of the state of an electron in an atom. The spin factor is usually written formally in the same way as a function of some "spin variable" s. Because little is known about the internal structure of the electron, this spin variable is invariably taken to be the component of the spin angular momentum along the axis of quantization. Thus, the "spin-up" function $\alpha(s)$, is zero everywhere except at $s = +\frac{1}{2}\hbar$, and the "spin-down" function, $\beta(s)$, is zero except at $s = -\frac{1}{2}\hbar$. Now if we are to maintain the statistical interpretation of $|\alpha(s)|^2$ or $|\beta(s)|^2$ as being a probability per unit "volume" in a two-dimensional spin space,

$$\int_{-\infty}^\infty [\alpha(s)]^2\,ds = \int_{-\infty}^\infty \delta\left(s - \tfrac{1}{2}\right)ds = 1$$

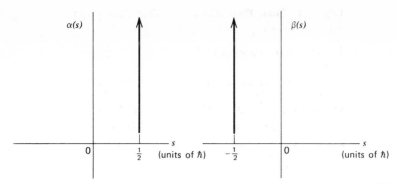

Fig. 7.14 Electron spin eigenfunctions as Dirac delta functions.

then the graph of $\alpha(s)$ or $\beta(s)$ versus s is an infinitely narrow but infinitely high spike (Figure 7.14), the limit being approached in such a way that the two normalization integrals are equal to unity.

$$\int_{-\infty}^{\infty} |\alpha(s)|^2 ds = \int_{-\infty}^{\infty} |\beta(s)|^2 ds = 1$$

The spin eigenfunctions thus behave like delta functions, but this cannot be precisely so. The integrals above require the functions to have units of $m^{-\frac{1}{2}} l^{-1} t^{\frac{1}{2}}$, whereas $\delta(s)$ would have units of $m^{-1} l^{-2} t$. Further, it is actually the integral $\int_{-\infty}^{\infty} \delta(s) ds$ which is equal to unity; the integral of the square of a delta function is divergent. Nevertheless, Figure 7.14 is still a convenient guide for thinking about spin and for assisting in working out the structure of esr and nmr spectra.

To conclude our discussion of the Dirac delta function we look at a possible meaning for the derivative of this function. In terms of a δ sequence, we can perform the following integration by parts.

$$\int_{-\infty}^{\infty} \delta_n'(t) f(t) dt = |\delta_n(t) f(t)|_{-\infty}^{\infty} - \int_{-\infty}^{\infty} \delta_n(t) f'(t) dt$$

The first term on the right goes to zero because we assume that we are using a sequence of functions $\delta_n(t)$ that vanishes for large $|t|$, much like the functions depicted in Figure 7.13. The second term on the right becomes $-f'(0)$ in the limit as $n \to \infty$. Hence we may define the derivative of the delta function to be another generalized function, which as the kernel of a functional, yields the value $-f'(0)$. In Table 7.4 are collected some further miscellaneous properties of the Dirac delta function that are both interesting and worthy of study.

Table 7.4   Some Properties of the Dirac Delta Function

$$\int_{-\infty}^{\infty} \delta(t-t_0) f(t)\, dt = f(t_0) \qquad\qquad \int_{-\infty}^{\infty} |\delta'(t)|\, dt = \infty$$

$$\delta(at+b) = \frac{1}{|a|}\delta\left(t + \frac{b}{a}\right) \qquad\qquad \delta(t) = \frac{d}{dt} H(t)$$

$$\delta(-t) = \delta(t); \delta'(-t) = -\delta'(t) \qquad\qquad t^2 \delta'(t) = 0$$

$$f(t)\delta(t) = f(0)\delta(t) \qquad\qquad t\delta'(t) = -\delta(t)$$

EXERCISES

1. Where would you expect to find discrete distributions of some variable which are nearly continuous and approximately Gaussian (a) in society, (b) in biology, (c) in the physical sciences?

2. Demonstrate that the series expression for erf(x) for large x is divergent and also asymptotic.

3. Show that the integral

$$\Gamma(n) = 2 \int_0^{\infty} \exp(-u^2) u^{2n-1} du$$

is indeed equivalent to Euler's integral definition of the gamma function.

4. As a generalization of the result of Example 65 show that

$$\langle v^n \rangle = \left(\frac{2kT}{m}\right)^{\frac{1}{2}n} \left[\frac{n+1}{2}\right]! \Big/ \left(\tfrac{1}{2}\right)!.$$

5. Express the integral $\int_{-1}^{1} (1+u)^k (1-u)^k\, du$ in simpler form.

6. Verify the identity $B(m,n) = \dfrac{m+n}{n} B(m, n+1)$.

7. Demonstrate that $(2n)!/(n! 2^n)$ is the product of the first n odd integers. For large n show that this is approximately $(2n/e)^n$, and then use this approximate formula to compute the product of the first 10 odd integers; compare with the more exact value.

8. An equation similar to the Legendre differential equation is the *Chebychev equation*:

$$(1-x^2)\frac{d^2 y}{dx^2} - x\frac{dy}{dx} + n^2 y = 0.$$

Put this equation into Sturm–Liouville form and determine the weighting function, $h(x)$. What useful mathematical properties will the solutions of Chebychev's equation possess?

9. Some of the Type I Chebychev polynomials are given below:

$$T_0(x) = 1 \qquad T_1(x) = x$$
$$T_2(x) = 2x^2 - 1 \qquad T_3(x) = 4x^3 - 3x.$$

Demonstrate that $T_1(x)$ and $T_3(x)$ are orthogonal over the interval -1 to $+1$. The Chebychev polynomials are sometimes first defined by the relation $T_n(x) = \cos(n \cos^{-1} x)$; show that $T_2(x)$ above follows from this.

10. Express the step function mentioned in Section 7.2 as a Legendre series. Retain the first three or four terms and graphically plot this polynomial for comparison with the actual step function.

11. Consider the Legendre series expression for the electrostatic potential ψ given in Section 7.2. The first term corresponds to the potential of a "pure" monopole (point charge); the second term corresponds to the potential of a "pure" dipole. What does the third term correspond to? Using the basic relation $\mathbf{E} = -\operatorname{grad}\psi$, work out the R, θ, and ϕ components of a pure dipole field. Compare your work here with that in Example 58.

12. Derive the last recursion relationship for the Legendre polynomials that was given in Section 7.2. Do the recursion relationships as given in that section work for the *normalized* Legendre polynomials?

13. A recurrence relation for the unnormalized associated Legendre functions is

$$P_{l+1}^m(x) = xP_l^m(x) + (1 - x^2)^{\frac{1}{2}}(l + m)P_l^{m-1}(x).$$

Derive this; start with the definition of the associated Legendre function.

14. Another recurrence relation is

$$(l+1)P_{l+1}^m(x) = (2l+1)xP_l^m(x) + m(2l+1)(1 - x^2)^{\frac{1}{2}}P_l^{m-1}(x) - lP_{l-1}^m(x).$$

Derive this from a recursion relation given earlier for the Legendre polynomials.

15. Determine whether or not the "p_x" and "p_y" functions given in Section 7.2 are eigenfunctions of the operator for the square of the angular momentum. Recall that you worked with this operator in Exercise 19 at the end of the second part of Chapter 6.

16. Work out the five spherical harmonics corresponding to $l=2$. Then select one of the five and make a polar plot similar to what was done in Figure 7.6. Of which orbital is this the angular part?

17. Debye pictured the motion of one proton in a water molecule (fluid state) as a random walk over the surface of a sphere (see Figure 7.15). The probability $P(\theta,\phi,t)$ that the proton will be at point B after a time t is to obey the second-order diffusion equation

$$\frac{1}{D}\frac{\partial P}{\partial t} = \nabla^2 P.$$

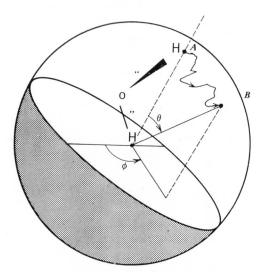

Fig. 7.15   Motion of one end of a water molecule.

The quantity D is a spherical diffusion coefficient, and the Laplacian contains derivatives only with respect to θ and ϕ. Show that a series of normalized spherical harmonics will satisfy the equation

$$P(\theta,\phi,t) = \sum_{lm} c_{lm} Y_{lm}(\theta,\phi) e^{-Dl(l+1)t}.$$

How can the coefficients c_{lm} be found if the initial probability distribution $P(\theta,\phi,0)$ is known?

18. Is Laguerre's differential equation of the Sturm–Liouville type? Does it become so if it is multiplied by e^{-x}?

19. Use Theorem 2 to differentiate Laguerre's equation k times and thus

show that

$$L_{n+k}^k(x) = (-1)^k \frac{d^k}{dx^k} [L_{n+k}(x)].$$

20. Refer back to Exercise 35* at the end of Chapter 5 where you separated the Schrödinger equation for hydrogen into an R, Θ, and Φ part. In the R part make the substitutions $x = 2r(-2mE/\hbar^2)^{1/2}$ and $R(r) = e^{-\frac{1}{2}x}x^s L(x)$, where s is some constant to be determined, and see if you can work the equation in x into the form of the associated Laguerre equation.

21. A generating function for the unnormalized Laguerre polynomials is

$$\frac{e^{-xz/(1-z)}}{1-z} = \sum_{n=0}^{\infty} \frac{L_n(x)}{n!} z^n \qquad |z| < 1.$$

Verify $L_4(x)$ which was given in Table 7.3. Use the generating function to obtain the following recurrence relation:

$$L_{n+1}(x) = (2n + 1 - x)L_n(x) - n^2 L_{n-1}(x).$$

22. In the solutions to the Φ equation part of the hydrogen Schrödinger equation, what is the mathematical effect of requiring the parameter m to be integral?

23. In electron spin resonance (esr) spectroscopy the sample is housed in a resonant cavity (a region where electromagnetic waves can oscillate). Suppose such a cavity is in the shape of a circular cylinder. Maxwell's equations lead to the scalar Helmholtz equation (recall Exercise 34** at the end of the second part of Chapter 6).

$$\nabla^2 B_z + \alpha^2 B_z = 0$$

for the z component of the magnetic vector (α^2 is a constant). Demonstrate that in cylindrical polar coordinates one obtains Bessel's equation.

24. Parabolic coordinates are defined by the transformation equations

$$
\begin{aligned}
x &= \zeta\eta\cos\phi && 0 \leqslant \zeta < \infty \\
y &= \zeta\eta\sin\phi && 0 \leqslant \eta < \infty \\
z &= \tfrac{1}{2}(\zeta^2 - \eta^2) && 0 \leqslant \phi \leqslant 2\pi.
\end{aligned}
$$

Show that Laplace's equation in parabolic coordinates also leads to Bessel's equation.

25. From the product of the generating functions $f(x,t) \cdot f(-x,t)$ for the Bessel functions of the first kind, show that one has

$$1 = [J_0(x)]^2 + 2[J_i(x)]^2 + 2[J_2(x)]^2 + \cdots +,$$

thus implying that $|J_0(x)| \leqslant 1$ and $|J_n(x)| \leqslant \frac{1}{2}\sqrt{2}$, for $n = 1, 2, 3, \ldots$.

26. Derive the useful recurrence relation $J_n'(x) = \frac{1}{2}[J_{n-1}(x) - J_{n+1}(x)]$.

27. Review the reasoning given briefly in the text for the statement that $n!$ is infinite for n a negative integer, and then assuming that basic factorial relations do carry over to negative real numbers, work out what the quantity $n! \, (-n)!$ is equivalent to.

28. By letting $t = e^{i\theta}$ in the generating function for the Bessel functions of the first kind, derive the expressions

$$\cos(x\sin\theta) = J_0(x) + 2\sum_{n=1}^{\infty} J_{2n}(x)\cos(2n\theta)$$

$$\sin(x\sin\theta) = 2\sum_{n=1}^{\infty} J_{2n-1}(x)\sin(2n-1)\theta.$$

What do these become in the special case of $\theta = \frac{1}{2}\pi$?

29. Examine the sequence of functions: $\delta_1(x) = 1/(2\cosh^2 x)$, $\delta_2(x) = 2/(2\cosh^2 2x)$, $\delta_3(x) = 3/(2\cosh^2 3x), \ldots, \delta_n(x)$. Make plots on the same set of axes of these first three members. Does $\lim_{n\to\infty} \delta_n(x)$ exist (discuss both the $x = 0$ and the $x \neq 0$ cases)? Does this sequence exhibit the first criterion for delta function behavior, that is, does the definite integral

$$\int_{-\infty}^{\infty} \delta_n(x)\,dx$$

exist and equal unity?

30. In esr spectroscopy the *isotropic hyperfine coupling constant* $|a|$ measures the splitting of spectral lines; this quantity is analogous to the spin-spin coupling constant J in nmr spectroscopy, except that a measures the interaction between an electron spin and a nuclear spin. According to a theory due to Enrico Fermi (Italian physicist, 1901–1954), the main contribution to a is governed by the density of unpaired electron spins at the surface of the nucleus of interest.

$$a = \frac{8\pi}{3}\, g\beta g_N \beta_N \rho(r_N)$$

$$\rho(r_N) = \int \psi^* \sum_k 2S_{zk}\delta(r_k - r_N)\psi \, d\tau$$

In this formula ψ is the many-electron wave function for the state (ψ^* is its complex conjugate), the spin component S_{zk} of the kth electron is $+\frac{1}{2}$ if the electron has spin α and $-\frac{1}{2}$ if it has spin β, and the Dirac delta function $\delta(r_k - r_N)$ ensures that the kth electron is at nucleus N. The calculation of a involves all the tools of modern quantum chemistry for any molecular free radical of interest, but can be performed easily for a free hydrogen atom in a $1s$ state.

(a) Show that for this state $|a| = 507$ G.

(b) If the Fermi contact term were the only term contributing to a, how many lines would you expect to see in the esr spectrum of atomic hydrogen in a pure $2p$ state?

(c) Experimentally, it is found that the hyperfine coupling constant for the α proton in the vinyl radical is 15.7 G.

$$\begin{array}{c} H \\ \diagdown \\ \diagup \quad C{=}C \\ H \end{array} \quad \begin{array}{c} \bigcirc\!\!\!\!\cdot \\ \diagdown \\ H \end{array} \qquad (15.7)$$

What does this mean in relation to your answer to part (a)?

31. What is the sum of $H(x + \frac{1}{2})$ and $-H(x - \frac{1}{2})$?

32. An alternative way to Example 68 of deducing the Laplace transform of the delta function is to actually start with some defining δ sequence. Take the general member of the sequence which is depicted in Figure 7.11, work out its Laplace transform, and then take the limit of this as $n \to \infty$.

33. To show that the derivative of the Heaviside step function is the Dirac delta function, as indicated in Table 7.4, one needs to have a defining sequence of continuous functions for $H(x)$. Make graphs of the following for a few integral values of n:

$$\tfrac{1}{2} + \frac{1}{\pi}\tan^{-1}(nx)$$

$$\frac{1}{\sqrt{\pi}} \int_{-x}^{\infty} n\exp(-n^2 u^2)\, du.$$

Do these functions seem to approximate $H(x)$? Do their derivatives form a δ sequence? You did this same kind of exercise back in 30* at the end of Chapter 2.

34. Write the Fourier transform of the Dirac delta function, and then by taking the inverse transform show that the following is an integral representation of the delta function:

$$\delta(t) = \frac{1}{2\pi} \int_{-\infty}^{\infty} e^{-iwt}\, dw.$$

35. Using the identity $|x| = 2xH(x) - x$, prove that the second derivative of $|x|$ is $2\delta(x)$.

36. Select some of the entires in Table 7.4 and verify their correctness.

37.* In Exercise 35** of Part 2 of Chapter 6 you found that the Stark effect for the hydrogen atom led to the differential equation

$$\frac{d}{dx}\left(x\frac{df}{dx}\right) + f\left[\frac{mE}{2\hbar^2}x - \frac{\alpha^2}{4x} + \frac{eE_0m}{4\hbar^2}x^2 + \frac{Am}{2\hbar^2}\right] = 0$$

where x here is ζ^2 there, the wave function is assumed to be of the form $\psi = f(\zeta)g(\eta)h(\phi)$, and α^2 and A are constants. First of all, verify that the above differential equation does result when the substitution $\zeta^2 = x$ is made, and then find a power series solution using the larger root of the indicial equation. How soon does the perturbation eE_0 enter? For hydrogen the mathematics involved in the Stark effect can be carried quite far; for other atoms and for molecules the differential equation approach is impractical, and perturbation theory is usually employed. The Stark effect on the rotational spectrum of molecules with permanent dipole moments permits the accurate determination of such moments.

38.* The Schrödinger equation for the three-dimensional isotropic harmonic oscillator in spherical polar coordinates is

$$\frac{-\hbar^2}{2m}\nabla^2\psi + 2\pi^2 m\nu^2 r^2\psi = E\psi.$$

Separate this and investigate the nature of the R equation.

39.* From your results in Exercise 20 and from material in the text, write out the complete forms for the normalized $2p_x$ and $2p_z$ wave functions for a hydrogenic atom of nuclear charge $+Z$. Now suppose that two C^{6+} nuclei are located along the z axis at $+0.77$ Å and -0.77 Å from the origin. At this distance, which corresponds to a carbon–carbon single bond length, compare the overlap integrals for lateral overlap (π bond) versus longitudinal overlap (σ bond).

40.* From the results of Exercise 28 and from the orthogonality properties of sines and cosines, derive the following integral representation of Bessel functions of the first kind:

$$J_n(x) = \frac{1}{\pi}\int_0^\pi \cos(n\theta - x\sin\theta)\,d\theta.$$

Also, show that the recurrence relation in Exercise 26 can be derived from the expression above.

41.* Consider a two-state system having energies E_1 and E_2 (see Figure 7.16) which is acted upon by a time-dependent perturbation $V(t)$ of the form $V(t) = V \cdot T(t)$. The wave function for the system at any time t is given by the linear combination

$$\psi = c_1(t)\psi_1 \exp\left(\frac{-iE_1t}{\hbar}\right) + c_2(t)\psi_2 \exp\left(\frac{-iE_2t}{\hbar}\right)$$

and quantum chemistry gives for the coefficient $c_2(t)$

$$c_2(t) = \frac{-i}{\hbar}\int \psi_2{}^* V\psi_1 d\tau \int_0^t T(t)\exp\left[\frac{i(E_2-E_1)t}{\hbar}\right]dt.$$

The probability P_{12} that the system, initially in state ψ_1, will be found in state ψ_2 at time t is given by $|c_2(t)|^2$. Suppose $T(t)$ is of periodic fluctuation $T(t) = 2\cos 2\pi\nu t$; show that near resonance $(\nu \cong \nu_{21})$ the probability behaves nearly like a delta function:

$$P_{12} \cong \frac{4\pi^2 t}{h}\left[\int \psi_2{}^* V\psi_1 d\tau\right]^2 \delta\left(E_2-E_1-h\nu\right).$$

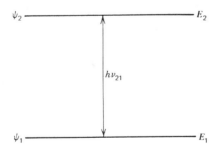

Fig. 7.16 A two-state system.

Annotated Bibliography

Historical Works

Ball, W. W. Rouse, *A Short Account of the History of Mathematics*, 4th ed., Macmillan, London, 1927.

Bell, E. T., *Men of Mathematics*, Simon & Schuster, New York, 1960. A book written with some wit, focusing on the lives of about a dozen mathematicians.

Bell, E. T., *The Development of Mathematics*, 2nd ed., McGraw-Hill, New York, 1945. A somewhat detailed account of mathematics history.

Bochner, S., *The Role of Mathematics in the Rise of Science*, Princeton University Press, Princeton, N.J., 1966. A scholarly look at a very complex historical topic.

Dunnington, G. W., *Carl Friedrich Gauss: Titan of Science*, Exposition Press, New York, 1955. A biography of the greatest mathematician of the nineteenth century.

Hankins, T. L., *Jean d'Alembert: Science and the Enlightenment*, Clarendon Press, Oxford, 1970.

Kline, M., *Mathematical Thought from Ancient to Modern Times*, Oxford University Press, New York, 1972. An excellent comprehensive history covering ancient Mesopotamian mathematics up to modern topology; much mathematics may be learned from reading this work.

Kramer, E. E., *The Nature and Growth of Modern Mathematics*, Hawthorn Books, New York, 1970. Similar to the preceding book but not on such a comprehensive scale nor as deep.

Newman, J. R. (ed.), *The World of Mathematics*, Vols I–IV, Simon & Schuster, New York, 1956. There is something for everyone in this marvelous set of volumes, with articles ranging from the historical, to the strictly mathematical, to the humanistic (such as a reprint of Oswald Spengler's essay on the nature of numbers taken from his philosophical masterpiece *The Decline of the West*).

Ore, O., *Cardano—The Gambling Scholar*, Dover, New York, 1965. Discussion of the life and works of Girolamo Cardano, including a reprint of his "Manual on Games of Chance."

Scott, J. F. and H. W. Turnbull (eds.), *The Correspondence of Isaac Newton*, 4 vols., Cambridge University Press, Cambridge, 1959–1967. Letters and notes to and from leading scientific personalities of the day; indispensable in any research on Newton.

Struik, D. J. (ed.), *A Source Book in Mathematics, 1200–1800*, Harvard University Press, Cambridge, Mass., 1969.

General Mathematical Works

Abramowitz, M. and I. A. Stegun, *Handbook of Mathematical Functions*, Dover, New York, 1965. Contains tables of values of the error, gamma, Bessel, and Legendre functions, elliptic integrals, Laplace transforms, etc.

Altshiller-Court, N., *College Geometry*, 2nd ed., Barnes & Noble, New York, 1952. Geometry of the triangle and the circle.

Apostol, T. M., *Calculus*, Vol. 1, 2nd ed., Blaisdell, Waltham, Mass., 1967; Vol. 2, Blaisdell, New York, 1962. See Vol. 2 for the calculus of several variables.

Apostol, T. M., et al., *Selected Papers on Calculus*, Mathematical Association of America, Inc., 1969. This is a good collection of articles on the standard calculus drawn from past issues of the *American Mathematical Monthly* and the *Mathematics Magazine*.

Arfken, G., *Mathematical Methods for Physicists*, 2nd ed., Academic Press, New York, 1970. Excellent book at a somewhat advanced level; topics include coordinate systems, series, complex variables, integral transforms, special functions.

Bermant, A. F., *A Course of Mathematical Analysis*, Part II, Macmillan, New York, 1963. Mainly a readable account of the calculus of two or more variables; topics include multiple and iterated integrals, line and surface integrals, Taylor's formula, and differential equations.

Bishir, J. W. and D. W. Drewes, *Mathematics in the Behavioral and Social Sciences*, Harcourt, Brace & World, New York, 1970. Elementary book covering sets, series, matrices, calculus, and probability; lots of worked examples and problems with answers.

Boas, M., *Mathematical Methods in the Physical Sciences*, Wiley, New York, 1966. Excellent; few applications are drawn from chemistry, however.

Brookes, C. J., I. G. Betteley, and S. M. Loxston, *Mathematics and Statistics for Chemists*, Wiley, London, 1966. Chapters 1–8 are relevant to material in this book.

Buck, R. C., *Advanced Calculus*, 2nd ed., McGraw-Hill, New York, 1965. A rigorous text that is a good source of proofs of theorems.

Burnside, W. S. and A. W. Panton, *The Theory of Equations*, Vols. I and II, Dover, New York, 1960. Contains much material on the solving of equations.

Butler, J. N. and D. G. Bobrow, *The Calculus of Chemistry*, W. A. Benjamin, New York, 1965. A very elementary book on arithmetic expressions and functions, derivatives, and integration.

Byron, F. W., Jr. and R. W. Fuller, *Mathematics of Classical and Quantum Physics*, Vol. I, Addison-Wesley, Reading, Mass., 1969. Organized around the theme of vector spaces; theorems are proved.

Chrystal, G., *Textbook of Algebra*, Vols. I and II, Chelsea, New York, 1964. A veritable gold mine of algebra and precalculus material from a scholarly standpoint.

Clapham, C. R. J., *Introduction to Mathematical Analysis*, Routledge & Kegan Paul, London, 1973, 80 pp. This is a short, well-written treatment of elementary calculus, suitable for a review of basics.

Courant, R. and F. John, *Introduction to Calculus and Analysis*, Vol. I, Wiley-Interscience, New York, 1965. Readable introduction.

Dettman, J. W., *Mathematical Methods in Physics and Engineering*, 2nd ed., McGraw-Hill, New York, 1969. An intermediate level text containing material and theorems on linear algebra, differential equations, and complex variables.

Edwards, J., *An Elementary Treatise on the Differential Calculus*, 3rd ed., Macmillan, London, 1896 (reprinted 1950). Contains much valuable material on expansions, partial differentiation, curves, maxima, and minima.

Edwards, J., *A Treatise on the Integral Calculus*, Vol. I, Macmillan, London, 1921 (republished by Chelsea, New York); Vol. II, Macmillan, London, 1922 (republished by Chelsea, New York). A very useful reference work.

Hardy, G. H., *A Course of Pure Mathematics*, 10th ed., Cambridge University Press, Cambridge, 1952 (reprinted 1967). A very famous and excellent text; highly recommended.

Hermann, R., *Lectures in Mathematical Physics*, Vol. I, Benjamin, New York, 1970. A somewhat advanced coverage of topics such as vectors, linear transformations, and ordinary differential equations.

Jahnke, E. and F. Emde, *Tables of Functions*, Dover, New York, 1945. Contains tables of values of the higher functions similar to the tables in the work by Abramowitz and Stegun.

Jeffreys, H. and B. S. Jeffreys, *Methods of Mathematical Physics*, 3rd ed., Cambridge University Press, Cambridge, 1956. An important, comprehensive reference work with applications to physics.

Kaplan, W., *Advanced Calculus*, Addison-Wesley, New York, 1952. Chapters 1, 3, and 5 are good on vector algebra and calculus.

Korn, G. A. and T. M. Korn (eds.), *Mathematics Handbook for Scientists and Engineers*, 2nd ed., McGraw-Hill, New York, 1968.

Lass, H., *Elements of Pure and Applied Mathematics*, McGraw-Hill, New York, 1957. See the first six chapters for material related to the contents of this book.

Lyusternik, L. A. and A. R. Yanpol'skii, *Mathematical Analysis*, Pergamon Press, Oxford, 1965. See Chapter III on series, Chapter IV on orthogonal systems and polynomials, and Chapter VI on special functions.

Madelung, E., *Die Mathematischen Hilfsmittel des Physikers*, Julius Springer, Berlin, 1922. A famous, old book—one of the first of its kind—and now largely of historical interest.

Mathews, J. and R. L. Walker, *Mathematical Methods of Physics*, 2nd ed., Benjamin, New York, 1970. An illuminating book written in the same vein as this one.

Merritt, F. S., *Mathematics Manual*, McGraw-Hill, New York, 1962. An elementary book written like a recipe book and containing material on algebra, geometry, simple calculus, series, differential equations, vectors, tensors, and matrices. Readable.

Nicolson, M. M. and D. G. Padfield, *Fundamentals and Techniques of Mathematics for Scientists*, Wiley, New York, 1961. A complement to this book.

Nielsen, K. L., *College Mathematics*, College Outline Series 105, Barnes & Noble, New York, 1958. A basic study of equations, analytic geometry, and the calculus.

Nielsen, K. L., *Modern Algebra*, College Outline Series 64, Barnes & Noble, New York, 1969. See chapters on linear algebra, transcendental functions, series, and probability.

Oakley, C. O., *The Calculus*, College Outline Series 48, Barnes & Noble, New York, 1957. Outline of the essentials of differentiation and integration.

Oakley, C. O., *Analytic Geometry*, College Outline Series 68, Barnes & Noble, New York, 1957. The essentials of plane and solid analytic geometry; well-written.

Oakley, C. O., *Analytic Geometry Problems*, College Outline Series 108, Barnes & Noble, New York, 1958. A collection of problems with solutions from plane and solid analytic geometry.

Olmsted, J. M. H., *Advanced Calculus*, Appleton-Century-Crofts, New York, 1961. An excellent comprehensive text containing worked examples and numerous first-rate problems.

Osgood, W. F., *Functions of Real and Complex Variables*, Chelsea, New York, 1935. See sections on infinite and Fourier series, the gamma function, and Cauchy theory. Lucidly written.

Perrin, C. L., *Mathematics for Chemists*, Wiley-Interscience, New York, 1970. Good coverage at about the same level as this book.

Pipes, L. A. and L. R. Harvill, *Applied Mathematics for Engineers and Physicists*, 3rd ed., McGraw-Hill, New York, 1970. A well-written reference work; see particularly Chapters 1 (complex variables), 2 (linear differential equations), 3 (linear algebra), and 4 (Laplace transforms), and Appendices C, D, E, and F.

Plumpton, C. and B. H. Chirgwin, *A Course of Mathematics for Engineers and Scientists*, Vols. 1–5, Pergamon Press, Oxford, 1961–1964. This series covers in great detail all the topics mentioned in this book; exercises with answers are included.

Smith, L. P., *Mathematical Methods for Scientists and Engineers*, Dover, New York, 1961. Useful complement to this book.

Spiegel, M. R., *Advanced Mathematics for Engineers and Scientists*, Schaum's Outline Series, McGraw-Hill, New York, 1971. Interesting, and of the usual good quality associated with this series.

Stephenson, G., *Mathematical Methods for Science Students*, Longmans, Green, London, 1961. Another useful complement to this book.

Weast, R. C. and S. M. Selby (eds.), *Handbook of Tables for Mathematics*, 4th ed., Chemical Rubber Co., Cleveland, 1970. This excellent reference work is the expanded version of the mathematics section of the *Handbook of Chemistry and Physics*.

Whittaker, E. T. and G. N. Watson, *A Course of Modern Analysis*, 4th and American ed., Macmillan, New York, 1943. This is a difficult but solid work on integration, series, complex numbers, differential equations, and the principal transcendental functions such as the gamma, Riemann zeta, Legendre, and Bessel functions.

Wilson, E. B., *Advanced Calculus*, Dover, New York, 1958. This book, written by a former student of Gibbs, contains an immense amount of useful material; the emphasis is clearly on operations rather than on rigor and theorem proving.

Specialized Mathematical and Applied Works

Aris, R., *Vectors, Tensors and the Basic Equations of Fluid Mechanics*, Prentice-Hall, Englewood Cliffs, N.J., 1962. See Chapters 2, 3, and 7.

Ayers, F., Jr., *Differential Equations*, Schaum, New York, 1952. Readable treatment of the subject.

Bois, G. Petit, *Tables of Indefinite Integrals*, Dover, New York, 1961. Strong on integrands containing complicated polynomial and transcendental expressions.

Brillouin, L., *Tensors in Mechanics and Elasticity*, Academic Press, New York, 1964. Exposition of the subject with applications to physics.

Bromwich, T. J., *An Introduction to the Theory of Infinite Series*, 2nd ed., Macmillan, London, 1926 (reprinted 1959). This is one of the great classic works on the subject; very highly recommended.

Champeney, D. C., *Fourier Transforms and their Physical Applications*, Academic Press, New York, 1973. Book is divided into Part I. Mathematical Foundations, Part II. Applications, and several appendices. Chapter 13 deals with X-ray, neutron, and electron diffraction from stationary scatterers.

Churchill, R. V., *Fourier Series and Boundary Value Problems*, 2nd ed., McGraw-Hill, New York, 1963. See Chapters I–V.

Churchill, R. V., *Complex Variables and Applications*, 2nd ed., McGraw-Hill, New York, 1960. Very readable introductory work.

Erdélyi, A., *Asymptotic Expansions*, 2nd ed., Dover, New York, 1956. An advanced monograph.

Farrar, T. C. and E. D. Becker, *Pulse and Fourier Transform NMR*, Academic Press, New York, 1971. A survey of the theory and the present state of the art.

Flügge, W., *Tensor Analysis and Continuum Mechanics*, Springer-Verlag, New York, 1972. Not too bad; see Chapters 1–4 and 11. Other chapters are applications to elasticity, kinematics, etc.

Gibbs, J. W., *Scientific Papers*, Vol. II, Dover, New York, 1961. Contains original writings by Gibbs on vectors.

Greenberg, M. D., *Application of Green's Functions in Science and Engineering*, Prentice-Hall, Englewood Cliffs, N.J., 1971. Section 3 of Part I contains an elementary discussion of the Dirac delta function. The Green's function technique for solving ordinary and partial differential equations (not covered in this text) is the main purpose of the book.

Hardy, G. H., *The Integration of Functions of a Single Variable*, 2nd ed., Cambridge University Press, Cambridge, 1916. This is No. 2 in the famous series Cambridge Tracts in Mathematics and Mathematical Physics, and is a summary of all of the standard tricks commonly presented in calculus books today for the "indefinite integration" of rational, algebraic, and transcendental functions.

Hardy, G. H., *Divergent Series*, Oxford University Press, London, 1949. A specialized monograph; all of Chapter XIII is on the Euler–Maclaurin summation formula.

Ince, E. L., *Ordinary Differential Equations*, Dover, New York, 1956. A famous and somewhat advanced-level coverage of the subject.

Jolley, L. B. W., *Summation of Series*, 2nd ed., Dover, New York, 1961. A collection of summation formulas.

Karamcheti, K., *Vector Analysis and Cartesian Tensors with Selected Applications*, Holden-Day, San Francisco, 1967. Chapters 1–4 on vectors and 8–9 on Cartesian tensors are good.

Knopp, K., *Infinite Sequences and Series*, Dover, New York, 1956. An authorative and readable exposition of the subject.

Lebedev, N. N., *Special Functions and their Applications*, Prentice-Hall, Englewood Cliffs, N.J., 1965. Contains interesting material on the gamma function, the exponential and related integrals, orthogonal polynomials, and spherical harmonics.

Ledermann, W., *Multiple Integrals*, Routledge & Kegan Paul, London, 1966. Coverage of line and surface integrals, and transformation of multiple integrals.

Lighthill, M. J., *Introduction to Fourier Analysis and Generalised Functions*, Cambridge University Press, London, 1958. Contains an interesting discussion of the Dirac delta function.

Narayan, S., *A Textbook of Cartesian Tensors*, 2nd ed., S. Chand, Delhi, 1961. A good, simple treatment.

Nielsen, K. L., *Differential Equations*, 2nd ed., College Outline Series 72, Barnes & Noble, New York, 1966. A treatment of ordinary and partial differential equations.

Rainville, E. D., *Infinite Series*, Macmillan, New York, 1967. Well-written introductory monograph.

Ramachandran, G. N. and R. Srinivasan, *Fourier Methods in Crystallography*, Wiley-Interscience, New York, 1970.

Rodiguin, N. M. and E. N. Rodiguina, *Consecutive Chemical Reactions*, D. Van Nostrand, Princeton, N.J., 1964.

Rogosinski, W., *Fourier Series* (translated by H. Cohn and F. Steinhardt), 2nd ed., Chelsea, New York, 1959.

Sneddon, I. N., *Fourier Transforms*, McGraw-Hill, New York, 1951. Contains much applied material of use in engineering.

Sneddon, I. N., *Elements of Partial Differential Equations*, McGraw-Hill, New York, 1957. Treatment of the subject from a practical or working standpoint.

Sommerfeld, A., *Partial Differential Equations in Physics*, Academic Press, New York, 1949. A famous book written from the standpoint of applications to physics.

Spiegel, M. R., *Complex Variables*, Schaum's Outline Series, McGraw-Hill, New York, 1964. Readable; definitely recommended.

Symon, K. R., *Mechanics*, 3rd ed., Addison-Wesley, Reading, Mass., 1971. See Chapter 10 for a good treatment of tensors.

Synge, J. L. and A. Schild, *Tensor Calculus*, University of Toronto Press, Toronto, 1949. See Chapter 1 for a general introduction.

Titchmarsh, E. C., *Theory of Functions*, 2nd ed., Oxford University Press, London, 1939. An advanced level book on the analysis of real and complex functions.

Wayland, H., *Differential Equations*, D. Van Nostrand, Princeton, N.J., 1957. Very readable, with applications to engineering.

Miscellaneous Articles

Apostol, T. M., "Another Elementary Proof of Euler's Formula for $\zeta(2n)$," *Am. Math. Mon.*, **80**, 425 (1973).

Ayoub, R., "Euler and the Zeta Function," *Am. Math. Mon.*, **81**, 1067 (1974).

Bridgman, P. W., "A Complete Collection of Thermodynamic Formulas," *Phys. Rev.*, **3**, 273 (1914).

Goldstein, L. J., "A History of the Prime Number Theorem," *Am. Math. Mon.*, **80**, 599 (1973).

Hardy, G. H., "The Integral $\int_0^\infty [(\sin x)/x]\,dx$," *Math. Gaz.*, **55**, 152 (1971).

Lentner, M., "On the Sum of Powers of the First N Integers," *Am. Stat.*, **27**, 87 (1973).

McShane, E. J., "A Unified Theory of Integration," *Am. Math. Mon.*, **80**, 349 (1973).

Papadimitriou, I., "A Simple Proof of the Formula $\sum k^{-2} = \pi^2/6$," *Am. Math. Mon.*, **80**, 424 (1973).

Rhodes, F., "$1 - 1 + 1 - 1 + \cdots = \frac{1}{2}$?," *Math. Gaz.*, **55**, 298 (1971).

Shaw, A. N., "The Derivation of Thermodynamical Relations for a Simple System," *Phil. Trans. Roy. Soc. (London)*, **A234**, 299 (1935).

Shiu, P., "How Slowly Can a Series Converge?," *Math. Gaz.*, **56**, 285 (1972).

Taylor, A. E., "Differentiation of Fourier Series and Integrals," *Am. Math. Mon.*, **51**, 19(1944).

Temple, G., "The Theory of Generalized Functions," *Proc. Roy. Soc.*, **A228**, 175 (1955).

Van Vleck, E. B., "The Influence of Fourier's Series upon the Development of Mathematics," *Science*, **39**, 113 (1914).

Wall, F. T., "Alternative Derivations of the Statistical Mechanical Distribution Laws," *Proc. Natl. Acad. Sci.*, **68**, 1720 (1971).

Whyburn, G. T., "What is a Curve?," *Am. Math. Mon.*, **49**, 493 (1942).

Youngs, J. W. T., "Curves and Surfaces," *Am. Math. Mon.*, **51**, 1 (1944).

Author Index

Subject Index